FRESHWATER VEGETATION MANAGEMENT

by
DR. EDWARD O. GANGSTAD
U.S. Army Corps of Engineers (*Retired*)

THOMAS PUBLICATIONS
P.O. Box 9335
Fresno, Ca. 93791

THIS BOOK FOR REFERENCE ONLY

READ THE LABEL CAREFULLY

About the Author

DR. EDWARD O. GANGSTAD
U.S. Army Corps of Engineers (*Retired*)

Dr. Gangstad, Aquatic Plant Specialist, transferred to the Office of the Chief of Engineers, 11 October 1966, from the Texas Research Foundation, Dallas,Texas, where he was employed as Principal Agronomist of the Hoblitzelle Agricultural Laboratory. Dr. Gangstad was graduated from the University of Wisconsin with a Masters Degree in Biochemistry (1947) and from Rutgers University with a Ph. D (1950) in Agronomy and minors in Plant Pathology and Plant Physiology.

His experience includes research and field studies on the physiology and pathology of plants at the Universities of Wisconsin and New Jersey; research and development studies on strategic long-vegetable-fibers and related programs in Florida with the United States Department of Agriculture; Office of Naval Research and the Department of Defense; and agrobusiness studies to develop renewable natural resources of the State of Texas with the Texas Research Foundation and management of natural resources for the Department of the Army and the U.S. Army Corps of Engineers.

Dr. Gangstad retired in 1985 after twenty-seven years of service with the Department of the Army.

TABLE OF CONTENTS

SELECTED TOPICS IN FRESHWATER VEGETATION MANAGEMENT

PREFACE

In many places, in the United States and other countries of the world, hydrilla, waterhyacinth, watermilfoil, salvinia and many other aquatic plants have had serious, some say "profound", effects on commerce, health and agriculture. Certain environmental conditions can cause them to suddenly outgrow other water plants. In fact, they literally choke many of the world's lakes and rivers. These weeds halt boat and barge traffic, disrupt the functioning of irrigation and flood control projects and hydroelectric power plants, provide homes for disease carrying mosquitoes and snails, and alter aquatic ecosystems by preventing sunlight from reaching other plants and animals which live beneath their mats. And they have "ruined the fishing" in any number of places.

Aquatic weeds are controlled by several methods. Heavy machines provide mechanical control, many kinds of insects, pathogens and other organisms provide biological control, and drawdowns, plastics sheets and colored dyes provide cultural control. However, chemical control continues to be the most common method. Certain herbicides and their various "formulations" are approved for aquatic use by the U.S. Environmental Protection Agency. However, old and new herbicides are subject to continuous testing for their effectiveness and safety.

Edward O. Gangstad

Springfield, Virginia
September, 1986

PART I

ENVIRONMENTAL ENGINEERING ASSESSMENT

CHAPTER 1. VEGETATION MANAGEMENT OF FRESHWATER RESOURCES

Chapter 1

VEGETATION MANAGEMENT OF FRESHWATER RESOURCES[1]

INTRODUCTION

There is an ever increasing demand of water resources, for recreational, agricultural, industrial and numerous other purposes. These water areas, like land areas, support a basic plant life. The kinds and amounts of aquatic plants vary within the different environments of streams, rivers, lakes ponds, marshes, wetlands and numerous man-made impoundments, which are a large part of the total fresh water resource.

The uses and management objectives for a particular body of water determine to a large extent, the need for management and/or control of aquatic plants in the freshwater resource. A given body of water may be used for irrigation, fishing, boating, swimming, waterskiing or water fowl hunting. Aquatic plant control may be required to meet the objectives of domestic, industrial recreational and/or agricultural consumption of the water.

Extensive infestations of obnoxious aquatic weeds cause problems in the recreational uses of the water resource, the operation and maintenance of irrigation, flood control, navigation and water supply systems, including a reduction in carrying capacity by retardance of flow by submersed aquatic plants, increased waterloss from the transpiration by emersed and marginal aquatic plants, the clogging and deterioration of structures in the distribution system by floating aquatic plants, and the limiting of operational control by ditchbank vegetation. They may also form favorable habitats for vector diseases transmitted disease organisms.

A discussion on the "Identification of Aquatic Plants" is given in Appendix A, a summary of "Formulas for Aquatic Herbicide Application" is given in Appendix B, and a "Glossary of Terms Used in Aquatic Weed Control" is given in Appendix C.

---

[1]The findings in this report are not to be construed as an official Department of the Army position unless so designated by other authorized documents.

CONTROL OF SUBMERSED PLANTS

Submersed plants complete their entire life cycle, exclusive of flowering and pollination under water. Watergrass (**Hydrochloa carolinensis)** and Eurasian watermilfoil (**Myriophyllum spicatum**) are submersed aquatic plants that grow in dense stands of mats and interfere with the operational use of the water resource. Chemicals for controlling submersed weeds (see Tables 1.1 and 2.1) can be applied in various ways. Granules may be spread from a boat, from the shore, or by aircraft. Granules are especially useful for spot treatments near boat landings or swimming areas. Liquid herbicides may be sprayed or pumped into the water from boats, or even by hand pumping from the shoreline. As a rule, the more evenly the chemical is distributed, the better the results will be. Spot treatment of problem areas with liquids in very large areas may be desirable. Usually more material per acre-foot of water is needed when making spot treatments than when making overall treatment, because the nontreated adjacent water will have a diluting effect. Where dense weeds cover an entire pond, only one-third of the pond should be treated at a time to prevent oxygen depletion due to decaying plant growth. When treating 1/3 of the pond, applications should be made at weekly or semi weekly intervals until the entire pond is treated (1,3,6,8,11,13,14,15).

CONTROL OF EMERGENT AND MARGINAL PLANTS

Emergent plants may grow in moist or swampy shoreline soils and extend into water three feet or more in depth. Many emergents are valuable duck foods, and should not be completely eliminated if waterfowl are wanted. Principal types include marsh plant species such as rushes, bulrushes, cattails, reeds, sedges, and arrowheads. (See Tables 1.1 and 2.1).

Foliar sprays should be applied in early summer as the leaves are approaching full size, but before flowering. If water is used as the diluent or carrier, a small amount of detergent or other wetting agent will improve coverage of the plant surfaces. The plant foliage should be completely wetted. Applications should be made during mid-day periods when the foliage above water is free from dew or rain.

Granular formulations act more slowly than liquids, but they may give more long-lasting results. If attaclay or a similar carrier is used, the herbicide may be spread with a cyclone seeder or by hand. The granules settle to the bottom and release the chemical that will be absorbed through the plant roots. As with foliar sprays, granular applications are made in late summer or fall, however, the effects may not be noticed until the following spring when the treated plants fail to develop. If granules are spread on choppy water, distribution will be uneven, and results may be unsatisfactory.

In making spray applications for controlling emergent weeds, there are two basic methods of calculating the dosage and application rate: (1) quantity of herbicide per surface area treated, and (2) quantity of herbicide per volume of spray solution.

For treating areas of one acre or more, the first method should be used. The important consideration with this method is the amount of herbicide applied per acre. The amount of carrier will vary with the spray equipment, nozzle sizes, and pressure. For treating areas of less than one acre, it is more practical to use the herbicide-per volume method and to spray foliage to the run-off point or until thoroughly wetted. With most herbicides, the container label will give directions for applications by both methods.

CONTROL OF FLOATING PLANTS

The most common floating plants are duckweed, water lily, spatterdock, waterhyacinth and watershield: The water lily types are valued by fisherman as long as ample room is left for fishing, but in areas used for boating, swimming, or water skiing, floating aquatic plants are serious nuisances and must be kept under control. For good control aquatic plants and the water surface should be treated by spraying, taking care to obtain even distribution in the area of plant growth. If water is colder than 60 F., or if plants are not growing actively, the area should not be sprayed. For floating plants that are rooted on the bottom, granular formulations usually give the best control. (See Tables 1.1 and 2.1)

CONTROL OF ALGAE

Most serious problems with algae are associated with domestic water supply reservoirs or small farm ponds. Control is most effective and least costly when undertaken before the algae become dense enough to constitute a problem. Some reservoir managers make a daily microscopic examination of the water to determine when treatment should be scheduled. Through experience with a given body of water, one may generally anticipate when chemicals should be applied. (See Tables 1.1 and 2.1)

The amount of chemical per treatment and the number of required treatments varies with the hardness of the water. In soft water, one treatment may suffice. In hard water, however, three or four treatments may be needed throughout the summer because the regrowth of algae can be quite rapid in such water. If results are not evident within seven days after treatment, another application may be made. However, trout are very sensitive to some chemicals, especially copper sulfate, and cannot tolerate levels required for control of certain species of algae.

METHODS OF APPLICATION

The applicator should consider only those herbicide formulations specifically registered and labeled for aquatic weed control.

The 3- to 5-gallon pressure-type sprayers available at most home garden centers and hardware and farm supply stores are adequate for treating small ponds. Ponds of 5 acres or more may be more efficiently treated with heavier, commercial-type spray equipment.

Granules can be spread by hand in small areas such as boat landings and swimming sites. Hand-operated, crank-type fertilizer and seed spreaders will do a satisfactory job in larger areas. Large versions of these spreaders are used for large-scale commercial granule applications. They operate on the principle of the cinder spreaders used on highways, and are capable of dispersing granules in 30- to 35 foot swaths. These units are often powered by a 12-volt D.C. motor that operates from an auto battery. Helicopters and airplanes have been used effectively to apply chemicals, particularly granules, in large-scale operations.

Chemicals, especially 2,4-D sprays, should be applied on a calm day when dangers from drifting can be avoided. With such precautions, damage to desirable vegetation is minimal, and operators are protected from excessive contact and inhalation of spray.

Chemical spillage, especially around stock pond areas or where pets and children may be exposed, must be cleaned up. Herbicides should never be stored where children can reach them. Labels should be studied and their instructions for safe and proper use observed.

Herbicide application can start at the margins of the lake or pond and progress toward the deep water. Fish and other organisms will tend to move ahead of the herbicide-treated water into the deeper areas where toxic concentrations can be avoided.

Lakes and ponds that have a high rate of inflow should be lowered prior to treatment so as to insure adequate contact time for the herbicide. The spillway should be closed and the treated water retained for at least 3 days before overflow. The amount of drawdown will vary according to the situation. Care must be taken to avoid excessive exposure of bottom areas. After the application is completed, the spray equipment should be flushed with large quantities of water, care being taken to avoid contaminating water supplies with the residue of the spray treatment.

Waters should be treated for aquatic weeds in late spring or early summer when plants are young and actively growing. Treatment at this time of year usually gives optimal control with a minimum of chemical. Applications in late summer or early fall require more chemical and usually give a slower, erratic control. Furthermore, access to normally dense aquatic vegetation is best in the spring or early summer before the plants reach the surface.

1. Be certain of the identity of the vegetation to be treated and the capability of the chemical to control it.
2. Obtain a permit to treat any lake or pond, whether for weed control, cleaning, or other purposes.
3. Never use more chemical than suggested on the label. Fish and other valuable aquatic life may be killed.
4. Use treated water only as suggested on the label.

ENVIRONMENTAL CHANGES CAUSED BY AQUATIC PLANT CONTROL

The sudden elimination of a dense growth of vegetation from an aquatic environment very often causes side effects that can produce significant changes in the biological and physical makeup of a lake, pond, or stream.

Following the death of larger weed plants in a pond or lake, a greenish or yellowish-brown turbid condition may be noticed. This condition is due to the presence of billions of microscopic algal cells which have utilized the nutrient for growth and reproduction. The blue-green algae are often responsible for a pea green appearance, whereas other algae and various one-celled organisms cause the yellowish-brown colors in water. When conditions are optimal for development of algae, a dense bloom can develop quickly. These dense blooms of plankton algae cut down light penetration and thereby inhibit the reestablishment of those species killed in treatment, but the algae may turn out to be more objectionable than the original weed infestation.

Some aquatic vegetation is necessary for the reproduction and survival of certain fish (pickerel, golden shiners, and others). It follows that where desirable fish are dependent on aquatic vegetation, portions of water should be left untreated. It should be recognized also, that certain aquatic plants which provide habitat in lakes and ponds for waterfowl and fish, may be in conflict with other types of water use. Although aquatic plants do add essential oxygen to the water, under some conditions, their respiration and decomposition of organic matter may reduce the oxygen to dangerously low levels for fish survival. Even though aquatic plants do play an important role in food chains;

too many plants may contribute to overcrowded and poor quality fish populations.

There is no easy cure-all for controlling undesirable aquatic vegetation. Dredging to deepen shallow edges may help, but may also create hazards and fish management problems.

Aquatic plant control with chemicals can be successful and very satisfactory. Once a weed problem is under control, diligent treatment of regrowth is necessary to maintain control. It is much easier and less expensive to conduct periodic maintenance or to make spot treatments than it is to wait until treatment of the entire area is necessary.

Aquatic weeds are threats to many areas of the country. Two species are of special importance, hydrilla (**Hydrilla verticillata**) in the southern United States, and Eurasian watermilfoil (**Myriophyllum spicatum**) in the northern United States, but pondweeds (**Potamogeton** spp.) and filamentous bluegreen algae are widespread pests in all areas of the country. Although effective herbicides are available, it is often difficult to control hydrilla, watermilfoil, pondweed and other obnoxious weeds with herbicides, not only because they are submersed and therefore hard to reach with conventional methods of chemical treatment, but also because public perception of possible adverse effects precludes herbicidal treatment (14,16).

CHEMICAL CONTROL

Aquatic plants may be killed, controlled, and maintained at acceptable population densities by herbicides and plant growth inhibitors. Management of aquatic plant biomass by synthetic chemicals is, in general, the easiest and least expensive method available, but it may have undesirable effects, such as lack of target plant specificity, toxicity to animals, and persistence of residues. Chemicals (3,4,13,14,18) tested for control of aquatic weeds are:

Floating weeds:

2,4-D - 2,4-dichlorophenoxytacetic acid,
diquat - 6,7-dihydrodipyrido[1,2-$_a$:2,1-c] pyrazinediium ion,
endothall - 7-oxabicyclo[2.2.1]heptane-2,3-dicarboxylic acid.

Immersed broadleaf weeds:

2,4-D,
dalapon - 2,2-dichloropropionic acid,
glyphosate - N-(phosphonomethyl)glycine,

Submersed weeds and algae:

2,4-D,
copper sulfate, copper carbonate, and organic compounds of copper.
diquat,
dichlobenil - 2,6-dichlorobenzonitrile,
endothall,

Irrigation and drainage ditch banks:

2,4-D,
dalapon,
dichlobenil,
diquat,
glyphosate,

Irrigation and drainage canals:

acrolein,
aromatic solvent,
copper sulfate, copper carbonate and organic compounds of copper.
2,4-D,
endothall.

IRRIGATION AND DRAINAGE DITCH BANKS

Weeds and brush on ditch banks area a major problem in the supply of irrigation water and subsequent drainage of overflow water. They reduce the flow of water and cause flooding, seepage, increased evaporation and transportation loss, decreased water delivery and decreased drainage of water. They obstruct inspection and maintenance operation of the irrigation system and cause salt and sedimentation deposits in the irrigation canals. Ditchbank weeds are also a potential of weed infestation of cropland or other uses for the water. Ditch banks provide an extremely variable weed habitat. Within a few feet of the waterline, emergent weeds may be a problem. Over the top of the ditch bank, drouth-tolerant species may predominate. Plant control methods will depend on the particular plant species to be controlled, and subsequent use of the water "down stream". When spraying ditchbanks, the sprayer should always travel "up stream" to avoid concentration of the herbicide in the irrigation canal. Registered herbicide for this site application are listed above and in Tables 1.1 and 2.1.

IRRIGATION AND DRAINAGE CANALS

Aquatic plants in flowing water are the most difficult to control and because the water is moving from one location to another, possible hazards of herbicide use are greater. Do not irrigate crops with the treated water unless this is permitted on the label. Some irrigation systems carry water for domestic use, industrial use, and recreation use as well as the irrigation of crops. As the number of use increases, greater restrictions and precautions are required. When floating and emersed plants are found in flowing water, it becomes necessary to control these plants. Herbicides use are similar to those used in static water and they are applied according to the rate for the area covered rather than the volume of water in the irrigation canal. When submersed plants and algae are treated, effective control can be achieved only by continuously applying enough herbicide at a given point to maintain the needed concentration and contact time. The greater the cross sectional area of the canal, and the greater the rate of flow, the larger the volume of water that must be treated. Few herbicides are available for control of submersed aquatic plants and algae in flowing water. Those listed above and in Tables 1.1 and 1.2 are registered for this purpose. Copper sulfate used for control of algae is toxic to trout but only moderately toxic to most other species of fish. Grade B xylene and acrolein are highly toxic to fish and many other forms of aquatic life and are used in water delivery systems that contain few or no fish, and the chemical residues do not contaminate potable or recreational water bodies. Where there is limited flow, or during the off season flow, more toxic herbicides may be used.

NEW METHODS OF CHEMICAL CONTROL

New methods by which chemical herbicides are applied to weeds are important with regard to extent of control and effects upon non-target species. Herbicides and growth regulators are now formulated with organic polymers to control drift, on granules of various compositions, in oil droplets, or with synthetic plastics, elastomers, waxes, or naturally-occurring polymers that slow or control the release rate of these chemicals. Although herbicides and plant growth regulators are relatively non-persistent in natural environments; they cause changes in aquatic ecosystems; and their impacts must be judged in relation to (1) toxicity to the target species, (2) relative toxicity to non-target species, (3) fate of residues and their significance to water, fishes, crops, livestock, and foods, (4) conditions that affect toxicity, efficacy, and persistence, and (5) synergizing or antagonizing activity of carriers, formulations, metabolites, degradation products, or other pesticides (4,5,11,13,14).

AQUATIC WEED CONTROL PROBLEMS

Inventory of weed problems. Although this is not specifically a chemical control problem, it is very important to control programs. We need to know the extent of weed problems also in order to plan trial and development research and control personnel need to know the distribution of aquatic weed species for the areas to be controlled. Moreover, the inventory should relate to user group perceptions, which are very important with regard to weed control. For example, irrigation managers desire weed-free water whereas fishermen may want a margin of plants around the lake (12,13,14,15,16,17).

Basic data on aquatic weeds. Relatively little is known about the basic ecology of aquatic weeds. It is not known why a species may be a pest in one lake, but is in a reasonable biomass in a nearby lake. Hydrilla may be a pest in a lake for one year, but not in the following year, after which, it may become a pest again. A species may attain high biomass in one portion of a lake, but not another. If we knew why these phenomena occur, safe methods for control might be devised. Herbicides used for control of aquatic plants are not developed in relation to any physiological characteristics of those plants. In fact, they are usually herbicides that were developed for use on terrestrial plants and later found to be effective against aquatic weeds (3).

Maintenance level for aquatic weeds. In many areas of Florida, waterhyacinth is no longer a problem because of effective maintenance programs. Acceptable maintenance levels should be achieved for other aquatic plants. This is, however, especially difficult for submersed plants, and different treatment will be required for different water bodies in relation to weed species and individual characteristics of those bodies. Just as important is the level of control as related to effects on the whole system and what degree of control is acceptable in relation to use (3).

Effectiveness of 2,4-D for maintenance control. The herbicide 2,4-D is an effective and environmentally safe chemical for control of waterhyacinth. Insects and pathogens probably aid in that control. Diquat is now being used in South Florida, but is not as efficient or environmentally safe as 2,4-D. Diquat kills many non-target plants, such as bulrushes, but because the public perceives 2,4-D as a dangerous chemical, although it is not, diquat is used instead (3).

Controlled release formulations. Experimental formulations of controlled release formulations that allow low concentrations of herbicides to be effective, have been developed. These are particularly effective in preventing regrowth after application to hydrosoil when it is exposed during drawdowns or periods of low flow. It is estimated that these formulations will be effective for at least a complete growing season or a full year. As yet, there are not enough data to determine effects of long-term exposure of non-target organisms to the lowest concentration of 2,4-D that inhibits growth (5).

BIOLOGICAL CONTROL

Structure and dynamics in natural communities are regulated by complex biological phenomena, one of which is the effect of a predatory species on population density of a prey species. An important part of such population density control is the dampening of plant biomass by herbivores. Overproduction by primary producers in a system is compensated through consumption by herbivores, whose numbers and biomass are controlled. The result of such a system is maintenance of a constant biomass for a period of time (9).

Biological weed control by man attempts to use natural predators to control biomass of weed species. It is clear that a reproducing population of plant predators will not eradicate weeds, and that numbers of prey and predator will oscillate both existing at concentrations acceptable to man (12,13,14).

Application of biological controls to weed problems has met with moderate success. For example, the alligatorweed flea beetle (**Agasicles hygrophila**) has controlled alligatorweed (**Alternathera philoxeroides**) in Florida, Louisiana and Texas. A large amount of work is continuing on the use of the waterhyacinth weevil (**Eichhornia neochetina**) on waterhyacinth as a potential biological control of that plant.

Researchers in biological control of aquatic plants have a tremendous responsibility to environmental protection because of the complexity of aquatic ecosystems. The risk is compounded when the modification is irreversible, as is typically the case in introduction of non-native species that subsequently reproduce. Nevertheless, potential benefits from introduction of insects and pathogens for control of nuisance aquatic plants can outweigh the risks if strict guidelines are followed. Suggested guidelines include (1) the need for an introduction must be clearly established, (2) the organism must have a desirable ecological and economic impact, (3) the species must have minimal niche overlap with native species, (4) it should cause minimal reduction of nontarget species, and (5) field releases should be studied and ecological impact determined. Disease interrelationships should be carefully examined, and methods for control of the introduced species should be established prior to large scale introduction.

Use of Insects

Host specificity. There is a large gap in our knowledge of host specificity with regard to insects and aquatic plants. It is difficult, if not impossible, to test an insect against all plants that may be exposed to it. Also, an insect may feed on many plant species in the laboratory, yet be found on only one or two species in the field (3,6). The cost of introducing insects is very high. Finding suitable species, quarantine, and testing can take 8 to 10 years at a cost of several million dollars. However, the cost per acre may be relatively low (17). Besides killing the weeds, an insect could alter an ecosystem in an unacceptable way if it did not affect a favored plant species, thus making moot the problem of host specificity.

Use of Plant Pathogens

Most work on plant pathogens, such as fungi, has been done on terrestrial species. Little is known with regard to methods for isolation, maintenance, and testing of aquatic pathogens. Aquatic pathogens are very specialized. They are often obligate parasites that cannot readily be cultured. We need to learn how to culture them and how to expose submersed weeds to them. Many pathogen species occur in soil and water attacking plants in both systems. In most cases, we do not know if it is safe to use them for aquatic weed control. Genetic manipulation may be an important tool in development of plant pathogens. However, most mutations result in loss of pathogenicity, rather that enhanced pathogenicity (2). Once a pathogen is isolated and proven to be useful for weed control, cost of mass culturing and production on inocula may be relatively inexpensive, except for obligate parasites. Since numbers of pathogenic organisms may decline as plant numbers decline, it may be necessary periodically to reinfest local areas.

Use of Herbivorous Fishes

Grass carp. The major comments with regard to use of the grass carp (**Ctenopharyngodon idella**) are reservations on its ability to control vegetation and on possible adverse environmental effects. Although grass carp have controlled weeds in some areas, they have not done so in others. They are also known to have caused changes in water quality; some people fear that the carp may reduce stocks of sport fishes, such as bass and bluegill; and control, when it occurs, is slow compared to chemical and biological methods (3,4,5).

Hybrid carp. The hybrid carp, a cross between the female grass carp (**C. idella**) and the male bighead carp (**Hypophthalmichthyes nobilis**), has been proposed for introduction for weed control. It is now being tested in several laboratories and field situations. An important advantage of the hybrid over the grass carp is that the hybrid consumes both plants and filamentous algae, whereas the grass carp eats only plants. Testing of hybrid carp for weed control has begun recently in the United States, and its use, singly and in combination with other control methods, has been moderately successful (3,4,6,12).

MECHANICAL CONTROL AND HABITAT MANIPULATION

Mechanical control of aquatic weeds involves collection of plants with subsequent treatment and return to the water, or removal from the infested water body (harvest method). The former may be appropriate for eutrophic systems, but the harvest method is used most often. Ordinarily, plants are harvested by a mechanical device and transported to the shore, where other mechanical devices collect the harvest and either deposit it there or transport it elsewhere for disposal or use.

The types of machinery used for harvesting aquatic weeds have been described by Nichols (10). Choice of such equipment as harvesters, transporters, and weed ploughs depends upon: (1) the type of plant to be harvested, (2) the type of water body, (3) the debris or other foreign matter encountered, (4) the nature of the shoreline, (5) the prevailing weather conditions, (6) the harvesting concept utilized, and (7) the plant disposal system contemplated (3). Also of importance with regard to the objectives of management plans are: (1) cost, (2) results, and (3) ecological implications (10).

There are two main concerns with regard to mechanical controls: (1) cost including energy consumption, and (2) disposal of harvested weeds. The cost of harvesting and disposal of weeds is often prohibitive, especially when harvesting must be done on a large scale. Often, as with waterhyacinth, weeds grow almost as fast as they are harvested, so that harvesting must begin again shortly after an area is cleared.

Water constitutes approximately 90% of the weight of aquatic weeds, and when harvested, a relatively large amount of water may be removed from a heavily infested system. Also, the heavy weight and large volume of the weeds make them difficult to transport from their point of origin. Nevertheless, research is being done to make aquatic weeds useful, and if this is successful, harvesting may become an economically feasible method of aquatic weed control (7,10).

Habitat manipulation for control of aquatic weeds includes such procedures as: water level manipulation, dredging, artificial shading, nutrient limitation and inactivations, and gravel, sand, and other types of blanketing. Habitat manipulation limits growth by alteration of one or more physical or chemical factors required by plants.

Mechanical control was the first control method used for waterhyacinths in Florida and Louisiana around the turn of the century. Over the first 50 years or so of this century, several chemicals were tried or actually used operationally with varying degrees of success. Some were toxic to humans and non-target organisms, whereas others were not effective or were too expensive.

Since 1948, various combinations of mechanical harvesting systems have been tested by several agencies, the Florida Game and Freshwater Fish Commission conducting most of the initial tests with mechanical methods for control of waterhyacinth. The Commission designed and built two types of control devices: one was a fixed-point take out that allowed plants to drift with wind and currents until they were piled on the shore; the other was designed to macerate the plants and pump the macerate through a pipe to shore or back in the water (7).

Neither method was highly successful, and since these early beginnings, very few mechanical systems have been used continually in the state of Florida. Neither private enterprise nor governmental agencies has helped to develop mechanical control systems because (1) they are too expensive in terms of dollars, labor, and fuel, (2) control over a large area is slow when compared to chemical control, and (3) they are inflexible, i.e., each piece of equipment, or configuration of equipment, is designed to work at a specific site under certain environmental conditions. Mechanical control is further complicated by the size and cumbersomeness of the equipment, need for trained personnel, easements, disposal areas, support logistics for fuel and transportation of personnel, and a myriad of other complicating factors (10).

EFFECTS OF MECHANICAL HARVEST

Dispersal of weeds. Eurasian watermilfoil and hydrilla propagate by fragmentation, i.e., pieces break from the stock and may develop into complete plants. Any two-stage operation of cutting and collection is bound to cause fragmentation, which for Eurasian watermilfoil and hydrilla is a highly significant means of dispersal. Cutting and collection may compound problems with these weeds. However, in a single step operation of collection only, dispersal by fragmentation may not be significant (7,10).

Disposal of harvested weeds. The cost of weed disposal is often great, and makes mechanical harvesting economically uncompetitive with chemical control. However, in some cases, the harvest may be disposed of in the lake or reservoir itself and this would decrease cost.

Actually, when herbicides are used, the plants decompose in the water. Harvest may be returned to the general water mass after shredding or it may be baled and deposited on the shore. One experiment has been tried in Orange Lake in Florida. In this trial, harvested material placed on shore, decayed quickly without apparent detrimental effects (10,14).

Removal of nutrients from the aquatic ecosystem. Removal of weeds may be an effective method for removal of nutrients in some lakes. Four or five harvests may cause significant decrease in nutrients in an oligotrophic lake, whereas it may have little or no value in where waters contain naturally high concentrations of nutrients (7,10).

Utilization of harvested weeds. If aquatic weeds are to be utilized economically, there is a need for development of commercial products. These products will have to utilize the plant material after the water is removed (aquatic plants are at least 90% water, by weight). Fresh aquatic plants are very heavy, and the cost of hauling harvest overland to a processing plant is great. Profit from any commercial product will not lower the cost of mechanical field operations and hauling, so the total cost of harvesting, hauling, and preparation of product appears to be excessive (7,10).

INTEGRATED CONTROL

Integrated control of aquatic plants utilizes methods of chemical, biological, and mechanical control concurrently or sequentially in a systematic program for initial biomass reduction and long-term maintenance. It has two purposes: effective control, and minimal environmental impact by reduction of unwanted effects of any single method. The latter is achieved through synergistic interactions of methods applied at rates below those when each is used singly. For example, there is evidence that herbicidal treatment for biomass reduction of hydrilla, followed by introduction of grass carp for maintenance, will reduce the need for repeated herbicidal treatment and have little or no effect on sport fishes (14).

SUMMARY AND CONCLUSIONS

A substantial amount of research has been done on development of methods for integrated control of aquatic weeds. Such development relies heavily upon new information. Methods for use of insects and plant pathogens in integrated systems takes considerable time to develop. Integration of chemical, mechanical, and fishes probably offers the best opportunity for current development and application at partic-

ular sites of infestation. Chemical weed management is often undertaken to increase and to extend the recreation fishing and boating
potential of a water resource. If aquatic weed management is properly
employed, it will indeed result in the desired objective. Except in extreme cases, there are few if any, detrimental effects.

REFERENCES

1. Bartley, T.R. and E.O. Gangstad. 1975 Enviromental aspects of
   aquatic plant control. Journ of the Irrigation and Drainage Division, ASCE. 100:231-244.
2. Conway, K.E., R.E. Cullin, J.E. Freeman, and J.A. Cornell. 1979.
   Field evaluation of **Cercospora rodmanii** as a biological control of
   waterhyacinth. Misc. Paper A-19-6, Environmental Laboratory,
   U.S. Army Engineer Waterways Experiment Station, Vicksburg,
   MS. 51 pp.
3. Gangstad, E.O. 1980. Weed Control Methods for Public Health Applications. C.R.C. Press, Boca Raton, FL. 229 pp.
4. Gangstad, E.O. 1982. Weed Control Methods for Recreation Facilities Management. CRC Press Inc., Boca Raton, Florida. 297 pp.
5. Harris, F.W. 1979. State of the art - Chemical control: Controlled
   release herbicides. In Proceedings, Research Planning Conference on the Aquatic Plant Control Program. Misc. Paper A-79-7.
   Environmental Laboratory, U.S. Army Engineer Waterways Experiment Station, Vicksburg, MS pp 50-55.
6. Holm, L., L. Weldon and R. Blackburn. 1969. Aquatic Weeds. Sci.
   166:699-709.
7. Koegel, R.G., H.D. Brun, and D.F. Livermore. 1972. Improving surface water conditions through control and disposal of aquatic vegetation. Univ. Wisc. Water Resources Center - Report OWRR-B-
   018, Madison, Wisc. 46 pp.
8. Lawerence, J.M. & L.W. Weldon. 1966. Identification of Aquatic
   Weeds. Hyacinth Control J. 4:5-17.
9. Margalef, R. 1968. Perspectives in Ecological Theory. University of
   Chicago Press, Chicago. 111 pp.
10. Nichols, S.A. 1974. Mechanical and Habitat Manipulation for
    Aquatic Plant Management. Tech. Bull. No. 77, Department of Nat-
    ural Resources, Madison, Wisconsin. 34 pp.
11. Newroth, Peter. R. Case Studies of Aquatic Plant Management for
    Lake Preservation and Restoration in British Columbia, Canada in
    Restoration of Lakes and Inland Waters. pp. 146-152. International
    Symposium on Inland Waters and Lake Restoration, September 8-
    12, 1980. Portland, Maine. U.S. EPA Office of Water Regulations

and Standards and Organization for Economic Cooperation and Development. Washington, DC.

12. Szehely, F. 1982. Environmental impact of large hydroelectric projects in tropical countries. Water Supply and Management 6:233-242. Texas University, Austin, Texas.

13. University-EPA-USDA Ad Hoc Committee. 1973. The development of data for registration of pesticides for specialty and small acreage crops and other minor uses. Department of Entomology, Michigan State University, East Lansing, Michigan.

14. University-EPA-USDA Ad Hoc Committee. 1977. Report of the SEA Research Planning Conference on Aquatic Weed Control. Department of Botany, University of California, Davis, California.

15. U.S. Department of Agriculture, ARS. 1968. Extent and cost of weed control with herbicides and an evaluation of important weeds, 1965. ARS 34-102, U.S. Government Printing Office, Washington, D.C.

16. U.S. Department of Agriculture, ARS. 1970. Selected weeds of the United States. Agricultural Handbook No. 366. U.S. Government Printing Office, Washington, D.C.

17. U.S. Department of Agriculture. 1977. Biological control of alligatorweed, 1959-1972. Tech. Bull. No. 1547, Agricultural Research Service, Washington, D.C. 98 pp.

18. Ware, G.W. 1975. Pesticides, An Autotutorial Approach. W.H. Freeman Co. San Francisco, CA. 191 pp.

Table 1.1. Common Waterweeds, Type of Waterweed, Prevention and Control.

Common and scientific name	Type of waterweed	How to prevent	How to control
Algae, filamentous, branched, Pithophora.	Algae	Uncertain	Algae-eating fish.
Algae, filamentous, single-filament	Algae	Avoid organic matter	Copper sulfate; algae-eating fish
Algae, microscopic	Algae	Do not fertilize	Copper sulfate.
Alligator weed, Alternathera philoxeroides.	Marsh plant	Uncertain	2,4-D; alligatorweed flea beetle
Arrow-arum, Peltandra virginica	Marsh plant	Deepen[4]	2,4-D.[2]
Arrow, Sagittaria spp	Marsh plant	Deepen;[4] sod[1]	2,4-D.[2]
Beakrush, Rynchospora spp	Marsh plant	Deepen;[4] graze[3]	2,4-D.[2]
Beggarticks, Bidens spp	Marsh plant	Deepen;[4] sod[1]	2,4-D.[2]
Bladderwort, Utricularia spp	Submersed waterweed	Uncertain	2,4-D granules
Bulrush, Scirpus ssp	Marsh plant	Deepen[4]	2,4-D.[2]
Burreed, Sparganium spp	Marsh plant	Deepen;[4] sod[1]	2,4-D.[2]
Buttercup, Ranunclus spp	Marsh plant	Deepen[4]	2,4-D;[2] 2, 4-D granules.
Buttonbush, Cephalanthus occidentalis.	Shrub	Sod;[1] pull	glyphosate.
Cattail, Typha spp	Marsh plant	Deepen;[4] graze[3]	dalapon; 2,4-D.[2]
Cordgrass, Spartina spp	Marsh plant	Graze;[3] deepen[4]	dalaphon.
Cowlily, Nuphar advena	Rooted plant with floating leaves	Deepen;[4] shade[5]	2,4-D granules.

See footnotes at end of table.

Table 1.1. Common Waterweeds, Type of Waterweed, Prevention and Control. (cont.)

Common and scientific name	Type of waterweed	How to prevent	How to control
Cutgrass, Leersia spp	Marsh plant	Graze[3]	2,4-D;[2] dalapon;
Duckweeds, Lemna, Wolffia, Spirodela	Floating plant	Uncertain	Ducks; 2,4-D;[2]
Eelgrass, Zostera marina	Submersed plant	Uncertain	2,4-D granules.
Elodea, Elodea spp	Submersed plant	Uncertain	2,4-D granules.
Fanwort, Cabomba spp	Submersed plant	Uncertain	2,4-D granules.
Floatingheart, Nymphoides spp	Rooted plant with floating leaves	Uncertain	2,4-D;[2] cut
Frogbit, Limnobium spongia	Marsh plant	Deepen[4]	2,4-D;[2]
Gaintcutgrass, Zizaniopsis milacea	Marsh plant	Graze[3]	Dalapon, glyphosate.
Grasses, Graminea	Marsh plant	Graze[3]	Dalapon; 2,4-D.[2]
Hornwort, Ceratophyllum demersum	Submersed waterweed	Uncertain	2,4-D granules.
Horsetail, Equisetum spp	Marsh plant	Deepen[4]	2,4-D.[2]
Hydrilla, Hydrilla verticillata	Submersed waterweed	Uncertain	Diquat, endothall
Lizards-tails, Saururus cernuus	Marsh plant	Deepen[4]	2,4-D
Lotus, American, Nelumbo lutea	Rooted plant with floating leaves	Deepen[4]	2,4-D.[2]
Ludwigia, Ludwigia spp	Marsh plant	Deepen[4]	2,4-D.[2]

See footnotes at end of table.

Table 1.1. Common Waterweeds, Type of Waterweed, Prevention and Control. (cont.)

Common and scientific name	Type of waterweed	How to prevent	How to control
Maidencane, Panicum hemitomon	Marsh plant	Deepen[4]	Dalapon.
Mannagrass, Glyceria spp	Marsh plant	Graze[3]	Dalapon; 2,4-D.[2]
Marestail, Hippuris vulgaris	Marsh plant	Deepen[4]	Dalapon; 2,4-D.
Mermaidweed, Prosperinaca spp	Submersed waterweed	Deepen[4]	Dalapon; 2,4-D.
Mudplantain, Heteranthera spp	Marsh plant	Deepen[4]	Dalapon; 2,4-D.
Naiad, Najas spp	Submersed waterweed	Uncertain	2,4-D granules.
Parrotfeather, Myriophyllum spp	Submersed waterweed	Uncertain	2,4-D granules.
Pennywort, Hydrocotyle spp	Marsh plant	Deepen[4]	2,4-D.[2]
Pickerelweed, Pontederia cordata	Submersed waterweed	Deepen[4]	2,4-D.[2]
Potamogeton, Potamogeton spp	Submersed waterweed	Uncertain	2,4-D granules; diquat; endothall ···
Reed, common, Phragmites communis	Marsh plant	Deepen;[4] graze[3]	Dalapon, glyphosate.
Rush, Juncus spp	Marsh plant	Deepen[4]	2,4-D.[2]
See footnotes at end of table.			
Sawgrass, Cladium jamaicensis	Marshplant	Deepen[4] or dry out	Uncertain.

See footnotes at end of table.

Table 1.1. Common Waterweeds, Type of Waterweed, Prevention and Control. (cont.)

Common and scientific name	Type of waterweed	How to prevent	How to control
Sedge, Carex spp	Marsh plant	Deepen[4]	2,4-D;[2] dalapon.
Smartweed, Polygonum spp	Marsh plant	Deepen;[4] cut	2,4-D.[2]
Spatterdock, see cowlily.			
Spikerush, Eleocharis acicularis and E. baldwinni.	Marsh plant	Deepen;[4] water level	Dalapon.
Stonewort, Chara spp	Submersed waterweed	Uncertain	Copper sulfate.
Sweetflag, Acorus calamus	Marsh plant	Deepen[4]	2,4-D.[2]
Tear-thumb, Polygonum spp	Marsh plant	Deepen[4]	2,4-D.[2]
Three-cornered grass, see bulrush.			
Waterchestnut, Trapa nutans	Floating plant	Uncertain	2,4-D.[2]
Waterfern, Azolla caroliniana and Salvinia rotundifolia.	Floating plant	Uncertain	2,4-D.[2]
Watergrass, Carolina, Hydrochloa	Submersed waterweed	Deepen;[4] graze[3]	2,4-D.[2]
Waterhemlock, Ciuta spp	Marsh plant	Deepen[4]	2,4-D.[2]
Waterhemp, Acnida spp	Marsh plant	Deepen[4]	2,4-D.[2]
Water-hyacinth, Eichhornia crassipes	Floatingplant	Uncertain	2,4-D amine salts.
Waterhyssop, Bacopa spp	Marsh plant	Deepen[4]	2,4-D.[2]

See footnotes at end of table.

Table 1.1. Common Waterweeds, Type of Waterweed, Prevention and Control. (cont.)

Common and scientific name	Type of waterweed	How to prevent	How to control
Waterlettuce, Pistia stratiotes	Floating plant	Uncertain	Diquat
Waterlily, Nymphaea spp	Rooted plant with floating leaves	Uncertain	2,4-D granules.
Waterplantain, Alisma spp	Marsh plant	Deepen[4]	Diquat
Waterprimrose, Jussiaea spp	Marsh plant	Deepen[4]	2,4-D;[2] 2,4-D granules.
Waterstarwort, Callitriche spp	Submersed waterweed	Uncertain	Diquat.
Waterstargrass, see mudplantain.			
Watershield, Brasenia schreberi	Rooted plant with floating leaves	Uncertain	2,4-D granules.
Waterwillow, Decodon verticillatus	Marsh plant Deepen[4]	2,4-D[2]	
Widgeongrass, Ruppia maritima	Marsh plant	Fresh water	2,4-D granules.
Willow, Salix spp	Tree	Graze;[3]	2,4-D.[2]

1. Establish good grass sod around the pond.
2. Esters of 2,4-D are mixed in diesel oil.
3. Graze with livestock or mow frequently.
4. Deepen edges.

Source: updated and adopted from, Agriculture Handbook NO. 447, 1973. Agricultural Research Service, U.S. Department of Agriculture, Washington, D.C.

See footnotes at end of table.

Table 2.1   Herbicides for Aquatic Weed Control by Site and Types of Weeds.

Algae in Lakes, Ponds, Reservoirs, and Irrigation Channels

Copper sulfate pentahydrate	0.5 to 2.0 ppmw (concentration) poured into water of irrigation channels or applied over water surface of impoundments early in the spring and at 2 to 3 week intervals thereafter.
	May be toxic to fish, especially trout. Safe in potable and irrigation water. Do not wait until severe algae problem develops before making application.
Dimethylamine salts or mono and di of endothall (Hydrothal 191)	0.05 to 0.2 ppmw (concentration) sprayed on the water or injected below the water surface when algal growth appears.
	May be toxic to fish in dosages in excess of 0.3 ppm. Do not use treated water for irrigation or agricultural sprays on food crops, for watering livestock or for domestic purposes within 7 days after application.

Algae in Ponds

Simazine (Aquazine)	1.4 to 3.4 lbs ai/A ft of water applied when 5 to 10% of the pond surface is covered with scum.
	Apply to ponds with little or no outflow only. Trees on shoreline may be injured or killed. Water from treated ponds should not be used for irrigation, livestock water or human consumption until 12 months following treatment. Fishing and swimming are permitted at any time.

Submersed Weeds in Flowing Canals and Ditches

Acrolein (Aqualin Herbicide)	0.1 ppmw (concentration) for 48 hrs in canal flows of more than 300 cfs, or 0.6 ppmw for 8 hrs in canal flows of less than 400 cfs applied when weed growth is no more than 4 to 6 inches tall.

Dimethylamine salts of mono and di of endothall	1 to 5 ppmw (concentration) sprayed on the water or injected below the water surface after growth has developed in late spring or early summer.
(Hydrothal 191)	Toxic to fish. Therefore manufacturer suggests that application be made by licensed applicators only. Do not use treated water for any purpose with 14 to 25 days after treatment depending on concentration applied. Marginal or sectional treatments rather than an overall type treatment is recommended.

Coontail and Milfoil in Lakes and Ponds

2,4-D granules (Several Mfgs)	20 lbs ai/A applied in spring or early summer before plants reach the water surface.
	Apply granules uniformly over water surface either by hand or with a rotary spreader. Do not use treated water for domestic or irrigation purposes. If weeds are abundant, treat 1/3 of the pond or lake at a time to avoid fish kill (due to low oxygen level from decomposing weeds). Safe for fish at rate given.

Emersed, Marginal and Bank Weeds Along Drainage Ditches

Dalapon (Dowpon-M)	15 to 25 lbs ai/A applied in spring or early summer before target species flower.
	Grass control only. Use at least 100 gpa of water carrier. Add at least 3 pints of a nonionic adjuvant per 100 gal of spray solution. Do not contaminate water used for irrigation or domestic purposes. See non-cropland section in this book for timing on cattail.
Glyphosate (Roundup)	Same as for irrigation ditches.
Petroleum oils	100 gpa sprayed on growing weeds.
	Do not contaminate domestic or irrigation water, or water containing fish. Control will be of short duration.
2,4-D (Several Mfgs)	2 to 3 lbs ai/A applied as foliage spray in the spring or early summer.

Treatments should be repeated every 3 to 4 weeks during the remainder of the season. Do not allow man or animal to drink treated water. Toxic to fish and many other aquatic organisms. Must have specialized equipment for application. Use only oxygen-free nitrogen for a pressurizing agent.

Petroleum distillate (xylene)

8 to 10 gal per cfs of water flow applied over a 30 to 60-minute period anytime after weed growth is well established but before it becomes matted at the surface or causes channeling of water.

Mix with emulsifier and inject under pressure, preferably in turbulent flow. Use 1-1/2 gal or emulsifier per 100 gal of xylene. Toxic to fish and many other aquatic organisms. Do not flood irrigate seedling crop plants with treated water.

Submersed Weeds in Nonflowing Canals and Ditches

Diquat (Diquat Water Weed Killer)

1 to 4 lbs ai/A injected below the water surface before weed growth reaches the surface.

Do not use treated water for animal consumption, swimming, spraying or irrigation for 10 days after treatment. Do not use treated water for drinking purposes until 14 days after treatment. Do not let spray come in contact with skin, eyes or clothing. Do not breathe spray mist. Wear protective clothing. Safe for fish at the rates given. Do not use in turbid water. This treatment is not effective on the attached algae, chara.

Submersed Weeds in Lakes and Ponds

Dichlobenil (Carsoron Aq-10G)

7 to 10 lbs ai/A applied before or immediately after week growth emerges from the hydrosoil.

Apply granules in early spring to exposed lake or pond bottom or over water surface. Do not use treated water for irrigation or drinking. Do not use fish from treated water for food or feed within 90 days after treatment.

Simazine
(Aquazine)

3.4 to 6.8 lbs ai/A ft of water applied in the spring while plants are actively growing and before they reach the water surface.

Apply to ponds with little or no outflow only. Trees on shoreline may be injured or killed. Water from treated ponds should not be used for irrigation, livestock water or human consumption until 12 months following treatment. Fishing and swimming are permitted at any time.

Diquat (Diquat
Water Weed
Killer)

0.25 to 2.5 ppmw (concentration) injected below the water surface before weeds reach the surface.

Do not use treated water for animal consumption, swimming, spraying or irrigation for 10 days after treatment. Do not use treated water for drinking purposes until 14 days after treatment. Do not let spray come in contact with skin, eyes or clothing. Do not breathe spray mist. Wear protective clothing. Safe for fish at the rates given. If weeds are abundant, treat 1/3 of the pond or lake at a time to avoid fish kill (due to low oxygen level from decomposing weeds). Do not use in turbid water. Not effective on the attached algae, chara.

Dipotassium salt
of endothall
(Aquathol)

1 to 5 ppmw (concentration) spread or sprayed on the water or injected below the water surface, after growth has developed in late spring or early summer, and water temperatures have reached a consistent 62° to 65°F.

Do not use fish from the treated water for food or feed with 3 days after treatment. Do not use treated water for watering of livestock or other domestic purposes within 14 days of treatment. Do not use treated water for irrigation of crops. This formulation, at given concentrations, is not effective on elodea or chara. If weeds are abundant treat 1/3 of the pond or lake at a time to avoid fish kill (due to low oxygen level from decomposing weeds).

Broadleaf control. Use at least 100 gpa of water
carrier for ground application and a least 7.5 gpa
for aerial application. Regrowth of perennials
such as Canada thistle may require retreatment
in the fall.

Emersed, Marginal and Bank Weeds Along Irrigation Ditches

Dalapon
(Dowpon-M)

10 lbs ai/A applied in spring or early summer
before target species flower.

Grass control only. Use at least 100 gpa of water
carrier. Add at least 3 pints of a nonionic
adjuvant per 100 gal of spray solution. Minimize
contact of spray on water surface. Do not spray
more than 2 miles of the same ditchbank during
any 24-hour period for ditches carrying less than
50 cfs water. Fishing restricted within calendar
year of treatment in treated waters.

Glyphosate
(Roundup)

.75 to 3.75 lbs ai/A applied when weeds are in
succulent condition (refer to label for growth
stage of perennial weeds).

Apply to dry ditches or canals only. Rainfall
occurring with 12 hours after application may
reduce effectiveness. Do not use glyphosate in
galvanized or mild steel tanks.

2,4-D (Several
Mfgs)

2 to 3 lbs ai/A applied as foliage spray in the
spring or early summer.

Broadleaf weed control. Use at least 100 gpa of
water carrier for ground application and at least
7.5 gpa for aerial application. Regrowth of
perennials such as Canada thistle may require
retreatment in the fall.

Broadleaf, Floating, Emersed, Marginal, and Bank Weeds of Ponds
and Lakes

2,4-D (Several
Mfgs)

2 to 3 lbs ai/A applied as foliage spray in the
spring or early summer.

Use at least 100 gpa of water carrier for ground
application and at least 7.5 gpa for aerial
application. Regrowth of perennials such as
Canada thistle may require retreatment in the fall.

Floating Weeds in Lakes, Ponds, Irrigation Canals, and Drainage
Ditches

Diquat (Diquat Water Weed Killer)	1 to 1.5 lbs ai/A applied whenever weeds becomes a problem.
	Apply in at least 150 gal per acre water carrier for ground application and at least 7.5 gal per acre for aerial application. Do not allow spray to drift or come in contact with adjacent crops. Do not use treated water for animal consumption, swimming, spraying or irrigation for 10 days after treatment. Do not use treated water for drinking purposes until 14 days after treatment. Safe for fish at the rates given. Do not let spray come in contact with skin, eyes or clothing. Do not breathe spray mix. Wear protective clothing.

Source: updated and adopted from, Agriculture Handbook NO. 447, 1973. Agricultural Research Service. U.S. Department of Agriculture, Washington, D.C.

IDENTIFICATION OF AQUATIC WEEDS

J. M. LAWRENCE and LYLE W. WELDON
Professor (Fisheries), Auburn University Agricultural Experiment
Station, Auburn, Alabama, and Research Agronomist, Crops
Research Division, Agricultural Research Service, U.S. Department
of Agriculture, Plantation Field Laboratory, Fort Lauderdale, Florida

INTRODUCTION

Aquatic plant growths in any body of water create problems involved with practically all water uses. A knowledge of the identity of over one-hundred species of aquatic plants which seriously affect water resources is necessary if effective and efficient control practices are to be employed. Since botanists may not be available to name every species of plant involved in a particular aquatic weed problem, the following simple outline of the major plant groups based upon their size, shape, and growth habits has been developed:

Plankton algae
Filamentous algae
Submersed weeds
Emersed weeds
Marginal weeds
Floating weeds

These major groups are further divided into sub-groups which include phyla, families, and genera of aquatic plants. Individual species are then placed under the appropriate genera.

Descriptions of these major groups, including a listing of the common and scientific name of many of the plant species in each group, and a descriptive illustration of some of the most important species are given in this paper.

The intent of this paper is not to present a taxonomic classification of aquatic plants. Rather, it is an attempt to set forth groupings of plants based upon morphological characteristics and occupancy of ecological niches that may be useful to a majority of persons involved in aquatic plant control at the present time.

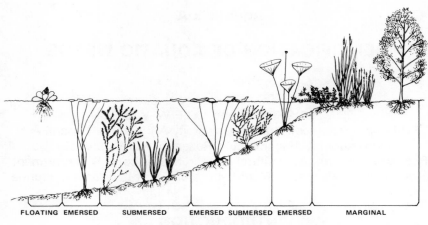

FLOATING EMERSED   SUBMERSED   EMERSED SUBMERSED EMERSED   MARGINAL

SPATIAL RELATIONSHIPS OF AQUATIC PLANTS

ALGAE

The freshwater algae are diverse in shape, color, size, and habitat. Some authorities have divided these algae into as many as nine phyla. A descrption of all species of algae would be as comprehensive as writing about all land plants, mosses, ferns, fungi, and seed plants.

For practical field work the algae are divided into two groups, plankton and filamentous algae, and are characterized by their growth form.

PLANKTON ALGAE

This group, sometimes called phytoplankton to separate them from the microscopic animal forms called zooplankton, include the truly aquatic, microscopic, single-cell, colonial, and simple filament forms of plants. They are the basic link in the conversion of inorganic constituents in water into organic matter. The rate at which this conversion occurs depends upon the abundance of algae in a given area at a given time. When present in sufficient numbers these plants impart colors to the water varying from green to yellow to red to black. They may also congregate at or near the water surface and form so-called "water blooms", or "scums".

Based upon their taxonomic characters, the major plankton algae have been separated into the following phyla:

GREEN ALGAE

Chlorophyta (Green algae). Unicellular or colonial, cells contain plastids in which chlorophyll is predominant.

Chrysophyta (Yellow-green or Yellow-brown algae). Including diatoms and desmids. Unicellular or colonial. Pigment in chromatophores in which yellow or brown often predominates. Diatoms appear more abundant in colder waters.

Euglenophyta (Euglenoids). Cells solitary, swimming by one (1) or two (2) flagella. A gullet and eye spot (red) present at anterior end of many species.

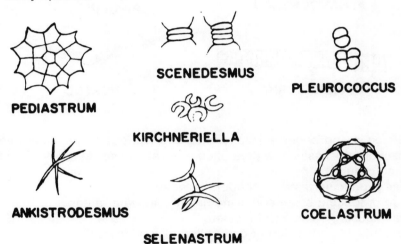

PEDIASTRUM

SCENEDESMUS

PLEUROCOCCUS

KIRCHNERIELLA

ANKISTRODESMUS

SELENASTRUM

COELASTRUM

BLUE GREEN ALGAE

Cyanophyta (Bluegreen algae). Unicellular or colonial, or simple filaments. Pigment in solution and coloring entire protoplast. Cell wall thin often covered with gelatinous sheath.

Cryptophyta. Cells solitary or colonial, swimming by means of 2 lateral or sub-apical flagella. Chromatophores large and brown.

Pyrrhophyta (Dino-flagellates). Cells solitary, swimming by means of 2 flagella, one commonly wound transversely around cell and the other extended posteriorly from point of flagella attachment.

Diatoms are most abundant in spring and fall (50°-60°F. optimum water temperature), the green algae are most abundant when water temperatures are 60°-80°F., and the bluegreen algae are never abundant at water temperatures less than 70°F.

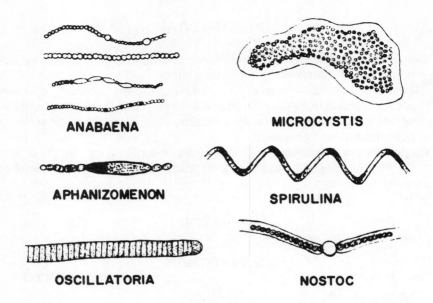

ANABAENA

MICROCYSTIS

APHANIZOMENON

SPIRULINA

OSCILLATORIA

NOSTOC

Biologist and engineers concerned with various management and utilization processes of waters often separate these algae into the following groups:

Algae producing tastes and odors in water.

Algae producing scum and slime growths in water areas.

Algae causing coloration of waters.

Algae causing corrosion of concrete and steel in contact with water.

Algae causing interference in coagulation processes.

Algae producing substances toxic to animal life.

Algae that are parasitic to plant and animal life.

A major beneficial role of plankton algae is removal of carbon dioxide from the water in the process of photosynthesis' during daylight, and the production of oxygen as a by-product of photosynthesis.

FILAMENTOUS ALGAE

Members of this group of algae belong primarily to the phylum Chrlorophyta. These plants are filaments of single cells united end to end, and may appear as a single thread, as branched filaments, as a net, or as erect, stem-like, whorled branches with forked "leaves". These plants have no true roots, stems or leaves.

Certain of the attached or supported single filament forms which grow in cooler weather have been utilized as control measures for certain rooted submersed aquatic weeds in fish ponds. Since these algae die at onset of hot weather, their death seemingly triggers the death of the supporting higher plants.

Other species of single as well as branched filament forms grow in both cool and warm weather and are generally considered a nuisance in whatever body of water in which they occur. Distribution of species of the following genera of algae seemingly is rather general throughout the United States:

Zygnema—Single filament form of algae, each cell with two star-shaped chloroplasts. Some species with conspicuous gelantinous sheath.

Spirogyra—Single filament form of algae. Diameter cells very small to fairly large. Chloroplast in cells definitely spiraled. May form green clouds of cottony growths in still waters.

Oedogonium—Single filament form in which cells are not cylindrical, being slightly larger at anterior end. Always with one or more ring-like scars at anterior end just below cross wall.

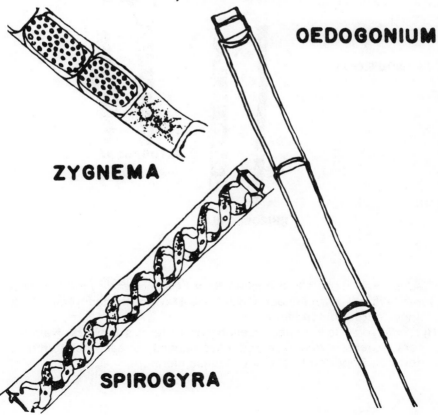

OEDOGONIUM

ZYGNEMA

SPIROGYRA

Mougeotia—Single filament form of algae with 1 band-like chloroplast per cell.

Rhizoclonium—Mainly single filament, coarse, wiry, form of algae. Cells slender usually three or more times as long as their diameter.

Pithophora—Irregularly branched filaments with barrel-shaped akinetes scattered throughout the filaments. Texture of filaments coarse, feeling like wet cotton to touch.

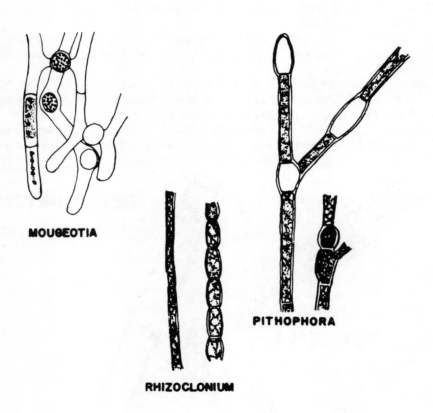

MOUGEOTIA

RHIZOCLONIUM

PITHOPHORA

Cladophora—Irregularly branched form of algae with cylindrical cells and without barrel-shaped akinetes. May form cladophora balls under northern conditions.

Hydrodictyon—Cells united at each end to form a network. Nets become extensive due to reproductive capacity of each cell to form a new net. Reported in ancient Chinese literature.

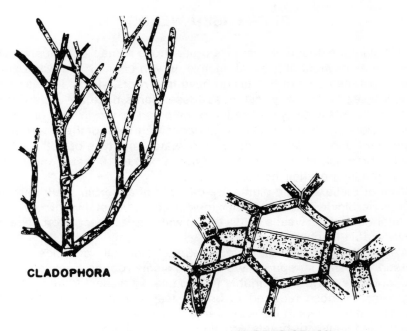

CLADOPHORA

HYDRODICTYON

Chara—Plants large, with erect stem-like whorled branches and forked leaves that are rough to the touch. Crushed plants produce musk-like odor.

Nitella—Plants large with erect, stem-like, whorled branches and forked leaves that are delicate in appearance and not rough to touch. Crushed plants do not produce musk-like odor

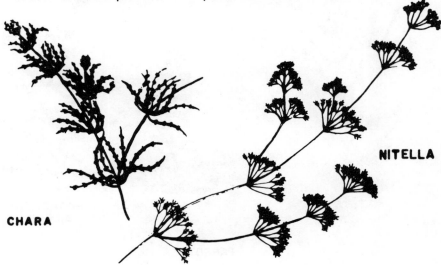

NITELLA

CHARA

SUBMERSED WEEDS

The plants included in this group are those rooted aquatics which produce all or most of their vegetative growth beneath the water surface. Most members of this group have true roots, stems, leaves, and produce seeds. In many instances these plants have an underwater leaf form, a totally different floating or emersed leaf form, and produce their flowers on an aerial stalk. Abundance of growth of these weeds is dependent upon depth and turbidity of water, and type of bottom. For most submersed plants a maximum depth of 8 to 10 feet in clear waters is the limit of their habitat.

Most of these aquatic plants are capable of absorbing nutrients as well as herbicides through either their roots or vegetative growth.

Major obnoxious weeds in this group with a brief description of each family are as follows:

Watermilfoil Family—*Haloragidaceae.* Perennial aquatics, submersed with slender sparingly branched stems rooting freely at lower nodes. Leaves whorled, variable from pinnately dissected into filiform segments to those reduced to bracts, leaf dissection variable from submersed to emersed forms. Flowers very small, borne either in axils of emersed leaves or bracts. Members of this family fairly well distributed throughout the United States.

Eurasian milfoil—*Myriophyllum spicatum*
Parrotfeather—*Myriophyllum brasiliense*
Broadleaf milfoil—*Myriophyllum heterophyllum*

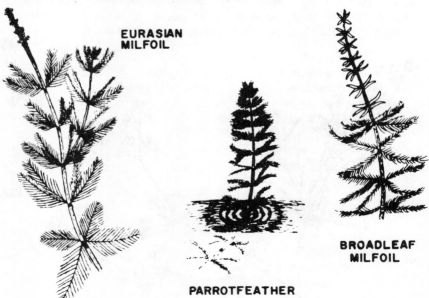

EURASIAN MILFOIL

PARROTFEATHER

BROADLEAF MILFOIL

Hornwort Family—*Ceratophyllaceae.* Submersed, rootless aquatic plants with slender main branch and scattered lateral branches. Lower end of stem frequently anchored in bottom mud. Leaves in whorls on stem, divided into slender, stiff, hooked, segments that are crowded toward apex by shortening of internodes to give shoots the "coontail" appearance. Only one genus but well distributed over the United States.

Common Coontail—*Ceratophyllum demersum*

Waterlily Family—*Nymphaeaceae.* Submersed aquatic plant with slender, branched stem, opposite or whorled, finely dissected leaves and with upper leaves that are entire and oblong and floating on surface. Flowers small, solitary on axillary peduncle and generally emersed. One species, widespread over eastern half of United States.

Cabomba—*Cabomba caroliniana*

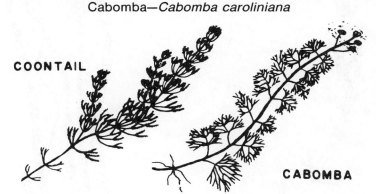

COONTAIL

CABOMBA

Pondweed Family—*Potamogetonaceae.* Fresh or brackish water submersed aquatic plants with creeping rootstocks. Leaves mostly alternate, may be opposite, on erect jointed stems. Leaves all alike or may be 2 kinds, all submersed or some of them floating. Submersed leaves thin and linear or all broad, emersed leaves broad, more or less elliptical and petioled. Seed heads small and crowded into spikes. Spikes raised to surface on long peduncle and/or submersed on short peduncle. Winter buds produced in axils of leaves of some species, creeping rootstocks of other species may terminate in small tubers. The largest family of truly aquatic plants, widely distributed throughout the United States, and one of the most troublesome groups of submersed aquatic plants.

Pondweeds—*Potamogeton* spp.
Sago pondweed—*P. pectinatus*
Waterthread pondweed—*P. diversifolius*
Curlyleaf pond—*P. crispus*
Widgeon grass—*Ruppia maritima*
Horned pondweed—*Zannichellia palustris*

Frogbit Family—*Hydrocharitaceae.* Perennial, slender-stemmed, branching, submersed aquatic plants with whorled thin linear leaves and fibrous roots, or submersed plants with long, linear clustered leaves at nodes of rhizomes. Flowers borne on peduncle above surface of water.

Brazilian waterweed—*Elodea densa*
American waterweed—*E. canadensis*
Eelgrass—*Vallisneria americana*

ELODEA

EELGRASS

Naiad Family—*Najadaceae.* Submersed aquatic plants with slender branches and fibrous roots. Leaves opposite or crowded into apparent whorls, finely toothed, dilated at base often with prominent stipules. About 35 species inhabiting fresh or brackish waters of temperate and tropical regions.

Naiads—*Najas* spp.
Southern naiad—*N. guadalupensis*
Slender naiad—*N. flexilis*

Pickerelweed Family—*Pontederiaceae.* Perennial or annual, floating or rooted aquatic plants with creeping rootstocks and fibrous roots. Leaves linear and thin on slender, branched, leafy stems. Flowers mostly solitary, appearing star-shaped, borne on spathe above water. Members of this family widely distributed throughout the United States.

Waterstargrass—*Heteranthera dubia*

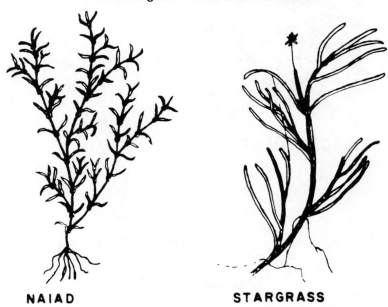

NAIAD   **STARGRASS**

Bladderwort Family—*Lentibulariaceae.* Submersed or floating, rootless plants with flaccid, finely dissected or fliform simple leaves. Many of leaf segments with small bladders that have little trap doors. These bladders may trap small aquatic animals which are digested and may serve as partial nourishment for the plant. Solitary flowers appear above water on short, erect pedicel and are either yellow or purple in color.

Bladderworts—*Utricularia* spp.

Sedge Family—*Cyperaceae*. Perennial plants having general appearance of grasses, fibrous roots and solid stems, submersed stems may root at joints. Leaves linear, parallel-veined, basal or alternate on stem, and with closed sheath. Flowers borne in axils of scales (glumes) in spikelets. Single species but with many varieties, distributed throughout the United States.

Slender Spikerush (Freshwater needle rush)—*Eleocharis acicularis*

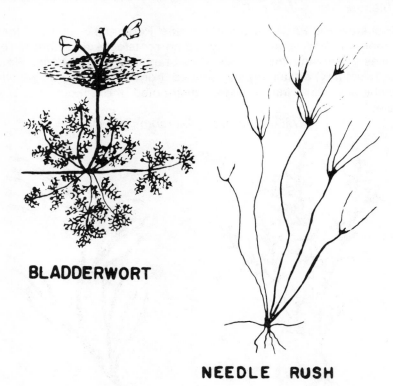

BLADDERWORT

NEEDLE   RUSH

EMERSED WEEDS

This group includes those plants that are rooted in the bottom muds and produce a majority of their leaves and flowers at or above the water surface. Some species possess leaves that are flat and float entirely upon the water surface. Other species have leaves that are saucer-shaped or whose margins are irregular or fluted. These latter types of leaves do not float entirely upon the water surface. Rather, they offer sheltered water areas beneath the leaf that are suitable habitats for mosquitoes. Leaf size and point of attachment is also variable in this group. Size ranges from a diameter of 2 inches to as much as 18 inches. Point of stem attachment may be at the leaf margin or within the leaf margin. The presence of these floating-leaf species provides sufficient shade to eliminate a suitable habitat for submersed weeds. These plants occupy clear water areas to depths of 10 feet or more.

Since emersed weeds and submersed weeds prefer the same type habitat, the elimination of emersed weeds usually will permit submersed weeds to become established. The advisability of emersed weed control depends upon the proposed management of a water area. While it is cheaper to control emersed weeds, it is generally conceded that certain of the floating, flat-leafed weeds produce fewer problems with water management than do the partially floating-leaf species or the submersed weeds.

The major obnoxious weeds in the emersed group with a brief description of families are as follows:

Cress Family—*Cruciferae*. Perennial aquatic herb with creeping stems, rooting at nodes. Leaves alternate and pinnately compounded, with peppery flavor. Introduced from Europe, but distributed over most of United States.

Watercress—Nasturtium officinales

Figwort Family—*Scrophulariaceae*. Creeping, fleshy herbs, rooting at nodes, leaves opposite, borne on stem and entire. Stems may be covered with crinkled hairs, flowers solitary, pale blue, purple, or white, borne on short stalk in axils of leaves.

Water Hyssop—Bacopa caroliniana

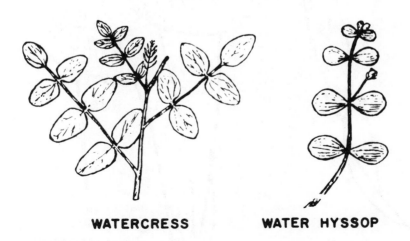

WATERCRESS   **WATER HYSSOP**

Waterlily Family—*Nymphaeaceae*. Perennial aquatic plants with large, creeping, often branched, rootstocks. Leaves may be large, elliptical or ovate in shape, sometimes emersed sometimes floating, submersed portions of stems and underside of floating elliptical leaves of one species covered with mucilaginous material. Flowers may be solitary and emersed or floating, or small and emersed.

Banana waterlily—*Nymphaea mexicana*
Fragrant waterlily—*N. tuberosa*
Spatterdock—*Nuphar advena*
American lotus—*Nelumbo lutea*
Watershield—*Brasenia schreberi*

Watershield has elliptical, flat, floating leaves that have a mucilaginous covering on the underside of leaves and submersed stems. There are few mosquito problems connected with watershield growths since the leaves are flat on water surface.

Spatterdock has similar habitat requirements to white water-lilies. The leaf is more heart-shaped and the flowers are almost oval with a distinctive seed case.

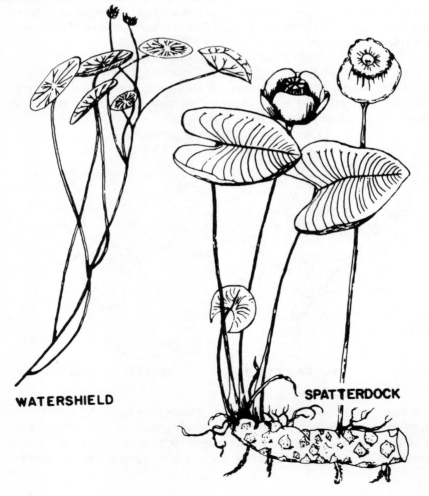

WATERSHIELD   SPATTERDOCK

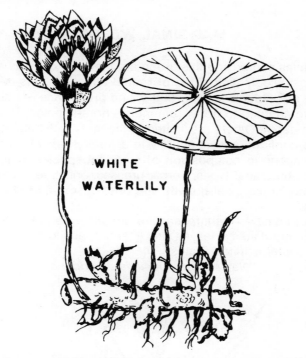

WHITE
WATERLILY

American lotus is probably the largest of the aquatic plants. It has large, emersed, leaves that are inverted like a saucer. The flower is relatively large, borne on an emersed stalk. The seed head is unique-being used in the dry state as a decorative item.

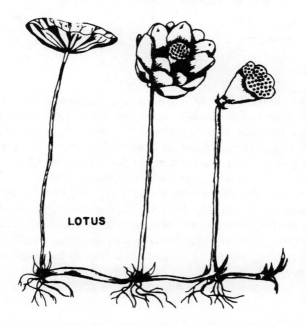

LOTUS

MARGINAL WEEDS

The species comprising this group are the most obvious and probably the most widely distributed of rooted aquatic plants. Members of this group are variable in size, shape, and preference of habitat. Many species are adapted to grow from moist shore-line soils into water up to 2 feet in depth. Others are limited to the moist soil habitat, while still others are confined almost entirely to a watery habitat.

The variations in composition of marginal species includes members of the broadleaf types, herbs, grasses, and trees. Major obnoxious species of marginal growth with brief description of families are as follows:

Acanthus Family—*Acanthaceae.* Perennial herbs with creeping rootstocks, and erect stems, leaves simple and opposite. Only one species limited to eastern United States.

Waterwillow—*Justicia americana*

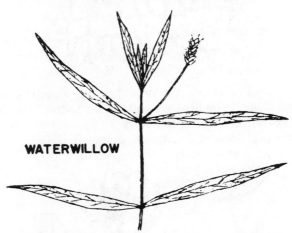

WATERWILLOW

Evening Primrose Family—*Onagraceae.* Perennial herbs with opposite or alternate simple leaves. Seeds borne in a box shaped capsule. Plants may be rect and branched or stems may be creeping and branched, rooting may occur at nodes. Distribution of aquatic members of this family confined mainly to Southeastern United States.

Waterprimroses—Jussiaea spp.

Amaranth Family—*Amaranthaceae.* Herb-like plants with opposite, entire, oblong, lanceolate leaves. Stems prostrate and creeping, jointed, branched and often rooted at nodes. Flowers a cluster similar to white clover blossom. May grow on dry land, on wet land into water or may float on water surface. Confined mainly to South Atlantic and Gulf areas.

Alligatorweed—*Alternanthera philoxeroides*

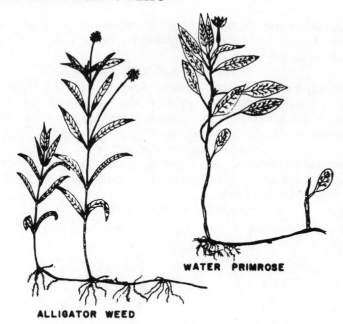

WATER PRIMROSE

ALLIGATOR WEED

Pickerelweed Family—*Pontederiaceae*. Stout, perennial, aquatic plant with thick, creeping rootstock and fibrous roots, Leaves in basal cluster and erect, with fleshy, sheathing petiole and heart-shaped to lance-shaped blades. Flowers a violet-blue cluster borne on stout erect stalk. Distribution confined to eastern half of United States.

Pickerelweed—*Pontederia cordata*

Water Plantain Family—*Alismaceae*. Mostly aquatic perennials with rosettes of sheathing basal leaves and scapelike stems from short, erect, rootstock, rhizomes or tubers, root system fibrous. Leaves variable, with long petioles, emersed or submersed types; submersed

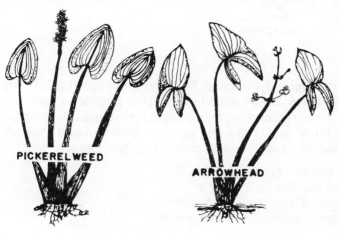

PICKERELWEED

ARROWHEAD

leaves subulate and elliptical. Emersed leaves elliptical to sagittate. Flowers on fruiting stalk and usually white in color. Each underground stem ends in edible tuber.

Arrowhead—*Sagittaria* spp.

Buckwheat Family—*Polygonaceae.* Moist soil perennial or annual plants with jointed stems with swollen nodes and creeping rootstocks, alternate simple entire leaves. Flowers in spikes. A few species of a single genus are aquatic and are distributed over United States.

Smartweeds—*Polygonum* spp.

Pepper Familly—*Piperaceae.* Tall aquatic plant from slender rootstock, leaves scattered and heart-shaped, flowers white. Confined to eastern half of United States.

Lizzardtail—*Saururus cernuus*

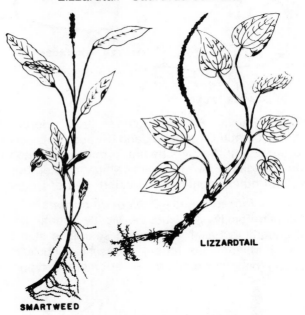

LIZZARDTAIL

SMARTWEED

Cattail Family—*Typhaceae.* Tall, erect, perennial plants with simple jointless stems, linear sheathing leaves, and large, branching rootstocks. Flowers borne in dense, rigid, spike usuallly emerging froma spathe, these spikes dry and persist into late winter. Rootstocks are rich in starch. Distributed over entire United States.

Blue cattail—*Typha glauca*
Common cattail—*T. latifolia*
Narrowleaf cattail—*T. angustifolia*
Southern cattail—*T. domingensis*

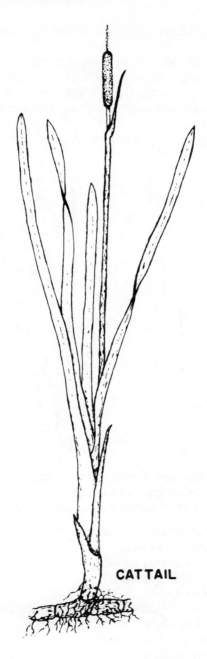

CATTAIL

Parsley Family—*Umbelliferae*. Low perennial herbs with creeping, stem-like rootstock often bearing small tubers. Leaves round and peltate on erect petioles from rootstock, may be floating or emersed.

Flowers small and white on erect petiole. Grows over both North and South America.

Pennywort—Hydrocotyle spp.

Arum Family—*Araceae*. Stout aquatic plants with alternate, fleshy, clustered leaves, rootstock short, erect, with fibrous roots. Leaves lanceolate in shape and either erect or floating. Flowers borne in clusters at apex of stout stalk.

Golden club—Oronthium aquaticum

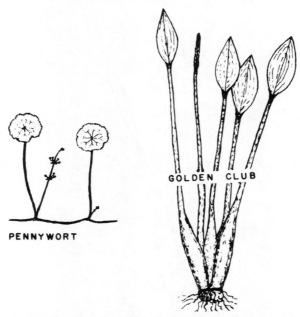

Grass Family—*Gramineae*. Plants with fibrous roots, nodose stems usually with hollow internodes and narrow, parallel-veined, 2 ranked leaves composed of a sheath and blade. Seed heads are variable.

Giant cutgrass—*Zizaniopsis miliaceae*
Rice cutgrass—*Leersia oryzoides*
Southern cutgrass—*Leersia hexandra*
Giant reed—*Phragmites communis*
Cordgrass—*Spartina* spp.
Southern watergrass—*Hydrochloa caroliniensis*
Knotgrass—*Paspalum distichum*
Water paspalm—*Paspalum fluitans*
Paspalm—*Paspalum repens*
Maidencane—*Panicum hemitomon*
Paragrass—*Panicum purpurascens*
Torpedo grass—*Panicum repens*

Water managrass—*Glyceria fluitans*
Sawgrass—*Cladium jamaicense*

Southern watergrass grows from the moist shoreline into waters up to 8 feet deep. The submersed portion of the plants are a mass of leafless stems with frequent rooting at the nodes. The emersed stems have tufts of leaf growths floating on or extending above the water surface for 4 to 6 inches. Occurrence rather infrequent, but it is potentially one of the more noxious plants.

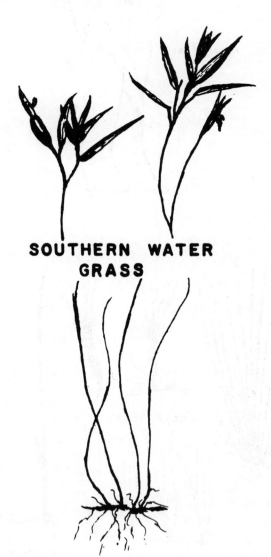

SOUTHERN WATER GRASS

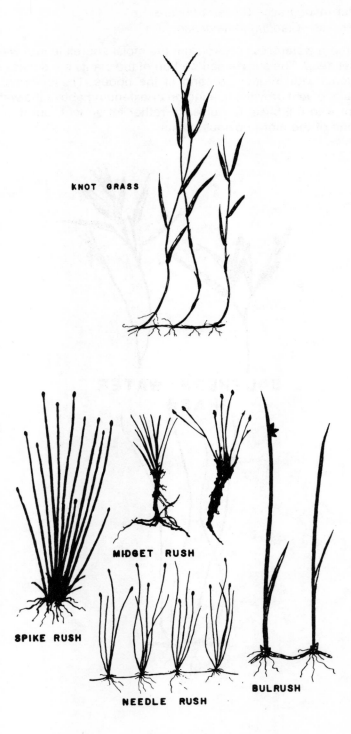

KNOT GRASS

SPIKE RUSH

MIDGET RUSH

NEEDLE RUSH

BULRUSH

Sedge Family—*Cyperaceae*. Perennial plants having general appearance of grasses or rushes with fibrous roots and usually solid stems, often having creeping rootstocks. Leaves linear, parallel-veined, basal or alternate on stem, and with closed sheath. *Carex* has 3-sided stems, 3-ranked leaves that are often finely serrated on margin and lower midrib. Flowers borne in axils of scales (glumes) in spikelets.

Sedges—*Carex* spp.
Spikerushes—*Eleocharis* spp.
Flatsedges—*Cyperus spp.*
Bulrushes—*Scirpus* spp.

Sedges (*Carex* spp.) cause varying degrees of marginal infestation of all water areas throughout the United States. In certain situations their presence and abundance are such as to present serious problems in water movement, water loss through evaporation, and public health hazzards. The two forms shown represent the varied forms in this genus.

SEDGE   SEDGE

Rush Family—*Juncaceae*. Perennial plants with appearance of grasses, leaves flattened somewhat, sheathing at base, lower bladeless and reduced to mere sheaths. Creeping rootance of grasses, leaves somewhat flattened; sheathing at base; lower leaves bladeless and reduced to mere sheaths. Creeping rootstock, stems simple, pithy and hollow, often with partitions. Leaves often hollow. Flowers in terminal cluster. About 200 species grow in marshes and bogs, a few grow in water.

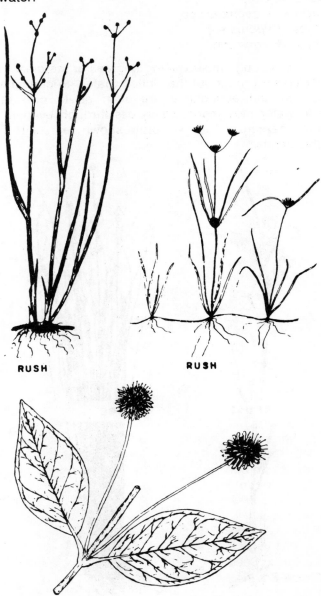

RUSH   RUSH

Madder Family—*Rubiaceae*. Large shrubs with leaves opposite or in 3's. Flowers in spherical heads on long bare stalks in axils of upper leaves. Mature fruits small brown balls. Grows on moist bank and into water a few inches in depth. Spread over eastern portion of United States.

Buttonbush—*Cephalanthus occidentalis*

Willow Family—*Salicaceae*. Large shrubs or trees with simple alternate leaves that are several times as long as wide, usually toothed. Flowers in catkins that generally appear in spring before leaves. Distributed all over United States.

Willows—*Salix* spp.

Birch Family—*Betulaceae*. Large shrubs or small trees, leaves scattered, entire, heavily veined, toothed. Seed heads are small burs in clusters, similar to pine cones.

Alders—*Alnus* spp.

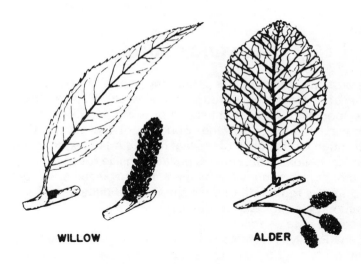

WILLOW   ALDER

Plains Cottonwood—*Populus sargentii*

Large tree with gray bark, deeply furrowed. Leaves broadly oval, often wider than long, 3 to 4 inches long and wide, long-pointed, coarsely toothed with curved teeth, smooth, light green, shiny. Great Plains and Rocky Mountains.

Salt Cedar—*Tamarix pentandra*

A large shrub or small tree to 30 feet. Stems support slender, contorted branches with small scale-like leaves on the young branches. Flowers are borne in dense panicles developing from base to apex in individual racemes. Seeds are very small with slender hairs at the apex. Located in Southwest United States.

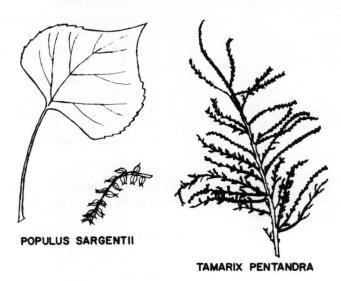

POPULUS SARGENTII

TAMARIX PENTANDRA

FLOATING PLANTS

This group has some species which are limited to their distribution while others are widespread throughout the world. Plants in this group have true roots and leaves, but instead of being anchored in soil they float about on the water surface. Bouancy of the plants is accomplished through modification of the leaf (including covering of leaf surface) and leaf petiole. Most species have extensive root systems which collect nutrients from the water medium. Most species are capable of reproducing at a rapid rate under favorable conditions, and are considered among the most obnoxious aquatics.

Major species are as follows:

Waterfern Family—*Salviniaceae*. Delicate, mosslike floating plants with small scalelike 2-lobed leaves; upper lobe aerial and lower lobe submersed. Reproduction by spores and by plant fragmentation. Plants green when young, turning pink, red, or brown with age. Plants confined to temperate and subtropical regions of United States.

Salvinia—*Salvinia rotundifolia*
Azolla—*Azolla caroliniana*

AZOLLA

SALVINIA

Pickerelweed Family—*Pontederiaceae*. Perennial or annual floating plants, with creeping rootstocks and large fibrous roots. Leaves in basal cluster, fleshy, ovate, and modified for boupancy. Flowers, a cluster borne on stalk above water. Seeds are produced, and they are viable under favorable conditions. Plants propagate vegetatively by sending out daughter plants on creeping rootstock. Confined to subtropical regions of the United States.

Waterhyacinth—*Eichhornia crassipes*

Waterhyacinth—A serious pest plant in water areas of subtropical and tropical areas throughout the world. Size of plants apparently determined by fertility of water environment and length of growing season. Causes problems in navigation, flood control and public health.

WATER HYACINTH

Arum Family—*Araceae*. Stout plants, mostly floating; leaves, hairy, fleshy and pliated, borne in rosettes from short stem bearing numerous adventicous branching roots. Propagation mainly vegetative by buds. Confined to subtropical areas of United States.

Waterlettuce—*Pistia stratioites*

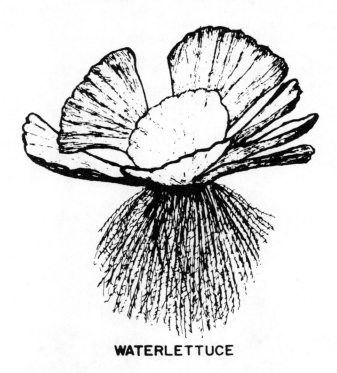

WATERLETTUCE

Water Chestnut Family—*Hydrocaryaceae*. Annual aquatic herbs with long, cordlike, sparsely branching, submersed stems which arise from a nut. Leaves are of 3 kinds: linear, mostly alternate; submersed, finely dissected and 2 at each node; emersed rosette clustered with inflated rhombic blades. Seeds a 2 or 4 pronged nut borne on short stalk. If seeds are air dried they die. Native of Europe, Africa, and Asia, limited distribution in northeastern United States.

WATER CHESTNUT

Water chestnut—*Trapa natans*
Duckweed Family—*Lemnaceae*. Plants free floating, minute, with un-differentiated flattened or globular plant body (frond) and without defi-nite stems or leaves. Fronds in colonies with or without roots. Reproduction is mainly vegetative by simple frond division.

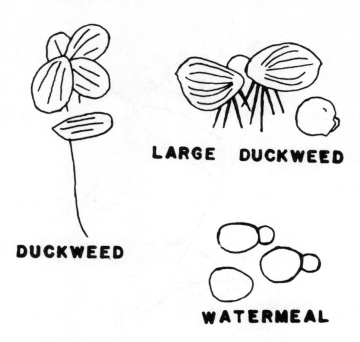

LARGE DUCKWEED

DUCKWEED

WATERMEAL

Common duckweed—*Lemna minor*
Giant duckweed—*Spirodela polyrhiza*
Watermeal—*Wolffia columbiana*

Duckweeds and watermeal usually occur as mixtures of several species. The growth of these plants in fresh waters is most abundant in areas protected from wind-wave action either by taller vegetation or shoreline configuration. Plants present serious problems by forming layer several inches thick on water surface. Such thick layers of plants are also very resistant to chemical control simply by physical inability to get chemicals on plants.

The following texts were used freely throughout the article to obtain good, simple descriptions as aids in identification: Eyles, Don E., J. Lynne Robertson, Jr., and Garnet W. Jax.

A Guide and Key to the Aquatic Plants of the Southeastern United States. 1944. Public Health Bulletin No. 286. 151 pp.

Palmer, C. Melvin. Algae in Water Supplies. 1959. Public Health Service Publication No. 657. 88 pp.

Prescott, G. W. How to Know the Fresh-Water Algae. 1954. Wm. C. Brown Company. 211 pp.

Fassett, Norman C. A Manual of Aquatic Plants. 1960. The University of Wisconsin Press. 405 pp.

Muenscher, Walter C. Aquatic Plants of the United States. 1944. Comstock Publishing Company. 374 pp.

Appendix B

FORMULAS FOR AQUATIC HERBICIDE APPLICATION

Volume of pond in cu ft = surface area in sq ft × average depth in ft

Volume of pond in ac ft = surface area in ac × average depth in ft

Volume of pond in ac ft = $\dfrac{\text{volume of pond in cu ft}}{43{,}560}$

ppmv = $\dfrac{\text{gal of 100\% ai}}{\text{volume in ac ft} \times 0.33}$

Total gal of chem required = ac ft × ppmv × 0.33

ppmw = $\dfrac{\text{lb ai of chem applied}}{\text{volume in ac ft} \times 2.72}$

Total lb ai required = ac ft × 1.72 × ppmw desired

Total gal of liquid formulation required = $\dfrac{\text{ac ft} \times 2.72 \times \text{ppmw desired}}{1 \text{ lb ai/gal of concentrate}}$

Liquid Measurements

1 gallon	=	4 quarts	0.1 gallon	=	12.8 ounces
1 gallon	=	8 pints	0.2 gallon	=	25.6 ounces
			0.25 gallon	=	32.0 ounces(1 qt)
1 pint	=	16 ounces	0.3 gallon	=	38.4 ounces
			0.4 gallon	=	51.2 ounces
1 cup	=	8 ounces	0.5 gallon	=	64.0 ounces
1/2 cup	=	4 ounces	0.6 gallon	=	76.8 ounces
1/4 cup	=	2 ounces	0.7 gallon	=	89.6 ounces
			0.8 gallon	=	102.4 ounces
1 tablespoon	=	1/2 ounce	0.9 gallon	=	115.2 ounces
8 tablespoon	=	4 ounces	1.0 gallon	=	128.0 ounces
16 tablespoon	=	8 ounces			

Solid Measurement

0.1 lb = 1.6 ounces	0.6 lb = 9.6 ounces
0.2 lb = 3.2 ounces	0.7 lb = 11.2 ounces
0.3 lb = 4.8 ounces	0.8 lb = 12.8 ounces
0.4 lb = 6.4 ounces	0.9 lb = 14.4 ounces

0.5 lb = 8.0 ounces   1.0 lb = 16.0 ounces

Units and Conversion Equivalents

1 ac = 43,560 sq ft
1 ac ft (ac ft) - 43,560 cu ft = 325,762 gal - 2,720,000 lb of water
1 cu ft/second (cfs) - 450 gal/minute (gpm)
1 cu ft - 7.48 gal - 62.4 lb of water
1 gal - 128 fl oz - 8.33 lb of water
1 ppm by volume (ppmv) - 1 gal/million gal of water
1 ppm by weight (ppmw) - 8.33 lb of chemical/million gal of water
1 ppmw - 2.72 lb of chemical/ac ft of water gal of liquid formulation

$$\text{required} = \frac{\text{lb ai required}}{\text{lb ai/gal of concentrate}}$$

$$\text{1 lb of dry formulation required} = \frac{\text{lb ai required} \times 100}{\text{\% ai in formulation by weight}}$$

(ai - active ingredient)

Formulas for Herbicide Application to Channels

cfs - cross section area in sq ft × average velocity in ft/second (fps)

Cross section area of rectangular channel in sq ft = average width in ft × the average depth in ft

$$\text{ppmv} = \frac{\text{gal of chemical} \times 1,000,000}{\text{cfs} \times 450 \times \text{minutes applied}}$$

$$\text{gal of chemical/cfs} = \frac{\text{ppmv} \times 450 \times \text{minutes applied}}{1,000,000}$$

$$\text{Total gal of chemical required} = \frac{\text{ppmv} \times 450 \times \text{cfs} \times \text{minutes applied}}{1,000,000}$$

$$\text{ppmw} = \frac{\text{lb of chemical} \times 1,000,000}{\text{cfs} \times 3.744 \times \text{minutes applied}}$$

$$\text{ppmv} = \frac{\text{gal of formulation} \times \text{lb ai/gal} \times 1,000,000}{\text{cfs} \times 3.744 \times \text{minutes applied}}$$

$$\text{lb of chemical/cfs} = \frac{\text{ppmv} \times 3,744 \times \text{minutes applied}}{1,000,000}$$

$$\text{gal of formulation/cfs} = \frac{\text{ppmv} \times 3,744 \times \text{minutes applied}}{1 \text{ lb ai/gal} \times 1,000,000}$$

Appendix C

GLOSSARY OF TERMS USED IN AQUATIC WEED CONTROL

Abscission
The formation of a layer of cells which causes the fruit, leaf, or stem to fall off the plant.

Adsorption
Penetration of a substance from the surface to below the surface.

Acid Equivalent (ae)
The theoretical yield of parent acid from an active ingredient content of a formulation.

Activator
Materials used in a pesticide formulation to increase the effectiveness of the toxic materials toward the target pest.

Active Ingredient (ai)
The chemical(s) in a formulated product that is (are) principally responsible for the herbicidal effects and that is (are) shown as active ingredient(s) on herbicide labels.

Acute Oral LD$_{50}$
The dosage required to kill 50% of the test animals when given in a single oral dose in toxicity studies.

Acute Toxicity
The amount of a substance, as a single dose, to cause poisoning in a test animal.

Adhesive
A substance that will cause a spray material to stick to the sprayed surface, often referred to as a sticking agent.

Adjuvant
Any substance in a herbicide formulation which enhances the effectiveness of the herbicide.

Adsorption
Adherence of a substance to a surface.

Aerobic
Living in air; opposite to anaerobic.

Aesthetic
Producing a pleasant or satisfying feeling to an exposure; enjoy seeing a beautiful flower or handsome animal.

Agitate
Keeping a mixture stirred up.

Algae
Nonvascular chlorophyll-containing plants, usually aquatic.

Alkalinity
Containing sodium and potassium carbonate salts. (Calcareous: Containing an excess of calcium usually in the form of the compound calcium carbonate-Limy.)

Anaerobic
Living in the absence of air, opposite to aerobic.

Anionic Surfactant
A surface-active additive to a herbicide having a negative charge.

Annual Plant
A plant that completes its life cycle in one year.

Antagonism
Opposing action of different chemicals such that the action of one is impaired or the total effect is less than that of one component used separately.

Antidote
A practical immediate treatment, including first aid, in case of poisoning.

Aquatic Plants
A plant that grows in water. There are three types: submergent, grow beneath the surface; emergent, root below the surface but plant extends above the water; and floating.

At Emergence
Treatment applied during the visible emerging phase of the specified crop or weed.

Band or Row Application
An application to a continuous restricted area, such as in or along a crop row, rather than over the entire field area.

Basal Treatment
A treatment applied to the stems of woody plants at and just above the ground.

Bed-up
To build up beds or ridges with a tillage implement.

Berm
Narrow shelf typically along the waters edge of canals formed by deposited silt.

Biennial
A plant that completes its life cycle in two years. The first year the seed germinates and the plant produces leaves, roots, and stores food. The second year it flowers and produces fruits and seeds.

Bioassay
The qualitative or quanitative determination of substance by response measurements of treated living organisms as compared to measurements on untreated, check, or standard living organisms.

Biological Control
Controlling a pest by its natural enemies; these may already occur in the area or be introduced.

Broadcast Application
An application over an entire area.

Broadleaf Plants
Botanically classified as dicotyledons. Plants have two cotyledon leaves in the seedling stage; true leaves are broad and have net-like or reticulate veins.

Brush Control
Control of woody plants.

Carcinogen
A substance capable of producing cancer.

Carrier
A gas, liquid, or solid substance used to dilute, propel, or suspend a herbicide during its application.

cfs
Cubic feet per second.

Chlorosis
Loss of green color in foliage followed by yellowing of the tissue.

Chronic Toxicity
Results produced in test animals exposed for long periods to chemicals.

Combustible
Will burn when near an open flame or spark.

Compatible
Mixable in the formulation or in the spray tank for application together in the same carrier without undesirably altering the separate effects of components.

Concentration
The amount of active ingredient or herbicide in a quantity of diluent expressed as percent, lb/gal, etc.

Contact Herbicide
A herbicide that is phytotoxic by contact with plant tissue rather than as a result of translocation.

Contaminate
To alter or render a material unfit for a specified use by allowing the pesticide to come into contact with it.

Control
May not mean eradication, but reduction of the weed problem to a point where it does not cause economic damage.

Crown
The point where the stem and root join in a seed plant.

Cuticle
Waxy, fatty material that covers plant surfaces such as leaves.

Cut-Surface Application
Treatments applied to frills or girdles that have been made through the bark into the wood of a tree.

Deciduous Plants
Those plants which are perennial in habit but lose their leaves during winter.

Deflocculating Agent
A material added to suspension to prevent particles from clumping together and settling out of spray tanks.

Defoliant or Defoliator
Any substance or mixture of substances for which the primary use is to cause the leaves or foliage to drop from a plant.

Degradation
The process by which a chemical is decomposed or broken down into less complex compounds or elements.

Deoxygenation
Depletion of oxygen.

Dermal Toxicity
Measures the amount of a pesticide or poisonous material that can be absorbed through the skin of animals to produce toxic symptoms.

Desiccant
Any substance or mixture of substances used to accelerate the drying of plant tissue.

Detergent
Primarily used as a cleansing agent. It is often used as a wetting agent to reduce surface tension of spray droplets.

Dewatered Ditch
A drained ditch.

Dicot (Dicotyledon)
A plant that has two seed leaves or cotyledons; broadleaf plants.

Diluent
Any gas, liquid, or solid material used to reduce the concentration of an active ingredient in a formulation.

Directed Application
Precise application to a specific area or plant organ such as to a row or bed or to the lower leaves and stems of plants.

Dispersing Agent
A material that reduces the cohesive forces between similar particles.

Dissolve
Refers to getting solids into solutions.

Dormancy
State of inhibited germination of seeds or growth of plant organs. A state of suspended development.

Dose (Rate)
The terms are the same; however, rate is preferred. Refers to the amount of active ingredient applied to a unit area regardless of percentage of chemical in the carrier.

Drift
The movement of airborne particles by air motion or wind away from the intended target area.

Efficacy
Capacity for serving to produce effects; effectiveness.

Emergence
The act of germinating seedlings of breaking through the soil surface.

Emersed Plant
A rooted or anchored aquatic plant adapted to grow with most of its leaf-stem tissue above the water surface and not lowering or rising with the water level.

Emetic
A material used to cause vomiting to rid stomachs of poisonous compounds.

Emulsifiable Concentrate (ec)
A concentration herbicide formulation containing organic solvents and adjuvants to facilitate emulsification with water.

Emulsifier
A surface active substance which promotes the suspension of one liquid in another.

Emulsion
The suspension of one liquid as minute globules in another liquid (for example, oil dispersed in water).

Epidermis
The outer cellular tissue of an animal or plant.

Epinasty
More rapid growth on the upper surface of a plant organ or part (especially leaves) causing it to bend downward.

Erosion
Wear away by wind or water.

Ester
A compound formed by reaction of an acid and an alcohol accompanied by the loss of water formed during the reaction.

Filler
A diluent in the powdered form.

Flag Stage
Stage of growth of cereals and other grasses at which the sheath and leaf have been produced from which the head will emerge.

Floating Plant
A free-floating or anchored aquatic plant adapted to growth with most of its vegetative tissue at or above the water surface and lowering or rising with the water level.

Foliar Application
Application of a herbicide to the leaves or foliage of plants.

Formulation
A mixture containing the active pesticide, the carrier, diluents, and other additives required to make the material ready for application.

Freeboard
Distance above water level.

gpa
Gallons per acre.

gpm
Gallons per minute.

Gradient
Steps or progress in the rate of growth (plant) or development (seed).

Granule or Granular
A dry formulation of herbicide in which the active ingredient is impregnated on small particles of carrier such as clay or ground-up corncobs.

Grass
Botanically, any plant of the Gramineae family. Grasses are characterized by narrow leaves with parallel veins; by leaves composed of blade, sheath and ligule; by jointed stems and fibrous roots; and by inconspicuous flowers usually arranged in spikelets.

Growth Regulator
A substance used for controlling or modifying plant growth processes without appreciable phytotoxic effect at the dosage applied.

Habitat
Environment (place) where plant grows naturally.

Hard Water
Generally defined as water containing 332 ppm of calcium carbonate. Water that contains certain minerals, usually calcium and magnesium sulfates, chlorides, or carbonates, in solution in sufficient amounts to cause a curd or precipitate instead of a lather when soap is added. Very hard water may cause precipitates in some herbicide sprays.

Hazard
The probability that injury or detrimental effects will result if a substance is not used properly.

Hazard Ratio
The relationship of the degree of risk.

Herbaceous Plant
A vascular plant that does not develop persistent woody tissue above ground.

Herbicide
A chemical used for killing plants or severely interrupting their normal growth processes.

High Volume Sprays
Spray applications of more than 60 gallons per acre volume.

Hormone
A naturally occurring substance in plants that controls growth or other physiological processes. It is used with reference to certain man-made or synthetic chemicals that regulate or affect growth activity.

Hydrosoil
Soil at bottom of the body of water.

Incorporate Into Soil
The mixing of a herbicide into the soil, generally by mechanical means.

Inert Ingredient
That part of compound without toxic or killing properties, sometimes called the carrier.

Inhibit
To hold in check or stop.

Integrated Control
Utilizes multiple approaches for pest control, giving consideration to minimum pesticide usage.

Invert Emulsion
The suspension of minute water droplets in a continuous oil phase.

Ionic Surfactant
One that ionizes or dissociates in water.

Jointing Stage
When the internodes of grass stems are elongating.

Label
All written, printed, or graphic matter on or attached to pesticide containers as required by law.

Lactation
Animals producing milk.

Lateral Movement
Chemical movement in a plant or in the soil to the side or horizontal movement in the roots or soil layer.

LC_{50}
Means of expressing the lethal concentrations of a compound in air as a dust, mist, gas, or vapor. It is a statistical estimate of the dosage necessary to kill 50% of a test animal population.

Leaching
The downward movement of a substance in solution through the soil.

Leaf Blade
The flat portion of a leaf.

Low-Volatile Ester
An ester compound with a high molecular weight and a low vapor pressure such as butoxy-ethanol, iso-octyl, or propylene glycol butyl ether ester.

Low-volume Spray
A spray application of 5 to 20 gallons per acre.

Marginal Plants
Those plants growing near shoreline.

Marl
A calcium carbonate deposit on algae.

Miscible Liquids
Two or more liquids capable of being mixed, which will remain mixed under normal conditions.

Monocot
A seed plant having a single cotyledon (monocotyledon) or leaf; includes grasses, corn and lilies.

Mutagen
A compound having the property to induce mutations.

Necrosis
Localized death of living tissue (as, for example, following desiccation, browning, and loss of function).

Node
Region of plant stem where leaf or leaves occur.

Non-ionic Surfactant
Chemically inert

Nonselective Herbicide
A chemical that is generally toxic to plants without regard to species (may be a function of dosage, method of application, etc).

Noxious Weed
A weed specified by law as being especially undesirable, troublesome, and difficult to control. Definition will vary according to legal interpretations.

Oral Toxicity
Toxicity of a compound when it is ingested.

Overall Treatment
Uniform application over the entire area.

Overtop Application
Applied over the top of transplanted or growing plants such as by airplane or raised spray boom of ground rigs. A broadcast application above the plant canopy.

Pellet
A dry formulation of herbicide and other components in discrete particles usually larger than 10 cubic centimeters.

Penetrant
Wetting agents that enhance the ability of a liquid to enter into the pores of a substrate.

Perennial
A plant that lives for more than two years.

Persistent Herbicide
A herbicide which, when applied at the recommended rate, will harm susceptible crops planted in normal rotation after harvesting the treated crop or which interferes with regrowth of native vegetation in noncrop sites.

Pesticide
Any substance or mixtures of substances used to control or kill insects, rodents, weeds, fungi, and other pests.

Pesticide Tolerance
The amount of pesticide residue which may legally remain in or on a food crop.

Photic Zone
Zone where light is sufficient for plant growth.

Photosynthesis
The manufacture of simple sugars by green plants utilizing light as the energy source.

Phylogenetic
Origin and evolutionary developments of plants.

Phytoplankton
Microscopic plant life living suspended in water.

Phytotoxic
Injurious or toxic to plants.

Potable Water
Drinkable water.

psi
Pounds per square inch.

Pubescent
In reference to hair on plants.

Quiescent
Quiet, still, inactive.

Rate
The amount of active ingredient or acid equivalent applied per unit area or other treatment unit.

Registered
Pesticides that have been approved for use by the Environmental Protection Agency.

Residual
To have continued killing effect over a period of time.

Residue
The amount of pesticide that is on or in the crop at the time an analysis is made.

Residue Tolerance
The amount of pesticide residue which may legally remain in or on a food crop.

Resistance
Same meaning as tolerance.

Rhizome
Underground root-like stem that produces roots and leafy shoots.

Seed
A reproductive body of a flowering plant.

Seedling Stage
Early stage of plant growth, within a few days to a few weeks after seed germination and emergence.

Selective Herbicide
A chemical that is more toxic to some plant species than to others (may be a function of dosage or mode of application).

Silty Water
Water clouded with very small particles of clay and sand.

Soil Application
Applied primarily to the soil surface rather than to vegetation.

Soil Injection
Placement of the herbicide beneath the soil surface with a minimum mixing or stirring of the soil as with an injection blade, knife, or tine.

Soil Layered
Placement of the herbicide in a discrete horizontal zone under a lifted or tilled layer of soil.

Soil Persistence
Refers to the length of time that herbicide application on or in the soil remains effective.

Soil Residual
A herbicide that prevents the growth of plants when present in the soil. Soil residual effects may be temporary or relatively permanent.

Soil Sterilant
See Soil Residual.

Solubility
The amount of a substance which will dissolve in a given amount of liquid.

Soluble Solid
A dry herbicide formulation that is soluble in the carrier liquid.

Solvent
A liquid such as water or oil used to dissolve other material such as herbicides.

Spore
A reproductive body of bacteria; algae, mosses, and ferns.

Spot Treatment
The application of a herbicide to a selected individual area.

Spray Drift
The movement of airborne spray particles from the intended area of application.

Spreading Agent
A substance to improve the wetting, spreading, or possibly the adhesive properties of a spray.

Static Water
Pond, lake, or reservoir water that has little or no inflow or outflow.

Stolon
The above-ground runners or slender stems that develop roots and shoots and new plants at the tips or nodes.

Stunting
In reference to plant, the retarding effect of growth and development.

Subacute Toxicity
Results produced in test animals by long-term exposure to repeated doses or concentrations of a substance.

Submersed Plant
An aquatic plant adapted to grow with most all of its vegetative tissue below the water surface.

Surface Tension
Due to surface molecular forces, a drop of liquid tends to form an apparent membrane that causes it to ball up rather than spread as a film.

Surfactant
A material which favors or improves the emulsifying, dispersing, spreading, wetting, or other surface modifying properties of liquids.

Surveillance
To keep watch on change in activity, growth, or performances.

Susceptibility
Lack of capacity to tolerate herbicide treatment.

Suspension
Finely divided solid particles dispersed in a solid, liquid, or gas.

Synergism
Complimentary action of different chemicals such that the total effect is greater than the sum of the independent effects.

Systemic
A compound which moves freely within a plant such that application to one area will result in movement to all areas of the plant to exert its effect.

Taxonomy
Science of classification—arrangement according to characteristics.

Teratogen
A compound having the property of causing congenital malformations in the fetus (birth defects).

Terrestrial Plant
A land plant.

Thallus
A nonvascular plant body with distinguishable roots, stems, or leaves.

Tolerance
Capacity to withstand herbicide treatment without marked deviation from normal growth or function.

Topical Application
Treatment of a localized surface site such as a single leaf blade, petiole, or growing point.

Transient
Not permanent; lasting for a short time.

Translocated Herbicide
A herbicide that is moved within the plant. Translocated herbicide may be either phloem mobile or xylem mobile, but the term is frequently used in a more restrictive sense to refer to herbicides that are moved in the phloem.

Translocation
Transfer of food or other materials such as 2,4-D from one part to another in plants (see Systemic).

Tuber
An underground plant storage stem of reserve food.

Turbidity
Suspended material in water preventing light penetration.

Turion
A scaly solitary shoot springing out of the ground; a young scaly sucker.

Vapor Drift
The movement of chemical vapors from the area of application.

Vascular Plant
Plants which have specialized food and water conducting cells.

Volatile
A compound is volatile when it evaporates or vaporizes (changes from liquid to a gas) at ordinary temperatures on exposure to the air.

Water Dispersible Slurry
A two-phase concentrate that contains solid herbicide suspended in liquid which is capable of suspension in water.

Water Soluble Powder
A finely ground herbicide powder which will dissolve in water.

Weed
A plant growing where it is not desired. Any plant that is a nuisance, hazard, or causes injury to man, animal, or the desired crop.

Weed Control
The process of limiting weed infestations or killing weeds for aesthetic, economic, public health, or other reasons.

Weed Eradication
The elimination of all live plant parts and seeds of a weed from a site.

Wettable Powder (wp)
A finely divided dry herbicide formulation that can be suspended readily in water.

Wetting Agent
Substance which serves to reduce interfacial tensions and causes spray solutions or suspensions to make better contact with treated surfaces.

Zooplankton
Microscopic animal life living suspended in water.

PART I

ENVIRONMENTAL
ENGINEERING
ASSESSMENT

CHAPTER 2. ENVIRONMENTAL CONCERNS FOR FISHERY MANAGEMENT

Chapter 2

ENVIRONMENTAL CONCERNS FOR FISHERY MANAGEMENT[1]

INTRODUCTION

The progress and potential for biological control of aquatic plants with fish, pathogens, competitive plants, and animals depends upon: (1) availability of a good natural enemy; (2) the nature of the weed (density, diversity, native or alien, type of problem and life history); (3) the strictness of the control required; (4) the weed's taxonomic position (enhances probability of selective control); (5) the resultant suitability and/or availability of enemies; (6) the nature of the plant community and the habitat management practiced; and (7) the applicability of other measures (chemical, mechanical, cultural, or integrated controls). We have learned to measure some of the biochemical, physiological, and ecological characteristics of these changes as they affect not only each species, but also the community metabolism and the interrelationship and dependence among organisms. It is this natural ecosystem that we must protect, particularly from the intrusion of aquatic pest plant species (47,65).

NUTRIENT ENTRAPMENT

An examination of the literature, indicates that there is no particular threshold of concentrations of plant nutrients in lakes, reservoirs, and streams, above which nuisance growths of algae would not be expected. However, the literature does indicate that the fertilizing elements contributing most to lake eutrophication are nitrogen and phosphorus. In addition to the basic building block, carbon dioxide, other mineral nutrients generally required for growth are sulfur, potassium, calcium, magnesium, iron, cobalt, and manganese (51).

Mackenthun concludes however that excessive aquatic growths can be avoided if the concentration of nitrate nitrogen is kept below 0.3 mg/l as N and the total nitrogen is less than 0.6 mg/l as N. He also concluded that if algae growths are to be prevented, total phosphorus

---

[1]The findings in this report are not to be construed as an official Department of the Army position unless so designated by other authorized documents.

should not exceed 100 ug/l (0.100 mg/l) in streams or 50 ug/l (0.050 mg/l) in lakes.

The threshold or critical nitrogen or phosphorus levels will differ for each body of water depending upon a number of factors, including the physical and chemical properties of the water, light penetration, and the hydraulic flow-through pattern. Thus, it is important to realize that nuisance aquatic growths do not always result from an over-abundance of chemical nutrients, since some physical factor may be restricting such growth. However, in a favorable physical environment, nuisance-level growths cannot occur if the concentration in the water of some essential chemical nutrient can be limited to concentrations below that required for luxuriant growth. Not only is there little agreement concerning the critical nutrient concentration, but there is disagreement concerning the specific form of the nutrients. Phosphorus has been shown to be highly mobile, and that it can change from the soluble to the insoluble form and *vice versa* in rapid sequence. In addition, the several forms of nitrogen can readily change from one form to another. The concentration observed at any time represents the instantaneous balance between supply and demand for a particular nutrient form, not necessarily the level of availability. It appears that action to prevent and control aquatic growths should be directed toward total concentrations of each of the basic nutrients rather than at any particular form or forms of these nutrients.

PROGRAMS OF CONTROL

The ideal program for control of pest species involves an integrated system of careful herbicide usage, biological control, and physical manipulation of the aquatic habitat. We understand most of the ecological changes caused by herbicides as well as the acute and chronic toxicity of these chemicals to fish and fish food organisms. Thus, other studies also involve food chain relationships and the fate, persistence, and toxicological significance of residues for the pesticide, its metabolites, and interaction with other chemicals in the aquatic ecosystem and their effect on environmental quality. Biologists in weed control and fishery management do meet on common ground in our mutual concern for the environment and the abundance of good fishing, hunting, and aesthetic quality (23,73).

The use of chemicals in the fishery environment entrails a serious responsibility with respect to water usage and conservation of the resource. The biotic potential of any given species of fish is regulated by the environmental resistance of its habitat. Physico-chemical characteristics of the water and the biological complex support and define the parameters of fish growth, reproduction and survival for each species. A change or imposition of any aspect of this habitat may have a profound effect upon the fishery and a reduction or depreciation of its productivity may result (71).

Sportsmen compete for space and demand quality recreation. By the year 2000, more than 60 million fishermen will converge on our waters with a pressure of about one billion fisherman days (58,75). A large proportion of this will be in the southeastern United States where the more serious aquatic weed control problems exist (73). Our interests in management of this aquatic ecosystem also converge on the control of dense growths of aquatic plants that are responsible for the clogging of fishing and boating access and elimination of the protective habitat for mosquito larvae. This excessive plant growth also affords cover that upsets the predator/prey relationship resulting in stunted fish population and poor fishing success.

At the 114th American Fisheries Society (AFS) Annual Meeting the Environmental Concerns Committee (ECC) proposed a protocol for establishing policy statements on issues of environmental concern to the membership. The original policy was adopted in 1977 and again in 1981. Each year the American Fishery Society members are requested to forward their own proposals to ECC (31,40,65)

WATER MANAGEMENT

Not all bodies of water are readily managed, nor do their problems have simple solutions. Quite the contrary, we have more to learn about aquatic ecosystems and how to properly manage them. Currently, no aquatic herbicide is registered that meets the criteria for all uses needed. Herbicides that may be necessary to manipulate plant populations in a body of water may be granted a special local need (SLN) registration in certain areas of the country. Since some herbicides are used directly in water for control of aquatic plants to enhance fish production and the sport fishery. Investigations have been centered on the fate of herbicide residues and effects on fish, and fish-food organisms (19,24,25,42,43,44).

Under the terms of a memorandum of understanding between the Environmental Protection Agency (EPA) and the Food and Drug Administration (FDA) published in the Federal Register (25) the procedures for establishing acceptable levels of pesticide residues in drinking water have been changed. The term "potable water tolerance" for acceptable levels of pesticide residues has been deleted and an "acceptable residue in drinking water (ARLDW) will be determined for various herbicides, generally without presentation of additional research information.

Problem Identification

Excessive aquatic weed growth is a universal problem throughout the world-affecting fish management, culture, and harvest. Blackburn (4) has pointed out the difficulties of managing farm ponds for sport fisheries and the importance of weed control. Interference in food fish culture has been described by Van der Lingen for Africa (76), Timmermans for Europe, (82) Ramachandran and Ramaprabku in India (64).

Emphasis in the United States has been placed upon the promotion of research on the ecological effects of weed control, social-economical factors, biological and integrated pest control, the toxicology of herbicides in fish, other aquatic organisms and wildlife, and the retention of herbicide residues in water, soil and the biota.

Control of aquatic plants in fisheries of the United States has been largely justified on the basis of eliminating vegetation that provides escape cover for forage fish or harbors obnoxious insects and vectors for fish diseases (5,17,50,51). In 1960, McCarthy (53) found that 78 percent of the 2,000 aquatic vegetation control projects were done with chemicals and 18 percent by mechanical harvesting. Mackenthun and Ingram (51) cited the main disadvantages of mechanical control: high cost of equipment and labor; temporary benefit; and problem of disposing of cut vegetation since it has little commercial value.

Mechanical techniques of weed control include: drawdown of water and overwinter freeze-follow; drying and burning; hand-pulling or cutting or raking, chain-dragging; hand or machine operated weed saws, cutters, and weed removal units (51). Stainers, filters, and skimmers have been used in algae control. According to Nelson, et al., (57) micro strainers with a 35 micron aperture 1effectively removed 46 to 97 percent of algae from Lake Michigan waters.

According to Moyle and Jones, (55) about 40 percent of the State agencies regulate the chemical control of aquatic nuisances by statue or executive order, another 40 percent by informal supervision, the remainder reported no regulation. Many State agencies have conducted research on aquatic weed infestations and chemical control methods. Several researchers have suggested that more scientific information is needed on the use of herbicides and algicides as fishery management tools; on the physiological activities and habitat limitations of aquatic plants; on the effects of chemicals and formulations on wide variety of plant species and aquatic environments. To quote Mackenthun and Ingram (51) directly: "A good herbicide or algicide must: (1) be reasonably safe to use, (2) kill the specific nuisance plant or plants, (3) be nontoxic to fish, fish-food organisms and terrestrial animals at the plant-killing concentration, (4) not prove seriously harmful to the ecology of the general aquatic area, (5) be safe for water contact by humans and animals, or provide suitable safeguards during the unsafe period, and (6) be of reasonable cost."

Ecological Considerations

The role of aquatic flora in relation to the fishery is often poorly documented and not well understood even in the most technically detailed studies. Generally, most research on weeds and weed control in fisheries has been focused on the removal vegetation by chemical, mechanical, or biological means. Very little effort, however, has been made to understand the flow of plant nutrients and energy in the aquatic ecosystem and now to manipulate the species of producer organisms and food chain organisms to maximize the harvestable yield. Thus, we must be concerned with basic research of aquatic ecology, plant and animal physiology, kinetics of pesticide residues and plant nutrients in water and soil, toxicology of pesticides, nutritional biochemistry, life history of aquatic food chain species (consumer organisms), and dependent relationships with aquatic plant and algae (producer organisms) (67,68).

Our efforts should be directed toward development of improved water management techniques and also toward the selection of fish for both improved quality of the fishery and efficient utilization of the energy flowing through the food chain. We must know the selectivity and preferences by fish for different food organisms and aquatic plants and the interdependence of plants with the variety of food organisms in the aquatic ecosystem. Excessive plant growth is commonly associated with the phenomenon of "overcrowding" and "stunted growth" of many pond fish populations, centrachids in particular, and correction of this situation often calls for drastic measures of both weed control and selective cropping or elimination of the entire population and restocking. Use of chemicals to manage these fish populations should be carefully examined along the lines suggested by Lennon and Berger (45).

Subsequent to aquatic weed infestation causing stunted fish growth, antimycin A, a short-lived piscicid, has thus been used selectively to alter the structure of fish populations and maximize production of sport fish populations (7,8,9). It has been used to remove scalefish from catfish ponds, or thin the stunted populations of bluegill, or yellow perch and reinstitute a desirable predator-prey relationship to improve the quality of the fishery (62).

Aquatic herbicides indirectly attack problems of overpopulation and poor fish growth caused by excessive plant cover and competition for nutrients. Herbicides are generally short-lived and do not accumulate or magnify in fish-food chain. However, the changes induced have a more subtle effect on the aquatic ecosystem and are transferred all the way up the food chain and dramatically alter the flow of energy. In this example, sodium endothall is used to selectively eliminate certain submersed rooted plants from the habitat and release these stored nutrients and energy to decomposer organisms (bacteria, etc.) which in turn feed diatoms, rotifers, protozoans, etc. This also changes some of the physical features of the habitat. Since protective cover for the weed clinging insect larvae, invertebrates, and small fish is reduced or eliminated, they are now more vulnerable to predation. Production of plankton is sharply increased but usually it has a beneficial effect on feeding both by primary consumers and by fishers at the secondary and tertiary trophic level. The net result is a more efficient system for benefiting the predatory species. By removal of excessive plant growth and redirecting energy flow, the fish growth rates improve, production increases, and the better catch per unit effort is evidence of improvement in the sport fishery (78,79,80,81,82,83).

Cost-Benefit Considerations

Benefits from the control of aquatic vegetation are measured in terms of increased production and harvest of fish: (1) release or rechanneling of nutrients and energy to fish food organisms; (2) greater availability of fish food organisms; (3) improved quality of fish food organisms; (4) better efficiency in the flow of energy through the food chain to fish; (5) maximize control of fish diseases and predators; (6) enhanced water quality—especially dissolved oxygen and pH conditions; (7) elimination of plant masses obstructing harvesting equipment or recovery of fish during draining of ponds; and (8) overcrowding and stunting of fish growth. Conversely, the losses caused by aquatic vegetation are measured by the loss in production of fish through: (1) inadequate nutrition or availability of fish food organisms; (2) failure of spawning, hatch, or survival of young and adults due to physical conditions of the environment; (3) adverse chemical conditions (high pH's, biochemical oxygen demand, toxins, etc.) resulting in poor growth, stress and mortality; (4) harboring pathogens and parasites of fish; (5) competition and predation by invertebrates, amphibians, reptiles, birds mammals; (6) excessive cover that limits availability or restricts distribution of more desirable species of food organisms. Losses also occur when the vegetation impedes the drainage of water from the ponds. Fish become stranded in the vegetation and are either lost to the harvest or cost time and inconvenience to rescue. Other indirect losses occur, such as: (1) damage to water-holding structures and drains; (2) attraction of other nuisance organisms (e.g., disease-carrying snails, muskrat damage to dikes, predatory birds, amphibians, insects, etc.); and (3) diversion of manpower and finances from other operational needs. Direct costs of weed control can also be assessed in terms of investments in chemicals, ma-chinery, and manpower (both in the learning or training and actual mechanics of operation).

Cost and benefit considerations are dictated by the overall economics and effectiveness of the chemical in channelization of energy in the ecosystem to increase quality or quantity of the harvestable yield. Biological research methods for evaluation of the cost-benefit aspects of pesticide use must include analysis of energy flow, limiting factors, and biomass produced at each tropic level with respect to the biotic potential of the species under management (27,28,54).

Chemical costs for weed control in channel catfish farming are assessed at $18/A by Mitchell, Travis and Usry, although Gallagher (26) cites $9 to $30/A depending on the time in production (1 to 2 years) and quality of control program (54). Detailed accounts of mechanical harvesting of waterhyacinth have been prepared by Van Dyke (77) and Phillippy and Perryman (63). In Shell Creek Reservoir the operation had a mean cost of $1,588.25/acre and mean capacity of 0.32 acres/day. In Gant Lake Canal similar harvesting equipment had a capacity of 0.47 acres/day at a mean cost of $406.05/acre. However, the harvesting costs were not determined to illustrate the costs and benefits in those situations where weed control would have prevented serious fish-harvesting losses and higher labor costs. Vegetation also causes serious growth and feed loss in the physical interference, chemical consumption of nutrients, high pH conditions and hazardous oxygen depletion problems.

PROBLEMS ASSOCIATED WITH THE USE OF CHEMICALS

Adequate labeling, recommendations, and guidelines for safe and effective use of herbicides requires appropriate data on toxicity, efficacy and residues involving various conditions. Research for the evaluation of weed control chemicals must develop the following information: (1) toxicity to the target species; (2) relative toxicity to non-target species of plants, invertebrates, fish, other aquatic animals, birds, mammals, and man; (3) fate of residues and significance in the water, fish, crops, livestock, and other foods of man; (4) conditions affecting toxicity, efficacy, and persistence of residues in the proposed pattern of use, e.g., water chemistry, temperature variations in susceptibility of species at various life stages and seasons, inflow dilution, contact time, rate of degradation, deactivation or detoxification; (5) potentiating or synergising activity of carriers, formulation or combinations with other contaminants and pesticide residues, metabolites and degradation products (32,33,34,35,36).

This requires an orderly system of toxicological screening and evaluation similar to that suggested by Lennon and Walker (46). Since herbicides may be applied in both standing (lentic) and flowing (lotic) situations, the bioassay methods must be sufficient to measure the concentration of herbicide and the contact time necessary for control of aquatic plants or toxicological effect on other aquatic organisms. Fate, persistence, and significance of the herbicide residues also must be determined to provide adequate information for the proper labeling and regulation of use for safety to man.

The research methods may include static, intermittent-flow, or constant-flow bioassay systems, depending on the length of the testing and the investigator's desire to more nearly simulate the lentic or lotic environmental conditions. Temperature, biomass-volume ratios, water chemistry, and light intensity or periodicity are also important considerations with regard to the reaction of aquatic organisms or plants to the chemicals.

In intensive bioassay testing of 72 promising herbicide formulations, Walker (78) found that toxicity of herbicidal chemicals to fish was a function of concentration, and the time of exposure and was dependent upon temperature. The toxicity of most aquatic herbicides was much less than other chlorinated hydrocarbon pesticides, but the order of selectivity to species was somewhat similar for various fish species even when subjected to suspensions of relatively insoluble chemicals. Small variations in the side chain, alteration in the salt or ester form, manipulation of the carrier, and use of wetting agent or emulsifier marketly affected toxicity of herbicides to fishers. Walker (78) also demonstrated the effect of water chemistry on the toxicity of herbicides to a variety of fishes. The rate and mode of chemical degradation or detoxification were important from the standpoint of absolute exposure time in relation to the concentration of the herbicide. The depression of oxygen tensions at higher concentrations of herbicides (i.e., chemical oxygen demand) or from decomposing and suppression of photosynthesis (i.e., biological oxygen demand or production) also can compound toxicity and the stress by asphyxiation and physiological injury to the gills. Histopathological findings of Cope, et al., (12,13,14,15,16,18) documented this very important aspect of herbicide toxicology in fishes.

Several investigators have found invertebrates to vary considerably in their sensitivity to aquatic herbicides in laboratory tests (50,51). Walker (77) conducted both simulated field tests with plastic-lined cardboard containers and field tests with plastic enclosures, open plots and whole ponds, to determine acute or chronic toxicity and ecological effects in 2,560 tests involving natural bottom fauna population and various submersed plant species. The population, species composition, and succession of aquatic plants and the bottom dwelling fish-food organisms varied considerably with each chemical and for-mulation. The limnological changes before and after the herbicidal control of aquatic plants are similar to those found in waters receiving organic pollution. This can profoundly influence production of decom-poser organisms, phytoplankton, zooplankton as well as the other pri-mary and secondary consumers. Thus, the uses of herbicides present many research problems and requirements of the disciplines, equip-ment, facilities, methods, and an orderly system of evaluation of chem-icals (24,25).

Bioassay Methods for Measuring Toxicity

The effects of chemicals on aquatic plant and animal life must be determined under a variety of physical, chemical, and biological cir-cumstances. Many factors contribute to the dependability, reproduc-ibility and accuracy of the bioassay. In collating all those suggestions by various authorities on this subject, the following items appear to be of significant importance in conducting and reporting results of bioassay:

1. Identify the species used as test organism.
2. State size and life stage of test organism—length and weight (means and range).
3. Document history and condition of test organism (source, genetics, exposure to chemicals, mortality, disease, nutrition, physiological and biochemical parameters).
4. Control temperature and acclimation prior to and during test.
5. Control water quality (provide chemical analysis) and acclimation prior to and during test.
6. Define procedures in handling fish (voidance time, acclimation to temperature, water quality, light periodicity, method of capture, in-troduction to test media, treatment of disease, types of stress).
7. Define test conditions (loading level); removal of waste materials, carbon dioxide, dissolved oxygen, pH and dissolved solids; static, intermittent or constant flow methodology; composition and intro-duction of toxicant and aliquots of solvent, inerts, formulation, car-rier; size of test containers, surface-volume relationship; number of organisms per test container, per concentration of toxicant, per control with and without solvents and other additives; length of ex-posure period; fate of toxicant through absorption, adsorption, me-tabolism, degradation, removal or detoxification).
8. Experimental design and statistical evaluation of data (adequate number of replicates and sample size for calculation of mean, con-fidence interval, and slope function; relative potency or toxicity in-dex in comparison to reference toxicant; selection of proper

concentrations and exposure time to determine both median and all or no effects of toxicant).

Measurement of Toxicity:

Toxicity is usually measured in terms of the effects of concentration upon a population of organisms for a given period of exposure. Although aquatic bioassay results have been expressed in a variety of terms, toxicity in the United States is most often calculated or estimated as median concentration affecting survival or "TL" or "median tolerance limit" (2,3). In addition to using TL_{50}, other expressions of toxicity measurement having comparable meaning are "median effective concentration" (EC_{50}), "median lethal concentration" (LC_{50}). The inclusion of percent figure in the term has additional advantages for expressing effect levels other that 50 percent (e.g., 0-, 10-, 90-, 100-percent, etc.). These levels have been described by many different authors: "incipient lethal level," "ultimate median tolerance limit," "lethal threshold concentration," "asymptotic LC_{50}," "kritische schwelle," "Schwellenwerte," "todlichkeitsgrenze," in addition to the LC_{50} or "no effect level" (1,4,19,20,21,22).

All expressions of toxicity must be further qualified by exposure time (e.g., 24-hour) TL_{50}, 48-hour EC_{50}, 96-hour LC_{50}). These measurements and the most recent proposed EC_{50}, LD_{50} and TL_{50} by the ASTM and APHA Committees on Standard Methods are derived from the universally used LD_{50} of pharmacology and toxicology in reference to "percent dose effect" experiments originating with Trevan (74). Others have elaborated upon the statistical calculation of the percent effect, relative potency, confidence limits, and fitting regression curves. The rapid graphical methods of Litchfield and Wilcoxon (48,49), using logarthmic probability transformations fitted visually, is now widely accepted, highly accurate, and easily accomplished with a minimum of training and mathematical experience.

Water Quality Considerations

Synthetic water with a uniform dissolved mineral content was prepared by Doudoroff (21) by adding reagent grade salts to distilled water. He used a calcium bicarbonate stock solution prepared by bubbling CO gas through a 210 mg CaCO per liter suspension. One liter of stock was diluted with 11 liters of distilled water and 3 ml of a mixed salt solution was added containing 0.4 mole NaCl, 0.3 mole MgSO and 0.025 mole K SO per liter to make a soft water with total alkalinity of 17.5 ppm CaCO and total hardness of 25 ppm. Waters of desired alkalinities and hardness (5 to 192 ppm and 7 to 275 ppm CaCO, respectively) were prepared by varying the dilution volumes of the two salt solutions. Lennon and Walker (46) and Marking (52) outlined formulas and the uses of reconstituted waters of selected hardnesses and ph for use by the USDI, Bureau of Sport Fisheries and Wildlife, in bioassay toxicity tests. Cains (10,11) recommended soft and hard synthetic dilution waters suitable for bioassay of fish and also algae with addition of certain trace materials. For screening pesticides in bioassays, Palmer and Maloney (60) used a Gerloff's modification of Chu No. 10 with nitrate doubled according to a previous formula in an illuminated culture room.

Natural water used for bioassay purposes should be carefully documented. Water hardness, alkalinity and dissolved salts (measured as specific conductance) have been demonstrated to influence the toxicity of pesticides and pollutants (6,7,8,27,28,29). This also commands enough importance that recommendations for proper treatment rates of certain piscicides have been made.

Dissolved oxygen concentrations in bioassay test solutions should not fall below 4 mg/l when warmwater fish are used as test animals, or 5 mg/l when cold water fish are used (2). The influence of different levels of dissolved oxygen upon the physiology and performance of fish, particularly those induced by low oxygen tensions, has been described in some detail by many authors using various respiration chambers or testing apparatus. Brown (5) reviewed these methods on effects of pollution on fishes.

Temperature ranks as one of the most important variables in toxicity of pesticides (2). Temperature control (3) in bioassay tests is very important in proper evaluation of efficacy, toxicity, and rate of degradation or detoxification of pesticides. As recommended by APHA, the test temperature should be selected that represents the usual and maximum temperatures of problem waters to which the bioassay results are to apply. Temperature control (3) can be achieved in specially insulated, constant-temperature room or large water bath equipped with circulation pump and thermostatic controlled refrigerant and/or heat source. Constant temperature chambers have been used for assay of aquatic plants and algae (29,42,43,44).

Test Organisms

The validity of toxicity measurements is often suspect and sadly compromised by use of test organisms that were not properly acclimated to test conditions (1,2,3,22,23). Cultured specimens with known history of handling, chemical exposure, biochemical-physiological parameters, and genetic origin are much preferred over wild stock. Accurate records on mortality, careful inspection for disease, and adequate feeding and handling are necessary for a meaningful bioassay program. Use of a reference toxicant, or representative chemical from the group under evaluation, serves as a useful measurement of the condition and susceptibility of the fish to chemical stress (46). It has been found that the same species of fish from different geographic areas, size, life stage, season, water qualities, and temperature vary in their susceptibility to toxicants. Thus, a careful documentation of these factors also appear necessary to assist the worker in the interpretation of bioassay data. Standard reference strains of fish is also useful in establishing baseline data.

Test Systems

The static bioassay is a satisfactory system to evaluate single dose methods of applying chemicals providing realistic loading rates (weight and number of fish per unit volume of water) and statistically valid sample size is used (2,3,4). Glass vessels or aquaria are usually accepted as standard containers for laboratory bioassays. However, plexiglass and plastic bags or containers have been found useful by several investigators. Plastic wading pools are very useful for yard tests to simulate field conditions with sunlight, temperatures, soil, and physico-chemical and biological features. Plastic enclosures constructed inponds give the most accurate evaluation technique for replication of tests under the same chemical, biological, and physical circumstances (78,79,80,81).

Ponds divided in half by plastic film also provide direct comparison of treatments. The systems also allow for detailed study of chemical effects on the species composition, biomass, energy-flow, and ecological succession through more than one season or generation. Absorption and leaching of chemicals through the 8 or 10 mil vinyl plastic film is not a problem. This plastic can also be used as a removable lining in concrete, fiberglass, or wooden tanks for easy decontamination. Vinyl-base paints, commonly used for swimming pools, can also be useful in aquaria and tanks (82,83,84,85).

Field Appraisal

Almost all agencies concerned with aquatic weed control develop a program to identify and survey weed problems, test control methods under a variety of field conditions, and support research activities. Lakes, ponds, and flowages are surveyed by area, and aquatic plant and algae are identified and cover mapped, usually by watershed such as that by Lesser (47) using acceptable authorities on plant nomenclature. Although limnological surveys are important in relation to the measurement of productivity for flora and fauna, comprehensive studies for waters of entire watersheds are seldom available despite the existence of standard procedures for collecting data (2,3,59,66). Several noteworthy improvements in sampling devices for collection of organisms in water and in bottom muds in shallow waters have been developed (37,38,41).

BIOLOGICAL CONTROL RESEARCH

Yeo and Fisher (86) recently summarized the progress and potential for biological control of aquatic plants with fish, pathogens, competitive plants, and snails at the first FAO International Conference on Weed Control. These points were stressed (1) availability of a good natural enemy; (2) the nature of the weed (density, diversity, native or alien, type of problem and life history); (3) the strictness of the control required; (4) the weed's taxonomic position (enhances probability of selective control); (5) the resultant suitability and/or availability of enemies; (6) the nature of the plant community and the habitat management practiced; and (7) the applicability of other measures (chemical, mechanical, cultural, or integrated controls).

The specificity of the biological control agent must be thoroughly tested and rigid quarantine procedures imposed to introduce only safe and controllable organisms (56). Preliminary investigations should include consideration of: (1) whether the weed inhabits a range greater than the control organism; (2) the length of time the control organism is active compared to the period the plant can grow, mature, and produce seed; and (3) whether all the environmental conditions that the weed grows in also favors the control organism. The National Academy of Science Subcommittee on Weeds (56) suggests that a good biological control agent is one that includes: (1) ability to kill the plant or prevent its reproduction in some direct or indirect way; (2) high ability to disperse successfully and to locate the target plant; (3) good adaptation to the weed host and the environmental conditions over a maximun part of the weed's habitat; and (4) reproductive capacity sufficient to overtake the increase of the target plant without too much delay (especially when any reason control is temporarily short-circuited or delayed by environmental factors).

Prior to deciding on introduction of the biological control organism, a systematic procedure should be developed to include: (1) preliminary exploration; (2) testing for plant specificity and ecological acceptability) (3) shipping and handling of material through quarantine; (4) developing culture and colonization methods; and (5) evaluation of results.

Preliminary Exploration

A thorough search of the literature and examination of the candidate control agent in its native environment is required (56). As pointed out by the Subcommittee on Weeds, this exploration should include: "(1) taxonomic position, biology, ecology, and economic importance; (2) native geographic distribution; (3) total present distribution; (4) probable center of its origin and that of its close relatives; (5) coextensive occurrence of related species; (6) occurrence of related and ecologically similar species in regions where the weed does not occur, but where exploration for an enemy agents seems desirable; and (7) the literature record of the weed's natural enemies."

Ecological Considerations

Safety in biological control relies heavily on the specificity of the organism to the target weed species (10,11,12,61). It also must be compatible with other desirable organisms in the ecosystem and to the croplands, domestic animals and human health. Although a great deal can be learned from the preliminary exploration, actual experimentation on the organism in the various ecological situations is necessary to confirm the acceptability, food relationships, and competition with other aquatic species, true degree of restriction in diet to the target species and range of conditions necessary or degrees of control attained or factors affecting rejection or failure to control. Thus, we must carefully establish the relevance of feeding tests to: (1) the laboratory or field conditions imposed; (2) spectrum of the plants selected for establishing selectivity; (3) relationship of physiological requirements such as reproduction, proper growth and maintenance, resistance to diseases and predators, etc.; and (4) the criteria established for the acceptability of the target plant(s) to the biological control agent.

Quarantine Facilities

Each type of biological control agent requires special facilities and precautions for handling and shipping to prevent escape. Transportation or shipping and handling procedures should be cautiously planned and regulated. Quarantine facilities, for importations, or from facilities to the field (for culturing or colonization), and the arrangements for special handling, labeling, communications or instructions on transfer points are needed for assuring success and safety in the quarantine procedure (56).

Culturing and Colonization

Although the methods for quarantine, culture, and colonization of terrestrial plants, insects, and some pathogens are well developed in the USA, Europe, and many other countries, such techniques are also needed and applicable to aquatic organisms. Candidates such as invertebrates (e.g., snails and insects), fish, birds, mammals, etc., described by Timmons (73), Yeo and Fisher (86) have been studied in the United States. However, several important aspects of culturing, colonization, and field evaluation are often overlooked. We must have adequate chemical, mechanical, biological, or natural climatic control methods for the candidate biological agent. For example, the white amur (**Ctenopharyngodon idella, Val.**) has demonstrated promise for controlling a broad spectrum of aquatic plants in Asia, Europe, and recently in the United States (69). We have developed management techniques (e.g., piscicides, sterilization, or monosex culture and other safeguards) for positive control of this fish. State and Federal agencies must be able to evaluate the economics, general acceptance, and make recommendations. They also must develop the necessary facilities for culture, transportation, handling, stocking, and management of the species before this biological method could be used.

Integrated Pest Management

The management and manipulation of the fish and wildlife habitats must, by just the complexity of the ecosystem alone, require biological methods of control integrated with selective chemical and mechanic methods. Success of the research in biological enhancement and introduction of exotic species or maintenance of native fish stocks relies heavily on development of effective control methods. This research and testing program that evaluates all aspects of energy flow dynamics and assessment of environmental impacts on aquatic plant and annual relationships.

HERBICIDE RESIDUES AND TOXICOLOGICAL SIGNIFICANCE

Residue analysis

A monitoring program should be maintained with emphasis directed to both fishes and their food chain organisms in each environmental ecotype. It should consider the kinetics of herbicide accumulation, persistence, mode of degradation, metabolites, mechanisms, and rate of disappearance are vital to establishing pesticide policy and furnishing guidelines to minimize hazards to fish, wildlife, and other consumers (27).

Toxicological significance

Occurrence of residues in fish, water, or components of the aquatic ecosystem must be evaluated relative to the potential hazards they pose. This toxicological significance can be judged only on the basis of sound biological work done on species both in their natural environs and in simulated and controlled conditions of the laboratory. Detailed physiological and biochemical studies of herbicide intoxication relative to various types of herbicide, combinations, concentrations, and modes of exposure can be properly evaluated with respect to residues, metabolites and their toxicological significance. Emphasis should be placed on determination of effects not only on the important fishes (egg to adult) but their food chain organisms and interaction of other environmental stresses. We should also evaluate chronic effects on growth, reproduction, fecundity, and subtle physiological changes (teratogenicity, pathology, compound stress, susceptibility to disease, predation, behavior, etc.).

SUMMARY AND CONCLUSIONS

The purpose of this literature review is to assess the usage patterns and benefits of using herbicides and to gain greater knowledge of the environmental effects of these compounds. The discussion covers herbicide use, available alternatives, and approaches to understanding and solving problems relating to fish and wildlife management. Adequate knowledge is currently available to cover the commonly recommended herbicide.

REFERENCES

1. Abram, F.S.H. 1967. The definition and measurement of fish toxicity thresholds. Advances in Water Pollution Research, Proc. 3rd Int. Conf., Munich, Germany (1966). Pergamon Press, Oxford, 1:75-95.
2. American Public Health Association, American Water Works Association, and Water Pollution Control Federation 1970. Standard methods for the examination of water and waste water including bottom sediments and sludges. Am. Pub. Health Assn., New York, NY, 13th Ed., 769 p.
3. Axelrod, H.R., R.E. Gossington, K.D. Kallman, S. McConnell, S.F. Snieszko, and C.R. Walker. 1973. Standards for care and maintanance of fish for laboratory research. National Academy of Sciences, Institute of Laboratory Animal Research, Committee for Care and Maintenance of Laboratory Animals, Subcommittee on Fish Standards. 245 p.
4. Blackburn, R.D. 1966. Weed control in fish ponds in the United States. F.A.O. Fisheries Report, 5(44):1-17.

5. Brown, Margaret E. 1957. The physiology of fishes. Vol. 1. Metabolism. Academic Press Inc., New York. 447 pp.
6. Burdick, G.E. 1960. The use of bioassays by the water pollution control agency. Trans. Second Seminar Biol. Prob. Water Pollution. U.S. Public Health Service, R.A. Taft Sanit. Engng. Ctr., Tech. Rpt. W-603:145-148.
7. Burress, Ralph M. 1968. Antimycin for controlling sunfish populations in ponds. Farm Pond Harvest. Winter, 1968, 2(1):11, 12 and 22. (Mimeo).
8. Burress, Ralph M. and Charles W. Luhning. 1970. Field trial of antimycin as a selective toxicant in channel catfish ponds. U.S. Bur. Sport Fish. and Wildl. Investigations in Fish Control.
9. Burress, Ralph M. and Charles W. Luhning. 1970. Use of antimycin for selective thinning of sunfish populations in ponds. U.S. Bur. Sport Fish. and Wildl. Investigations in Fish Control.
10. Cairns, John, Jr. 1968. The sequential comparison index—a simplified method for non-biologists to estimate relative differences in biological diversity in stream pollution studies. J. FWPCA, 40:1607.
11. Cairns, John, Jr. 1969. Fish bioassays—reproducibility and rating. Revista de Biologia, 7(1-2):7-12.
12. Cope, Oliver B. 1961. Standards for reporting fish toxicity tests. The Prog. Fish-Cult., 23(4):187-190.
13. Cope, Oliver B., Joseph P. McCraren, and Lafayette Eller. 1969. Effects of dichlobenil on two fishpond environments. Weed Sci., 17(2):158-165.
14. Cope, Oliver B., Edward M. Wood, and George H. Wallen. 1970. Some chronic effects of 2,4-D on bluegills. Trans. am. Fish. Soc.
15. Crosby, D.G. and R.K. Tucker. 1966. Toxicity of aquatic herbicides to *Daphnia magna*. Sci., 154 (3746):289-291.
16. Cummings, J.G. 1969. Use, regulation and registration of chemicals used in fish culture and management. Ann. Meeting of American Fisheries Society, New Orleans, La.
17. Davis, H.S. 1963. Culture and disease of game fishes. Univ. Calif. Press 332 pp.
18. Davis, James T. and W.S. Hardcastle. 1959. Biological assay of herbicides for fish toxicity. Weeds, 7(4):397-404.
19. DeMarco, J., J.M. Symons and G.G. Robert. 1967. Behavior of synthetic organics in stratified impoundments. Fed. Water Poll. Contr. Admin. Cincinnati, Ohio.
20. DeVaney, T.C. 1968. Chemical vegetation control manual for fish and wildlife management programs. U.S. Fish and Wildl. Svc., Res. Publ. 48. 42 pp.
21. Doudoroff, P., B.G. Anderson, G.E. Burdick, P.S. Galtsoff, W.B. Hart, R. Patrick, E.R. Strong, E.W. Surber, and W.M. Van Horn.

1951. Bio-assay methods for the evaluation of acute toxicity of industrial wastes to fish. Sewage Indus. Wastes, 23:1380-1397.

22. Doudoroff, P. and M. Katz. 1953. Critical review of literature on the toxicity of industrial wastes and their components to fish. II. The metals, as salts. Sewage Indus. Wastes, 25:802-839.

23. Doudoroff, P. 1956. Some experiments on toxicity of complex cyanides to fish. Sewage and Industrial Wastes. 28:1020-1040.

24. Ellis, M.M. 1937. Detection and measurement of stream pollution. U.S. Bur. of Fisheries. Bull. 22(58):365-437.

25. Federal Register. 1982. Vol. 47, pp 25746-25748.

26. Gallagher, J.E. 1969. Clearance and registration of chemical tools for fish culturists and fisheries biologists. Ann. Meeting of Amer. Fisheries Soc. New Orleans, La.

27. Gangstad, E.O. 1978. Weed control methods for river basin management, CRC Press Inc., Boca Raton, Florida. 232 pp.

28. Gangstad, E.O. 1982. Weed control methods for recreation facilities management. CRC Press Inc., Boca Raton, Florida. 297 pp.

29. Hart, W.P., P. Doudoroff, and J. Greenbank. 1945. The evaluation of the toxicity of industrial wastes, chemicals, and other substances to freshwater fishes. Atlantic Refining Co., Phila., PA, 317 pp.

30. Hays, H.W. 1969. Uses, regulations and registration of chemicals for fish culture and management. Ann. Meeting of the Amer. Fisheries Soc., New Orleans, La.

31. Tarzwell, C.M. 1960. Biological problems in water pollution. U.S. Dept. Health Educ. and Welfare. W 60-3 285 pp.

32. Hiltibran, R.C. 1965. The chemical control of some aquatic plants. III. Natural History Survey Section of Aquatic Biology:1-5.

33. Hiltibran, R.C. 1963. Effect of endothall on aquatic plants. Weeds 11:256-267.

34. Hiltibran, R.C. 1965. The effect of diquat on aquatic plants in central Illinois. Weeds, 13(1):71-72.

35. Hiltibran, R.C. 1967. The effects of some herbicides on fertilized fish eggs and fry. Trans. Am. Fish. Soc., 96(4):414-416.

36. Hiltibran, R.C. and M.G. Johnson. 1965. The effect of rotenone on oxygen uptake by liver mitochondria of the bluegill, *lepomis macrochirus*. State Academy of Science 58:140-143.

37. Hughes, Janice S. and James T. Davis. 1962. Comparative toxicity to bluegill sunfish of granular and liquid herbicides. Proc. Southeastern Assn. Game and Fish Commissioners, 16:319-323.

38. Jackson, H.W. 1970. A controlled-depth, volumetric bottom sampler. The Prog. Fish-Cult., 32(2):113-115.

39. Jones, R.O. 1962. Tolerance of the fry of common warm-water fishes to some chemicals employed in fish culture. Southeastern Assn. of Game and Fish Comm. 16:436-445.

40. Kallman, B.J., O.B. Cope and J.R. Navare. 1962. Distribution and detoxification of toxaphene in Clayton Lake, New Mexico. Trans. Amer. Fish Soc. 91:14-23.

41. Larimore, R. Weldon. 1970. Two shallow-water bottom samplers. The Prog. Fish-Cult., 32(2):116-119.

42. Lawrence, J.M. 1962. Aquatic herbicides data. Agr. Handbook No. 231.

43. Lawrence, J.M. 1966. Aquatic weed control in fish ponds. F.A.O. Fisheries Report 44, Vol. 5, p. 76-91.

44. Lawrence, J.M. and R.D. Blackburn. 1962. Evaluating herbicidal activity of chemicals to aquatic plants and their toxicity to fish in the laboratory and in plastic pools. Auburn Univ., Agr. Expt. Sta., pp. 1-23.

45. Lennon, R.E. and B.L. Berger. 1970. A resume on field applications of actinomycin A to control fish. U.S. Bureau Sport Fish and Wildlife, Investigations in Fish Control 40:1-19.

46. Lennon, R.E. and Charles R. Walker. 1964. Investigations in fish control: I. Laboratories and methods for screening fish-control chemicals. U.S. Bur. Sport Fish. and Wildl. Cir. 185:15 pp.

47. Lesser, Charles A. 1966. Aquatic vegetation survey. Delaware Game and Fish Comm., 65 pp.

48. Litchfield, J.T. and F. Wilcoxon. 1949 A simplified method of evaluating dose-effect experiments. J. Pharmacol. Exp. Ther., 96:99-113.

49. Litchfield, J.T. and F. Wilcoxon. 1953. The reliability of graphic estimates of relative potency from dose-per cent effect curves. J. Pharmacol. Exp. Ther., 108:18-25.

50. Mackenthun, K.M. 1969. The practice of water pollution biology USDI Fed. Water Poll. Contr. Adm. 281 pp.

51. Mackenthun, K.M. and W.M. Ingram. 1967. Biological associated problems in freshwater environments. USDI Fed. Wat. Poll. Cont. Admin., pp. 270-273.

52. Marking, Leif L. 1966. IFC: 10. Evaluation of p,p'-DDT as a reference toxicant in bioassays. Bur. Sport Fish. & Wildl., Resource Publ. 14, 10 pp.

53. McCarthy, H. 1961. Survey study on methods of controlling aquatic weeds and their effectiveness. FWD Corp., Clintonville, Wis., pp. 1-27 (Mimeo.).

54. Mitchell, Travis E. and Meda J. Usry. 1967. Catfish farming—a profit opportunity for Mississippians. Miss. Res. Develop. Ctr., 83 pp. (Mimeo.).

55. Moyle, J.B. and B.R. Jones. 1957. Summary of aquatic nuisance control activities in the United States in 1956. Minnesota Dept. of Conservation. pp. 1-9 (Mimeo.).

56. National Academy of Science. 1968. Scientific aspects of pest control Publication 1402, Washington, D.C.

57. Nelson, O.F., K.M. Mackenthun, and L.A. Lueschow. 1961. Micros-training at Kenosha, Am. Water Works Assn., Wis. Section, Milwaukee, Wis. (Spt. 28), 15 pp. (Mimeo.).

58. Outdoor Recreation Resources Review Commission (ORRRC). 1962. Sport fishing—today and tomorrow, ORRRC. Study Rpt. 7. U.S. GPO, Washington, D.C. 136 pp.

59. Palmer, C.M. 1952. An incubation from for algal cultures in water supply taste and order research. News Bull., Phycolo. Soc. Am., 5(16):9-11.

60. Palmer, C.M. and T.E. Maloney. 1955. Preliminary screening for potential algicides. Ohio J. Sci., 55(1):1-8.

61. Pimentel, D. 1971. Ecological Effects of Pesticides on Nontarget Species, Executive Office of the President, Office of Science and Technology, Washington, D.C. 220 pp.

62. Pintler, H.E., and W.C. Johnson. 1958. Chemical control of rough fish in the Russian river drainage, California. California Fish and Game 44 (2):91-124.

63. Phillippy, C.L. and J.M. Perryman. 1972. Mechanical Harvesting of Waterhyacinth (*Eichhornia crassipes*) in Gant Lake Canal, Sumter County, Florida. Fla. Game and Fresh Water Fish Comm. 21 pp.

64. Ramachandran, V. and T. Ramaprabku. 1966. Investigations on aquatic weed control with special reference to the use of chemicals. FAO Fisheries Rpt, 5(44):92-108.

65. Rosen, R.A. and L.B. Starnes. 1985. Environmental Policy: The AFS and you. Fisheries 10(2):6:9.

66. Sanders, Herman O. and Oliver B. Cope. 1968. The relative toxicities of several pesticides to three species of stoneflies. Liminol. Oceanogr. 13:165-169.

67. Strange, R.J. 1976. Nutrient release and community metabolism following application of herbicide to macrophytes in microcosms. J. Appl. Ecol. 13:889-897.

68. Strange, R.J. and C.B. Schreck. 1976. Response of aerobic community metabolism to chemical treatment of aquatic macrophytes. J. Aq. Plant Manag. 14:45-50.

69. Smith, C.R., and Shireman, J.V. 1983. White Amur Bibliography. University of Florida, Gainesville, Fla., and the U.S. Army Engineer Waterways Experiment Station, CE, Vicksburg, Miss. (in Press).

70. Stokes, William. 1969. Requirements for establishing tolerances for aquatic herbicides. Weed Soc. Am., Las Vegas, Nev., 8 pp.

71. Surber, Eugene W. 1948. Chemical control agents and their effects on fish. Progr. Fish Cult. 10:125-131.

72. Timmermans, J.A. 1966. Control of aquatic vegetation if fish ponds in Europe. FAO Fisheries Report 5(44):61-75.

73. Timmons, F.L. 1964. Scope of aquatic and marginal weed problem and status of the use of herbicides for their control. Weed Sci. Soc. Meeting, Las Vegas, Nev., (2/13/69), 16 pp.
74. Trevan, J.W. 1927. The error of determination of toxicity. Proc. R. Soc. B., 101:483-514.
75. U.S. Department of the Interior. 1968. National Survey of needs for hatchery fish. Bur. Sport Fish. and Wildl. Res. Publ. 63, 71 pp.
76. Van Der Lingen, M.I. 1966. Control of pond weeds. FAO Fish. Rpt., 5(44):53-60.
77. Van Dyke, J.M. 1971. Mechanical Harvesting of Waterhyacinth (*Eichhornia crassipes*) in Shell Creek Reservoir, Charlotte County, Florida. Fla. Game and Fresh Water Fish Comm. Tallahassee. 25 pp.
78. Walker, C.R. 1961. Toxicological effects of several herbicides to bottom dwelling fish-food organisms in Missouri ponds. Res. Rpt. North Central Weed Control Conf., 18:104-106.
79. Walker, C.R. 1963. Toxicological effect of herbicides on the fish environment. Proc. Air and Water Pollution Conf.:8:17-34.
80. Walker, C.R. 1963. Toxicological effects of herbicides on the fish environment. The Univ. Missouri Bull., 64(24):17-34. Also, Water and Sewage Works, 3(3):113-116, 3(4):173-175.
81. Walker, C.R. 1964. Pond renovation with Penco herbicide 47 and Penco pond renovator. Proc. 19th North Central Weed Control Conf., 27: Weed Abst., 13(1):Abst. 137.
82. Walker, Charles R. 1968. Herbicides in the aquatic environment: a summary of research activities by various agencies. Proc. 8th Meeting of the Weed Sci. Soc., Am., New Orleans, 7 pp.
83. Walker, Charles R., Robert E. Lennon, and Bernard L. Berger. 1964. Investigations in Fish Control: 2. Preliminary observations on the toxicity of antimycin A to fish and other aquatic animals. U.S. Bur. Sport Fish. and Wildl. Cir. 186, 18 pp.
84. Warner, R.E. 1967. Bioassays for microchemical environmental contaminants with special reference to water supplies. Bull. Wld. Health Org., 36:181-207.
85. Whitworth, Walter R., and Thomas H. Lane. 1969. Effects of toxicants on community metabolisms in pools. Limnology and Oceanography, 14(1).
86. Yeo, R.R. and Fisher. 1967. Dissipation of diquat and paraquat, and effects on aquatic weeds and fish. Weeds, 15(1):42-46.

Figure 2.1 Florida Game and Fresh Water Fish Commission personnel collecting fish samples at Lake Conway, Florida, with Wagner Rings. (Courtesy of Florida Game and Fresh Water Fish Commission, June 1978).

Figure 2.2 An innovative feature that provides a rapid method of cleaning boat hulls and eliminating aquatic weeds that adhere in the boat hull. (Courtesy of the U.S. Army Corps of Engineers, Nashville District, July 1976).

Figure 2.3 Compared to waters in other parts of the United States, the nutritional load of Florida lakes is plentiful, creating aquatic plant problems. View of Lake Ochlawaha, Florida showing a typical infestation of hydrilla. (Courtesy of the U.S. Army Corps of Engineers, Jacksonville, Florida, July 1974).

PART I

ENVIRONMENTAL ENGINEERING ASSESSMENT

Chapter 3

WHITE AMUR FISH FOR AQUATIC PLANT CONTROL[1]

INTRODUCTION

During the last several decades, research to discover means of controlling obnoxious aquatic plant growth has included evaluation of various species of herbivorous fishes. It has been purpose of this research to determine the efficiency of the white amur fish (**Ctenopharyngodon idella**) as a biological control agent for aquatic weed populations in natural habitats, with evaluation of the effects of space and plant nutrients resulting from the destruction of weeds in the aquatic ecosystem. This research information provides the basis to establish a system of knowledge for control and operational procedures for use of white amur fish for aquatic plant control (1,2,3,4,5,6,7,9,10,11,14,15).

LARGE-SCALE OPERATIONS MANAGEMENT TESTING

Beginning in 1975, the U.S. Army Engineer Waterways Experiment Station (8) began planning for a Large-Scale Operations Management Test (LSOMT) to investigate the suitability of the white amur (**Ctenopharyngodon idella**) as a potential biological control for aquatic plants, especially hydrilla (**Hydrilla verticillata**). Because the State of Florida had an aquatic plant problem and was receptive to using the fish under the concept of an LSOMT, Lake Conway near Orlando, Florida, was selected as the study site. Lake Conway is an urban lake consisting of five interconnected pools with a combined surface area of approximately 7.4 km². The project was envisioned as consisting of a one-year study for compilation of baseline data (prestocking period) and approximately three years of poststocking study. By September 1976, the following contracts had been awarded and work started: water chemistry and sediment quality—Orange County Pollution Control Authority; aquatic macrophyte populations-Florida Department of Natural Resources; phytoplankton, zooplankton, and benthic invertebrate populations, and an ecosystem model—University of Florida; and

---

[1]The findings in this report are not to be construed as an official Department of the Army position unless so designated by other authorized documents.

fish, aquatic bird, and mammal inventories—Florida Game and Fresh Water Fish Commission. In June of 1977, a contract was awarded to the University of South Florida to characterize and monitor the amphibian and reptile populations.

In September of 1977, a monosex population of the white amur was introduced into Lake Conway (8) at an average stocking density of one fish per 0.1 hectare. This value, previously determined from a stocking rate model was designed to control aquatic plant populations, particularly those of hydrilla, in Lake Conway. From this point on (poststocking period), populations were monitored in Lake Conway to evaluate the impact, if any, of the white amur on the component systems of the lake community through September 1980. In September 1979, radiotracking was added to the project's methodologies to gain insight on feeding habits of the white amur. Baseline studies and the first, second and third year poststocking studies have been published.

The hybrid carp, a cross between the female grass carp (**C. idella**) (8) and the male bighead carp (**Hypophthalmichthyes nobilis**), was proposed for introduction for weed control and is now being tested in several laboratories and field situations. An important advantage of the hybrid over the grass carp is that the hybrid consumes both plants and filamentous algae, wheras the grass carp eats only plants.

In 1961 Soviet and Hungarian researchers (8) crossbred female grass carp (**Ctenopharyngodon idella**) with male bighead carp (**Hypophthalmicthys nobilis**), another fish of Asian origin, to produce what appears to be a sterile hybrid. Hybrid grass carp are now being produced commercially in the United States, but in very limited numbers. Their potential use for aquatic weed control provides an environmentally attractive means for dealing with a serious and growing water system maintenance problem in irrigation canals.

In 1980, the Bureau of Reclamation's Division of Research (8) in a cooperative agreement between the Reclamation's Lower Colorado Region, U.S. Fish and Wildlife Service, Coachella Valley Water Users Organization, Imperial Irrigation District of California, and three State of California agencies, initiated a study with hybrid grass carp to evaluate their effectiveness in controlling aquatic weeds in test canals and their effects on the aquatic environment. The Division of Research staff's responsibility in these studies was to determine the effectiveness of the hybrid fish in controlling aquatic vegetation.

GRASS CARP IN USSR AND OTHER EUROPEAN COUNTRIES

An investigative trip (17) was made to evaluate the effects of the grass carp in areas where it had been introduced and to exchange information with scientists conducting research on this fish. The objective was to gain a better understanding of the impact that the grass carp might have on areas where it was not native so that an evaluation could be made of potential effects if it were used in the State of Florida for the control of certain aquatic plant problems.

The Netherlands

The Netherlands is a small country of approximately 200 by 200 km in area, but with about 150,000 ha of surface waters. Much of this water is in canals and drainage ditches. These waterways remove water from the land and function for transportation and recreation. Much of Holland is below sea level with dikes to hold back the North Sea and the Rhine River. Water must constantly pumped from the polders (diked-off land) to permit growth of terrestrial plants. Aquatic weed control in the Netherlands is necessary to ensure proper water flow in the waterways. Problems with aquatic weeds have been reported as early as the 13th century.

Filamentous algae is the major weed problem during the winter months without ice cover and in the spring. As the water temperature increases, higher aquatic plants such as **Potamogeton crispus, Potamogeton lucens, Edodea nutallii, Elodea canadensis,** pondlilies, and some of the duckweeds begin to grow. Oddly enough, **Hydrilla verticillata** is considered by several Dutch scientists to be endemic but now is rarely found. **Elodea nutallii** is a native Dutch species that was apparently crowded out after **Elodea canadensis** was introduced. However in recent years, **E nutallii** began replacing **E. canadensis** apparently as a result of eutrophication. **Elodea canadensis** is considered an indicator of pristine waters.

In general, the Dutch would prefer to use mechanical methods to clear their canals. The canals must be cleaned periodically to remove the build-up of organic matter and debris. The decay of vegetation deposited along the bank is thought not to release sufficient nutrients to contribute significantly to new aquatic weed problems. However, associated with mechanical harvesting is high turbidity and low dissolved oxygen which frequently results in massive fish kills.

Because of these concerns over the effects of herbicides and mechanical methods, the Dutch initiated studies on biological methods for the control of their aquatic weed problem. In 1966 grass carp were imported from Hungary and from Taiwan and beginning in 1972 grass carp have been artificially spawned at a new and modern fish hatchery near Lelystad under the direction of Mr. Huisman. This facility has about 220 ha of grow-out pond and has access to the warm water effluent of an electric generating plant. The hatchery annually spawns pike (**Esox lucius**), carp (**Cyprinus carpio**), and recently introduced rainbow trout (**Salmo gairdneri**). The grass carp is spawned in December and January when the hatchery is normally idle.

The brood fish are removed from 2 to 4 C water and slowly warmed to 23 C prior to injection with hormones. The length of warming and rise in temperature is based on the sum of heat-day degrees required to achieve greater than 1,050 physiological heat units. The oxygen consumption of the fish as related to temperature is used to calculate these units. Apparently temperature is the most critical factor involved in ripening of the grass carp and not light intensity or photoperiod which affects salmonids. During the warming period the males and females are kept in separate containers but under the same temperature regime.

The Human Chorionic Gonadotropin (HCG) injections are administered intramuscularly. The Dutch researchers were amazed to learn that in Florida these intraperitoneally injections were successful (although this method is successful with other species). The resolving dose of pituitary extract is the only injection given intraperitoneally. The males are injected with only pituitary extract.

Using the sum of heat-day degrees to mature brood stock, ovulation occurs in approximately 85% of the females injected. The fertilized eggs are placed in cone shaped hatching jars, the water is sand filtered, aerated, and heated and then de-nitrogenated at the storage area or tanks by splash screens. They use approximately 100 g of eggs per 15 liters of water with just enough flow to keep the eggs floating. Too much flow apparently mechanically damages the eggs and interferes with normal development with a resulting decrease in the percent hatch. Gentle rolling is critical and is perhaps one of the problems associated with incubation. After hatching, the fry swim up and out an overflow into a tray and are then transferred to large bins.

The fry are fed freshly hatched **Artemia** (brine shrimp) until they reach a weight of 25 to 35 mg. A light is suspended over one end of the tank to attract the **Artemia**. The outflow from the tank is at the other end so that the debris is separated from the fry. The same water is used as in the incubation and compressed air is never used.

The advanced fry are fed trout pellets which contain 50% crude protein. This percent of crude protein is lowered to 30% as the fry grow to large fingerlings. The larger fingerlings apparently cannot effectively utilize the high protein-low fiber diet. They obtain a 24% survival of the eggs to fingerlings (2-g fish). It takes about 6 weeks to produce the 2-g fish.

Fingerlings 25 to 30 g in weight are transferred to buoyed cages 1.5 by 3 m in surface area with 6.5 m³ by volume. There are 24 cages located in warm water effluent that is 7 C above ambient water temperature. The flowing water prevents a buildup of metabolites and growth inhibitors, and one cage is equivalent to a grow-out area of approximately 4-acre feet in a closed pond system. Stocking is approximately 1 kg of fish for each 10 liters of water volume in the cage. Approximately 1,500 to 2,000 fingerlings are stocked in each cage. About 600 to 700 kg of 350-g grass carp are harvested after 1 year. On rare occasions up to 1,500 kg per cage are harvested. Growth in the cages is fairly slow due to low water temperature and survival is approximately 80%. Food conversion from fingerlings to the 350-g fish is 1.61. Feeding in the cages is by demand feeders. The most active feeding occurs in the morning and again in the late afternoon or evening.

Impact studies revealed that grass carp caused less ecological damage than herbicides. A 3-year study indicated that macrofauna and plankton species diversity was not decreased. Planktonic species did not decrease in this study or in subsequent ones. Dramatic changes in water quality have not been observed except in small containers.

Dutch authorities consider that approximately 10% of 15,000 ha of their waters are suitable for stocking with grass carp. Present stocking of grass carp is at the rate of 250 kg of 300 to 350-g fish per ha. In 1976 they stocked 20 ha and plan to stock 200 ha or about 50,000 kg of grass carp in 1977.

Fishermen abound in Holland; one in fourteen of the population being considered an avid freshwater sport fisherman. These fishermen spend some 5 million guilder (about 2 million dollars) annually to help pay for stocking of fish. Pike, carp, rutt, roach, and rainbow trout are caught for fun and returned to the water. Because of widespread interest in freshwater fisheries and the uncertain impact of grass carp, all areas to be stocked with grass carp are secured with screens that have parallel bars spaced 3 cm apart. These screens are placed in a vertical or horizontal position in the waterway. This 3-cm spacing seems adequate to keep the fish in and at the same time permits debris to flow through.

The Dutch fishermen use doughballs and **Salix** (willow) leaves for hook-and-line capture of the grass carp. However, this fish is reluctant to take bait once it has been hooked and escapes, or is returned to the water. The Dutch are confident that they can use hook-and-line techniques to remove grass carp from their waterways. They also have shown that electrofishing is quite successful in their canals and ditches because grass carp cannot escape the electrical field.

Czechoslovakia

Czechoslovakia is a country in central Europe stretching out between 48° to 51° northern latitude and 12 to 22° eastern longitude. It has a mild climate with an average temperature of 20 C in the summer and -5 C in the winter. It covers some 128,000 square kilometers and has a population of over 14 million people. Prague, the principal city, is the capital of the Czechoslovakia Socialist Republic and of the Slovak Socialist Republic.

The territory of Czechoslovakia is in the river basin of two main rivers—the Elbe (Bohemia) and the Danube (Moravia and Slovakia). There are hundreds of mineral springs both hot and cold which are used for therapeutic and medicinal purposes. There are over 22,000 lakes and ponds scattered throughout the country with the majority of them in the southern part.

In Czechoslovakia small fry of white amur was repeatedly imported from the Soviet Union in the mid-sixties. At present there are a sufficient amount of sexually mature breeding fish. Their hatching is carried out in southern Moravia (better temperature conditions) but also in the experimental establishments of the Research Institute of Fish and Hydrobiology in Vodnany, southern Bohemia.

Poland

Poland is located in northcentral Europe and lies between 48° to 55° in latitude and 14° to 24° eastern longitude. Warsaw, the capital, has some 1.5 million people with a total of about 35 million inhabitants in this country. The northern part of Poland borders the Baltic Sea into which empties the two main rivers of this country, the Odra and the Wisla. The southern part of the country is mountainous with trout streams while the northern part is flat with slow flowing and turbid waters.

A number of aquatic plants are present in Poland but are problems only under certain circumstances such as in the warm water effluent ponds of electric power plants and other shallow-water ponds. Plants which may cause problems are **Chara** *spp.,* **Elodea canadensis, Potamogeton** *spp.,* **Myriophyllum** *spp.,* **Typha** *spp.,* and **Phragmites** *spp. Herbicides and mechanical control methods have been utilized in the past to control these plants, but now the grass carp is used exclusively for their aquatic weed problems.*

In 1964 Poland imported grass carp fry from Russia but they now spawn the grass carp artificially every January. The present hatchery has 100 ha of water with the ponds ranging in size from 0.2 to 10 ha in surface area. During the 1977 season some 25 to 30 million fingerlings were produced which is considered insufficient for Poland's needs. A second hatchery is being built so that production can be increased. The Polish use a technique similar to that in Holland of warming the brood stock to mature them in January. However, only two injections are given to the female brook stock to achieve ripening. Both injections are carp pituitary extracts which are administered intramuscularly. Weiss jars which have cone-shaped bottoms and straight sides are used for incubation. Water at a temperature of 20 to 23 C enters form the bottom and slowly rolls the eggs. The overflow from the jars is to a cloth-lined basket.

Grass carp in Poland grow at a slow rate as compared to that in Florida. The weight of 3-year-old fish is generally 1.0 kg. In Florida some fish may grow at a rate of 1.0 kg or more per month. The cool water temperature and lack of vegetation are the two major factors for the slow rate of grass carp growth in Poland. Water temperature in the late summer can reach as high as 28 C but this warm temperature is of short duration. Most of the stocking of grass carp is in combination with carp. Carp stocked at 500 kg per ha destroy macrophytes and grass carp have little to eat. Grass carp stocked alone in ponds produce an average of 200 kg of fish per ha. The production in lakes is much lower.

Almost all of Poland's 60,000 ha of ponds and lakes are stocked with grass carp. The fish has not been stocked in the Odra and Wisla rivers but escaped grass carp are now present there. Small numbers have been in these two rivers for approximately 12 years but natural reproduction has not occurred. Karol Opuszynski and Dr. Backel of the Institute of Inland Fisheries do not believe that Polish rivers are suitable for spawning. The grass carp is generally captured at 3 years of age from ponds and natural bodies of waters using seines.

Interest in the silver carp (**Hypophthalmichthys molitrix**) is greater than the grass carp and research in Poland is now aimed at a polyculture of carp and silver carp. This polyculture increases production over twice that of either species alone. The silver carp does not compete for the food of the carp or the grass carp.

Austria

The grass carp is used extensively for control of aquatic weeds in Austria and to a limited extent as a sport fish. The fish has been stocked in most lakes and ponds and has been in Austrian rivers for over 12 years, but it has not reproduced naturally. They have been artificially spawned for the past 7 years. Any number of grass carp can be bought and stocked by anyone in Austria without a permit.

While in Austria we visited Alexander von Mensel at his private research hatchery facility near Wettmannstatten. This facility cover 170 ha and has 80 ha of ponds. Von Mensel produces 5 to 6 million grass carp annually using 20 to 25 brood fish. The annual fish production at this hatchery is 40 tons of carp, 40 tons of silver carp, 15 to 20 tons of grass carp, and 10 tons of Tinca (**Tinca tinca**). Grass carp are usually sold as fingerlings but there is also a market for larger fish by sport fishing clubs.

The techniques used by von Mensel for artificial propagation of the grass carp are similar to those used in Holland. The fish are spawned in the spring after at least 1,500 degree days have elapsed. Preparation of ponds for stocking with grass carp fry differs from other techniques in that an organic complex formulation of phosphoric acid is applied at a rate of 1.0 g per m³ to the ponds 24 hr in advance of the fry. The compound used is a Bayer product called Neguvon [(2,2,2-trichlor-1-hydroxy-ethyl)-phosphonate-dimethylester]. The young fish are fed a powdered meal, and after they are larger, grass is cut and placed in the ponds. Sufficient terrestrial vegetation is placed in the pond so that the grass carp have consumed it within 3 days.

Weed control recommendations with grass carp are to use 400 to 600 2 to 3-inch fish per ha if no predators are present. At this stocking rate weed control can be expected in 1 year. If pike or other predator fish are present, the recommended stocking rate is 200 to 300-700g fish per ha.

West Germany

In West Germany the grass carp is being studied at the Bundeforschungsanstalt fur Fischerei (BfF) in Ahrensburg under the direction of Volker Hilge and in southern Germany at the Bayerische Landesanstalt fur Wassenforschung at Wielenback under the leadership of Martin Bohl.The grass carp they produce is for their own research studies and extra fish are sold to the farmers for weed control purposes.

The BfF is studying the grass carp along with intensive culture of common carp. One of the most interesting things we saw at this research facility was a method for holding and rearing brood stock grass carp. Five brood fish of about 15 kg in weight were held in an all-glass aquarium of 1,000 liters in volume. This aquarium also contained two large brook carp. Grass clippings were added in the morning and evening in sufficient quantities so that the grass carp had all they could eat. The aquarium was supplied with 6 to 8 liters per minute of aerated water from a well at 23 C. The grass carp had been held for 2 years under these conditions and grew from 7 kg to 15 kg during this time. Because the water temperature is constant at 23 C year-round, the grass carp apparently matured in response to photoperiod. The aquarium is located in a greenhouse which is subjected to natural photoperiod conditions. Thus, apparently grass carp may mature without a previous exposure to a cool period or changes in water temperature.

The hormonal injections used by V. Hilge are two doses of carp pituitary extract with the first dose one-tenth that of the final dose. The injections are given 24 hr apart. The dosage is calculated from the body diameter using the graph in Figure 12.2.

The BfF (formerly the Max Planck Institute) several years ago investigated the feasibility of selectively breeding carp to reduce the number of intramuscular bones. However, this program was abandoned because (1) it was expensive, (2) the number of floating rib bones on three to four genetic loci, (3) complete removal of bone was not possible, and (4) in most cases the variant must be dissected or x-rayed to determine the number of bones.

The number of grass carp for control of weeds in ponds depends on the amount of vegetation and the size of grass carp. Stocking rates vary from 70 to 1,000 individuals per ha. Sizes of 1, 2, 3, and 4-year-old grass carp average 40 g, 250 g, 1.5 kg, and 3 kg, respectively. These fish are then stocked at rates up to 1,000, 400, 200 and 70 fish per ha for the 1, 2, 3, and 4-year-old grass carp, respectively. Natural waters require about one-half the stocking rate of pond culture.

Aquatic plants that cause problems in Germany are **Potamogeton crispus**, and other pondweeds (**Potamogeton** spp.), **Typha** spp., **Pharagmites** spp., **Elodea canadensis**, and **Lemna** spp. A **Ranunculus** spp. is not eaten at all by the grass carp even when no other vegetation is available. The grass carp will eat the young shoots of waterlilies, and will control these plants in about 3 years. One problem of using grass carp in Germany is that the plants begin growth in the spring when the water reaches 4 C and the grass carp effectively consume the vegetation only at temperatures above about 20 C. Thus, many plants produce luxurious growth before the grass carp begins to feed. In trout ponds **Chara** spp. and **Spirohyra** spp. are problems and the water is too cold for effective control by the grass carp. Grass carp also is reluctant to eat vegetation coated with calcium carbonate.

In Great Britain the Ministry of Agriculture, Fisheries, and Food is charged with the utilization and protection of the country's fresh waters. The final authority, however, resides within each of the 10 autonomous water management districts. Each district governs and taxes its own area, and even controls the importation of fishes into its waters.

The Fens, a dyked area about 10 ft below sea level, has intensively farmed areas of organic muck soil. An active weed control program is required for drainage canals in ths area. Some of these canals drop only 3 inches in a mile and weed growth can seriously reduce water flow. Water temperature of the Fens tends to be considerably warmer (greater than 20 C) than in other waters (ca. 20 C), thus providing an environment suitable for good growth of the plants.

Aquatic plants that cause problems in Great Britain's waters are emergents such as **Phragmites communis**, **Glyceria** sp., **Carax** sp., and **Typha latifolia** L.; the submersed **Myriophyllum verticillatum**, **Myriophylum spicatum** L., **Potamogeton pectinatus** L., **Potamogeton natans**, and **Callitriche** sp.; and some of the floating **Lemna** spp., **Hipparus** sp., and **Nuphar** spp. **Elodea canadensis** and **Egeria densa** are the only two exotic problems. The aquatic weed problem varies between different parts of the country and usually is caused by a mixture of plants including some of the algal species.

In 1976 the average cost for controlling aquatic plants in a canal 10 m wide by 1.0 km in length (1.0 ha) was estimated at 190 for a weed cutting boat (twice a year); 990 for hand cleaning; 280 for a weed cutting and harvesting bucket; 400 for dredging; 130 for a dragline; 180 for diquat; 170 for terbutryn; 47 for glyphosate; and 70 for dalapon (1.0 = $1.73). In order to provide for an additional method of control and to reduce costs, the grass carp is being considered for control of aquatic weed problems.

Early experimental research with the grass carp was promising; good control of some aquatic weed problems could be expected after stocking 200 kg of grass carp per ha. A study with 200 to 300-g grass carp in small enclosed bodies of water showed that these fish preferred **Potamogeton pectinatus**. **Ranunculus circinatus** and **Callitriche** sp. were next in preference. Not consumed was **Myriophyllum spicatum L.**, which tended to become the dominant vegetation after consumption of other vegetation. These grass carp also tended to avoid **Potamogeton natans**. In later studies large grass carp did not consumer **Ranunculus circinatus**.

Impact studies of the grass carp on native species have shown that survival of the common bream (**Abramis brama** L.) was not affected. Bream in ponds with the grass carp had a better growth rate than bream in the control pond. The British scientists point out that this experiment needs repeating before definite conclusions can be reached.

The United Kingdom has strict laws regulating importation of fishes in regards to parasites and diseases. Until recently no exporter of grass carp could meet the disease-free requirements, resulting in a critical shortage of research specimens. Recently 16,000 grass carp have been cleared for import from Yugoslavia, and British scientists plan large scale field tests on the feasibility of controlling aquatic weeds. Interest in testing the grass carp has been expressed by 9 of the 10 water management districts. British scientists also plan an artificial spawning program that will supply disease-free grass carp for future research programs.

Russia

The Union of Soviet Socialist Republics (USSR) covers over 22,400,000 square km or one-sixth of the world's inhabited surface. It stretches 5,000 km from north to south in the northern hemisphere and nearly 10,000 km from west to east sprawling across 11 times zones. The USSR is a vast country with environmental conditions of extreme heat in the southern regions and intense cold in the arctic north.

Only about 10% of the USSR's land is arable because of the vast area occupied by tundra, forests, and dry land. A wide belt of more than 7,000,000 square km of forest area stretches across the country from east to west. Huge irrigation systems are being built to bring more freshwater to the dry lands in the south to increase the amount of land for cultivation.

The Soviet Union has a large reserve of freshwater. For example, the Russian Republic has some 20 million ha of lakes, 5 million ha of reservoirs, and 0.5 million km of rivers. Although fisheries management of these waters is largely for commercial fisheries, there are a number of sportfishing areas. The Kuban Riber, for example, has a series of lakes in the upper reaches set aside for sportfishing and commercial fishing is not allowed in these areas.

Fish farming is an important economic enterprise in the Soviet Union with aquaculture of freshwater species predominating over marine fish. Freshwater fishes are reared on large collective farms such as the Akkurgan (white hill) Fish Collective, on which is located the Middle Asis Laboratory of Pond Fishes. This collective, near Tashkent in the Republic of Uzbeck, is on the Syr Dar'ya River from which it obtains its water supply.

The Akkurgan fish farm produces annually over 5,000 tons of common carp and phytophagous fishes. It has 2,500 ha of hearing ponds ranging up to 200 ha. This fish farm with its staff of eight scientists and some 500 workers is the basis of a community over 3,000 people. Scientists from Moscow University and local institutes come to Akkurgan to conduct research during the summer. This fish farm therefore functions not only as a center for fish production but also as a research facility. Stanlia Ryabora is the Chief of Fisheries Research at the farm.

The most important fish species at Akkurgan is carp. Other fishes cultured are the grass carp, spotted bighead, silver carp, snakehead, and perch. A total of 25 million yearlings are produced annually. The primary polyculture is a combination of 60% silver carp and 40% carp. Perch and snakehead are used as predators for trash fish, and are also harvested. The grass carp is used primarily for weed control but is also sold for human consumption.

In 1962 80% of the ponds at Akkurgan were severely infested with submerged aquatic plants. The grass carp was obtained from China in 1965 to control these weeds. This collective farm now produces about 10 million grass carp larvae which are distributed throughout the USSR, and subsequently grown and used for weed control purposes. The grass carp is one of the live fishes sold by the fish markets and is becoming one of the preferred live fishes. Live fish are available from August to May.

The ponds at Akkurgan are routinely stocked with 50 grass carp per ha to prevent aquatic plants from becoming a problem, and 150 to 200 fish are stocked per ha to bring existing weed problems under control.

An underwater mechanical saw-boat is used to help control the **Phragmites** sp., Pigweed, and Cattails.

Artificial spawning techniques and hormone injections are used to reproduce most species of culture species including grass carp. Procedures are similar to those used elsewhere in the world. For grass carp, brook fish are collected for spawning in late May or early June when the water temperature reaches 21 to 22 C. River water is diverted to a reservoir and pumped to an elevated storage tank. The water is then filtered prior to being used in the spawning. Two injections of carp pituitary extract are given to 15-kg brook stock at 24-hr intervals. Human chorionic gonadotropin (HCG) is used only if a supply of pituitary extract is not available. The grass carp have been spawned using HCG exclusively (not generally successful in the United States). Ovulation is obtained in 80 to 85% of the females injected. Males are also injected simultaneously with the second dose given to the females. The eggs are incubated in large cylinders with conical bottoms (similar in appearance to Weiss jars except they are about 200 liters in volume). Deformities of larvae are common and seem to be quite variable. The fry collected in mesh baskets placed under the overflow of the hatching jars are transferred to porcelain bath tubs equipped with screened overflows.

The 4-day-old grass carp larvae are stocked in ponds at the rate of 4 million individuals per ha. To stimulate zooplankton production, the ponds are fertilized with 25 kg of ammonium nitrate and superphosphate per ha before the larvae are stocked and again after 7 days. Organic material is also added to the ponds. The larvae remain in the ponds for 12 to 14 days and the 100-mg fish are transferred to other ponds where they are fed pellets of meal and wheat. By the end of the summer the fish average 25 to 30 g, large enough to be used for weed control. Post-larval mortality is only 20%. The predators causing the most damage are gulls and snakes.

In addition to fish farming, grass carp and other herbivorous fish are stocked in natural systems in order to increase commercial fisheries. A specific function of the Grachi Kluch hatchery is to produce fish for stocking in open waters of the Kuban River system. The first stocking of artificially spawned grass carp in the Kuban River was with 22,000 yearlings in 1961. From 1961 to 1969 some 700,000 yearling grass carp were stocked and an additional 150,000 grass carp placed in the river from 1969 to 1974. No grass carp have been stocked since 1974. During the period of 1961-1969, 3 million 2-year-old silver carp were stocked in the Kuban and an unknown amount has been stocked since then. In 1976 50 million buffalo fry were stocked in the Kuban system.

The commercial catch of grass carp in some locations is incidental to the main purpose of stocking grass carp for weed control. One such system is the Kara Kum Canal system in Turkmenia SSR. Stocking began here in the early 1960' shortly after opening of the canal. Commercial catch data indicate a build-up of grass carp in the canal and connecting rivers and reservoirs in 1970 followed by a decline. The number of grass carp is declining in spite of annual stocking of millions of fingerlings in the branch irrigation canals and reservoirs.

In the Kara Kum system the primary use of grass carp was for weed control. Soon after the construction of the Kara Kum Canal, Phragmites and pondweeds began growing in sufficient quantities to interfere with water flow and other uses of the system. Phytophagous fishes, including the grass carp, were stocked in the canal in an attempt to control these weeds. The number of grass carp stocked, documented in the literature, were in the millions. Weeds in the main canal of the Kara Kum system were initially controlled through use of an integrated approach using the grass carp and mechanical methods. The Soviets estimate their mechanical cleaning costs at $12,500 per km of canal. Mechanical control is no longer necessary in the main canal except to reestablish bank configuration. Reproduction apparently is still sufficient to maintain control in the main canal and in connecting canals deeper than 1.0 m. However, the fish may migrate long distances and populate distant sites as witnessed by their movement in the Kara Kum system to the delta of the Amu Dar'ya 1,000 km away. They do not readily enter shallow canals, especially intermittent ones, hence it is necessary to stock annually millions of grass carp fingerlings in branch canals not connected directly to larger feeder canals. Also, drainage ditches do not connect with the canals and these must be stocked annually.

Grass carp are used for weed control in the Kuban rice fields and can increase rice production an extra 1.0 to 1.5 tons per ha. The fish are stocked in the spring at a size of 20 to 30 g and at a rate of 100 individuals her ha. By the fall they are about 300 g and some 25 to 30 kg of grass carp are recovered per ha from these fields when they are dewatered.

The Volga River was first stocked 20 years ago with several hundred brook fish from the Amur river. During the past 20 years some 50 to 70 million fingerlings have been released in the delta region. Grass carp stocked in the Volga River in an attempt to control the dense growth of **Potamogeton** spp. and **Chara** spp. in the delta region were totally ineffective in controlling the abundance of aquatic vegetation. The Soviet scientists estimated a grass carp population of only one fish per 10 ha in this river. Grass carp has not reduced the growth of problem plants and stocking many fish is expensive. Many scientists recommend that no more grass carp be stocked in the Volga River. They prefer that more effort and money be spent toward trying to increase the natural reproduction of grass carp in this river.

Few impact studies have been conducted in the USSR to assess the effect of the grass carp on the aquatic ecosystem. An 8-year project conducted by V.B. Verigin and the late G.N. Nikolsky showed that the grass carp had no effect on native fishes, including piscivorous species. The grass carp in this study consumed the sumberged vegetation and then starved to death by the end of the study (4).

In one study cited by several Soviet fishery workers pike and perch in a lake were eliminated after grass carp had destroyed their spawning vegetation. This, however, was an isolated case of an effect manifested in a small lake heavily stocked with grass carp. In most locations grass carp did not completely eliminate vegetation and hence had little effect on other species. In the Kara Kum Canal and adjacent waters apparently pike were effected by grass carp but pike perch catch was greatly increased.

Soviet scientists considered disease to be one problem associated with introduction of grass carp. In Leningrad we talked to Dr. Oleg N. Bauer of the Zoological Institute on problems associated with parasites of the grass carp and other fishes. He indicated that over 40 species of parasites and diseases were brought into the Soviet Union with phytophagous fishes of which 36 are species specific. The parasitic tapeworm, **Bothriocephalus gowkongensis** was first identified in 1955. Dr. Bauer thinks that this parasite was not brought from China with shipments of grass carp but rather the parasite was already infecting carp and was transferred from them to the grass carp. In 1961 **B. gowkongensis** was again found in the Soviet Union in Turkmen SSR. Fish infected with this parasite were unkowningly placed in the pond which supplied water to all the other ponds. The parasite was widely distributed before it was detected. Some of these parasite-infected fish were stocked in natural waters. However, it has been determined that this parasite has not caused problems in natural systems and in pond culture systems it can be controlled with DEVERMIN. **Bothriocephalus gowkogensis** is not a problem for large grass carp since they shed the parasite when they change from a zooplanktonic to a herbivorous diet.

Carp retain **B. gowkongensis** much longer than the grass carp. This tapeworm has been found in **Gambusia** and **Ictaluris**, and if the temperature is right, it will probably infect all freshwater fishes. One of the ways to obtain parasite free fish is through the shipment of larvae spawned in water free of the parasite. Poland does not have the tapeworm and apparently Germany is free of it also. In Russia this tapeworm occurred extensively during the first few years after it was found but is now present in a lower frequency in all their fish farms in the central southern portion of the country.

Grass carp have been found to be much less susceptible to viral disease than other fishes cultured in ponds. Grass carp are used in ponds to dilute species concentrations of fishes which in turn reduces problems with viral diseases without altering productivity. Inflammation of the airbladder has been one problem associated with viral diseases in grass carp. Grass carp are less susceptible to carp diseases than the carp themselves. Alimentary disease problems are more prevalent when grass carp are feeding on pellets than when they have plenty of vegetation to eat. Dr. Bauer thinks that when the grass carp are placed in natural systems the distribution of parasites is too widely dispersed to be of any consequence.

The most significant information gained from the visit to the Soviet Union concerned reproduction requirements and places of naturalization. The grass carp's native range includes the Amur River in the eastern part of the USSR. This fish has been stocked widely throughout the USSR and has reproduced in the (1) Syr Dar'ya River, (2) Kara Kum Canal system, (3) Volga River, (4) Kuban River, and (5) Ili River. A report of reproduction of herbivorous fish in the Terek River may not include grass carp. The grass carp constitutes up to 5.0% by number of the natural fish populations in these rivers where it has become acclimatized. In some of these syetms the percent composition of grass carp was at one time higher but has now declined.

The Syr Dar'ya River originates in the Tien Shan Mountains and flows north for some 900 km to the Aral Sea. The Okkurgan Fish Farm was the source of fish entering the Syr Dar'ya, probably as escapees in about 1967. They are now stocked annually. The grass carp spawns annually in such tributaries as the Chirachick River when it reaches a flood stage in excess of 1.0 m.

The Kuban River is another river where the grass carp have become acclimatized and have reproduced. This river originates on the slops of Mt. Elbrus primarily from the Ulucum Glacier and flows into the Azov Sea some 940 km from the mountains. Approximately 100 years ago the Kuban emptied into the Black Sea, but not empties into the Azov Sea as a result of the construction of irrigation canals.

The major tributaries of the Kuban River are the Psekubs, Laba, Belaya, and the large and small Zelenchuk. The Kuban River has a very fast current during the early stages of its journey, often in excess of 2.0 m per second, and an annual discharge of 12 km^3. The river is very turbid with an average of approximately 1 kg per m^3 suspended solids.

A dam was constructed in 1974 across the lower end of the Kuban near Krasondar which resulted in the formation of a reservoir with a surface area of 42,000 ha and an average depth of 5.5 m. The reservoir is 42 by 10 km. The primary purpose of the reservoir is to provide a water source for irrigation of rice. Last year this region produced 600,000 tons of rice and with the completion of the reservoir their goal is to harvest 1 million tons of rice. The reservoir will also play an important role in their freshwater fisheries. In 1978 commercial fishing is to begin on the Kuban River and reservoir.

The grass carp have spawned in the Kuban River and the Belaya tributary prior to the construction of the reservoir. The developing grass carp eggs were carried downstream and larvae were dispersed in the rice fields of the delta area. The reservoir has reduced the flow in the lower part of the Kuban, and some Soviet scientists doubt that natural reproduction will sustain the population in this river. Prior to construction of the reservoir, natural reproduction of the grass carp was not particularly effective (young grass carp constituted about 1% of the fish population in some rice fields having 10,000 young per ha). Possibly, the population in the Kuban would not persist at present levels without hatchery stocking.

The Syr Dar'ya is the only river in the Uzbeck Republic where the grass carp spawns. The spawning sites are presumed to be the confluences of tributaries downstream of islands. Spawning in this river, as in the other rivers of the USSR, coincides with a change in water level (usually an increase) greater than 1 meter. Accompanying the change in water level is a flow rate of at least 1.0 m per second and accompanied by very turbid water. Spawning has been triggered by artificial manipulation of water level by release of water from reservoirs.

The Kara Kum canal system is an extremely large irrigation scheme of some 14 million km of canals and ditches designed to irrigate thousands of ha of arid land. The main canal is about 900 km in length and originates with the diversion of water from the Amu Dar'ya River near the Afghanistan border. The canal presently terminates near the city of Ashkhabad but when the system is completed it will empty into the Caspian Sea some 3,000 km from the Amu Dar'ya River. The phytophagous fish spawn in a relatively short section below the dam controlling entry of water into the canal. In late spring when the snow and glacier ice begins melting, water level rises in the Amu Dar'ya River, but the sluice gates in the canal are partially closed to maintain relatively constant flow in the canal. During peak flow the water is about 2 m in height above the dam creating a flow of 6 to 8 m per second through the sluice gates. The fish are unable to swim against this strong current and thus gather just below the dam. The rapid flow of water, attempts to jump the dam, and contact with each other apparently stimulates these fish and they spawn below the dam. The fertilized eggs are carried in the current to the Kelif Reservoir which is approximately 100 km downstream from the dam. The location of this reservoir downstream corresponds to natural systems where the grass carp spawns successfully.

Soviet scientists hypothesize that lakes or reservoirs downstream from the egg-laying site is a necessary requirement for survival of young grass carp. A river or canal does not produce sufficient zooplankton as food nor plants as cover for survival of fry. Immediately after hatching the fry need a large slow-flowing area with vegetation which provides cover from predators. Also, this area must produce an abundance of food (zooplankton) for the fry. These conditions were ideal in the Kara Kum Canal when reproduction of the grass carp was first observed. Because of biological removal of the aquatic vegetation in the nursery area, optimum conditions no longer exist in the system and the number of grass carp in the system has declined.

In the Soviet Union the grass carp has reproduced in several locations outside its native range, (1) the Syr Dar'ya River, (2) the Kuban River, (3) The Volga River, (4) the Ili River, and (5) the Kara Kum Canal. Phytophagous fish have spawned in the Tereck River but it is not clear whether the grass carp is included. These systems differ considerably but all are large and have seasonal changes in water flow. Reproduction is not monitored annually so there is some uncertainty as to whether reproduction occurs every year. Year-class analysis is difficult because millions of fry and fingerlings from hatchery operations are released annually into all of these systems. These releases are considered by some to be totally unnecessary whereas other Soviet fish culturists consider the stocking to be essential to maintenance of population and believe that many existing populations would eventually die out without stocking.

The requirements for reproduction of the grass carp are quite precise. The Soviet scientists do not know exactly what parameters or combination of conditions are necessary for spawning, but they have noted some striking similarities in the areas where the grass carp reproduced. They believe that sufficient information is available so that natural reproduction can be increased and the cost of artificial propagation can be reduced.

The primary requirement for reproduction is that the grass carp be in a flowing stream. These fish have never spawned in static water even though they develop eggs and viable sperm. Under these conditions the females reabsorb the eggs after they are formed. The grass carp can be forced to mate and lay eggs in static water by use of hormone injections. Eggs laid under these conditions may be fertilized by the males but soon settle to the bottom and disintegrate.

Flowing water is essential for egg laying in grass carp. A sudden change in water level and increased velocity further stimulates spawning. A water current of 1.0 m per second is generally associated with turbulent water. The changes in water conditions may excite the fish and initiate mating behavior. The turbulence is critical in maintaining the eggs in the water column during their negatively buoyant water hardening phase. Second, below the area of turbulence, a sustained average flow of at least 1.0 m per second is required to uphold the eggs in the water column. Third, a lake or reservoir some distance from the egg laying site is critical for survival of the young grass carp.

There is some variation in the distance of flowing water required for successful reproduction of the grass carp. The Soviet scientists think that 170 km is necessary (i.e. in waters with an average flow rate of 0.6 m per second); however, the distance of flow in the Kara Kum is only 80 to 100 km. Temperature affects development of the eggs. Therefore, the required distance of flow is related to temperature and the rate of flow. For example, the grass carp spawned once in the Kara Kum Canal when the water temperature was 18.5 C. At this temperature and flow rate the eggs probably reached the reservoir before they hatched because of the slower development. The eggs would settle to the bottom in the reservoir and perish. Using development times for eggs hatching under laboratory conditions and flow rates from the field, it is possible to calculate that egg development could be accomplished over a distance of 50 km.

Other factors affect reproduction to varying degrees. A constant temperature of 20 C or higher results in good egg development. Fluctuations of 5 to 6 C reduce survival. Temperatures higher than 29 C result in an increase of deformed fry and low survival. Turbidity in hatchery situations reduces egg development by mechanically disrupting the membrane through an abrasive action. However, turbidity helps to protect the larvae from predators. Also, vegetation enables young fish to escape predators. Large numbers of microplankton such as rotifers are required by the larvae once the egg sack has been absorbed. All these conditions for mating behavior, spawning, and egg and larval development must be optimal and in proper conjunction for good survival of grass carp. Even when these conditions are optimal no more than 5% of the total fish population is grass carp.

UTILIZATION OF HERBIVOROUS FISH IN CHINA

The fish production areas in China (5) are divided into five major areas: the Amur River basin, the Yangtze-Yellow River basin, the South China area, the North West Area and the Tsang Pu-Lu River basin.

The major fish species are divided into two groups; the herbivores and the carnivores. The herbivores include the carp species, the black roach, the big heads, Peking bream and the mullet species. The carnivores include the Chinese perch, snake-head, sheat fish, sturgeon, yellow cat fish, pike, and taimen.

Generally, the herbivores prefer to feed in calm, still waters, while the carnivores feed in fast flowing or slow waters. The black roach or black amur is to be of special significance in China for the control of snails that harbor liver and lung flukes and other schistosomes that are harmful to man.

REQUIREMENTS FOR REPRODUCTION OF THE WHITE AMUR

A. Mating and egg laying
   1. Rapid change in water level of at least 1.0 m. This change is usually an increase but can also be a decrease.
   2. Turbulence or vertical upwelling that stimulates mating behavior.
   3. Water temperature of 20 C (68 F) or higher, although there are several reports of egg laying at slightly lower water temperatures.
B. Egg Development
   1. Warm temperatures are needed for egg development.
      a. A temperature of 20 C or higher.
      b. Fluctuations of 5 to 6 C reduce survival.
   2. Flowing water is essential for incubation.
      a. A large and series of upwellings is required to keep the eggs suspended until they water harden (absorption of water). During the water harden process the eggs become more buoyant.
      b. After water hardening a flow rate of 1.0 m per second keeps the eggs in suspension.
      c. A stretch of water 100 km long is necessary for carrying eggs, although under some conditions only one-half this distance would be required.
   3. Turbidity reduces egg survival in hatcheries but may protect them from predators in nature.
C. Larval development (up to zooplankton feeding)
   1. Immediately after hatching the transparent fry begin vertical movement. This behavior keeps them in the water column for movement to backwater areas containing food.
   2. During the period of vertical movement they may be vulnerable to predation by plankton feeding fishes and invertebrates.
   3. Turbidity tends to reduce visibility and offers protection to the larvae.
   4. Larvae are carried by currents to vegetated backwater habitats which offer a place for shelter.
   5. Microzooplankton such as rotifers provide the initial food of larval white amur.
D. Survival of young white amur
   1. Fry up to an average length of 1.3 cm feed on large zooplankton.
   2. Fry of the 1.3-cm length are extremely vulnerable to predation in natural systems.
   3. Turbidity and presence of vegetation enhances survival.

E. Population densities of white amur.
   1. All the conditions for mating behavior, spawning, and egg and larval development must be optimal for good survival.
   2. In most cases of successful reproduction and after stocking, the number of white amur is low because of predation.
   3. Chinese fishery workers consider that stocking millions of fry in systems having reproduction populations is a waste of effort.
   4. The white amur is a minor component of commercial fisheries in natural systems and generally consists of no more than 5% of the total commercial fish population.
F. Impact of white amur on natural systems
   1. White amur have had no affect on commercial catches of fishes.
   2. Water quality may be improved because of increased circulation after vegetation removal.
   3. Algae blooms do not occur; silver carp are always stocked along with the white amur and the silver carp control algae.

SUMMARY AND CONCLUSIONS

The white amur is effective for control of aquatic plant problems in small enclosed bodies of water. In large, open natural systems the white amur are not generally effective in eliminating aquatic plants and controlling aquatic weed problems.

In Europe and China the white amur is used not only for aquatic weed control but is also harvested from polyculture sustems for human consumption. Reproduction and massive stocking in natural systems has not resulted in the establishment of large populations or a deterioration of the natural ecosystem.

REFERENCES

1. Avault, J.W., Jr. 1965. Preliminary studies with grass carp for aquatic week control, *Prog. Fish-Cult.*, Vol 27: 207-209.
2. Bailey, W.M. 1975. "Operational Experiences with the White Amur and Weed Control Programs." Proceeding, Symposium on Water Quality Management Through Biological Control, Jan. 23-30, 1975, Gainesville, Fla., P.L. Brezonic and J.L. Fox, eds., Report ENV-p7-75-1, Department of Environmental Engineering Science, University of Florida, Gainesville, Fla.
3. Bailey, W.M., and Boyd, R.L. 1973. "A Preliminary Report on Spawning and Rearing of Grass Carp **(Ctenopharyngodon idella)** in Arkansas." Herbivorous Fish for Aquatic Plant Control Program,

E.O. Gangstad, ed., U.S. Army Engineer Waterways Experiment Station, CE, Vicksburg, Miss., pp 1-16.

4. Beach, M.L., Lazor, R.L., and Burkhalter, A.P. 1977. "Some Aspects of the Environmental Impact of the White Amur **(Ctenopharyngodon idella**, Val.) in Florida, and Its Use for Aquatic Weed Control," Proceeding, Fourth International Symposium on Biological Control of Weeds. T.E. Freman, ed., University of Florida, Institute of Food and Aquacultural Sciences, Gainesville, Fla., pp 269-289.

5. Gangstad, E.O. 1980. Utilization of Herbivorous fish in China *in* Weed Control Methods for Public Health Applications. CRC Press, Boca Raton, Florida.

6. Krupauer, V. 1971. The use of herbivorous fishes for ameliorative purposes in central and eastern Europe, *Proc. Eur. Weed Res. Counc. 3rd Int. Symp. Aquatic Weeds*, pp 95-103.

7. Michewicz, J.E., Sutton, D.L., and Blackburn, R.D. 1972. The white amur for aquatic weed control, *Weed Sci.*, 20: 106-110.

8. Miller, A.C. and Decell, J.I. 1984. Use of the White Amur for Aquatic Plant Management. Instruction Report A 84-1, U.S. Army Engineer Experiment Station, CE, Vicksburg, Miss.

9. Verigin, B.V. 1961. Results of work on acclimatization of far eastern phytophagous fishes and measures for their further assimilation and study in new regions, *Vopr. Ikhtiol.*, 1: 640-649.

10. Singh, S.B., et al. 1967. "Observation of Efficacy of Grass Carp, **(Ctenopharyngodon idella** (Val.)) in Controlling and Utilizing Aquatic Weeds in Ponds in India," Proceedings, Indo-Pacific Fisheries Commissioners Couz., Vol 12, No. 2, pp 220-235.

11. Smith, C.R., and Shireman, J.V. 1981. "Grass Carp Bibliography," University of Florida, Institute of Food and Agricultural Science, Center for Aquatic Weeds.

12. Stanley, J.G. 1976. "Production of Monosex White Amur for Aquatic Plant Control," Contract Report A-76-1, U.S. Army Engineer Waterways Experiment Station, CE, Vicksburg, Miss.

13. Stanley, J.G., Miley, W.W., II, and Sutton, D.L. 1978. "Reproductive Requirements and Likelihood for Naturalization of Escaped Grass Carp in the United States," Transactions of the American Fishery Society, Vol 107, No. 1, pp 119-128.

14. Sutton, D.L. 1974. "Utilization of Hydrilla by White Amur," Hyacinth Control Journal, Vol 12, pp 66-70.

15. Sutton, D.L. 1977. "Grass Carp (**Ctenopharyngodon idella** Val.) in North America," Aquatic Botany, Vol 3, pp 157-164.

16. Sutton, D.L. 1977. "Utilization of Duck Weed by the White Amur," Proceedings, Fourth International Symposium and Biological Control of Weeds, T.E. Freeman, ed., University of Florida, Institute of Food and Agricultural Sciences, Gainesville, Fla., pp 257-260.

17. Sutton, D.L., Miley, W.W., II, and Stanley, J.G. 1977. "Report to the Florida Department of Natural Resources on the Project: On Site Inspection of the Grass Carp in the USSR and Other European Countries," Agricultural Research Center, University of Florida, Fort Lauderdale, Fla.

18. Theriot, R.F., and Sanders, D.R. 1975. "Food Preferences of Yearling Hybrid Carp," Hyacinth Control Journal, Vol 13, pp 51-53.

19. Transactions of the American Fishery Society. 1978. Vol 108, No. 1.

20. U.S. Fish and Wildlife Service. 1973. Injurious Wildlife; proposed importation regulations, Fed. Reg., Vol 38, No. 244, Part IV, 20 Dec 1973, pp 34970-34976.

Figure 3.1 White amur fish (**Ctenopharyngoda idella**) used as a biological control agent for aquatic weed populations in natural habitats. (Courtesy of Dr. P.L. Sutton, University of Florida, Fort Lauderdale, Florida, July 1978).

Figure 3.2 Standard dose curve used for estimating the required mg of carp pituitary for hormonal injections of female grass carp based on their body diameter (cm).

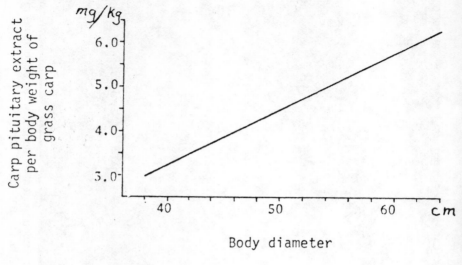

Figure 3.3   Natural spawning occurs (a) at the turbulence generated in the confluence of two streams (b) downstream from an island where turbulence and eddies are generated by flow of the water.

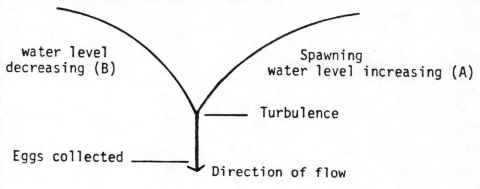

water level
decreasing (B)

Spawning
water level increasing (A)

——— Turbulence

Eggs collected ———

Direction of flow

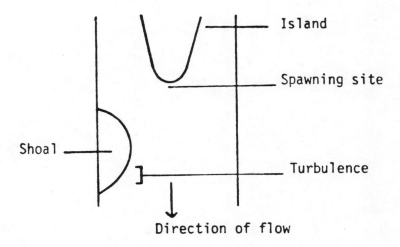

——— Island

——— Spawning site

Shoal ———

——— Turbulence

Direction of flow

PART II

EVALUATION OF SELECTED AQUATIC HERBICIDES

Chapter 4

HERBICIDAL, ENVIRONMENTAL AND HEALTH EFFECTS OF ACROLEIN[1]

INTRODUCTION

Acrolein is a highly reactive liquid herbicide that is used to control submerged aquatic weeds in irrigation and drainage canals. It is extremely toxic to mammals, fish and other aquatic life. It is highly volatile and flammable, and its vapors are a powerful irritant to the eyes and respiratory passages. Because of these properties, the chemical must be metered or pumped from a closed container into the water without contact with air. If it is necessary to work with acrolein, it should be handled with care and caution.

Excessive growths of aquatic weeds may create serious problems for man and aquatic fauna. In the water conveyance systems of the western states, aquatic weeds can seriously impede the delivery of water to agricultural areas and municipal water supplies. Increased siltation, resulting from decreased water flow, may alter watercourses and render them unnavigable. Although not a panacea, acrolein can provide adequate control of aquatic weeds within the time and expense of biological or mechanical control.

HERBICIDAL EFFECTS

Acrolein is applied full strength (92%) directly to the water, under supervision of licensed operators. It is metered from specially adapted equipment at a rate not to exceed 15 parts per million at any one time during application. Many applications are made at a 0.1 ppm concentration over a 48 hour period. It is a general biocide and is toxic to fish under average conditions of application. Fish kills are avoided by treating one-half of the area at a time. Low levels of acrolein act as a fish repellent. Acrolein is of special value to control the submersed weeds such as **Potamogeton**, **Najas**, **Zannichellia**, **Ceratophyllum**, and **Spirogyra**. The registered use, tolerance and use limitations are given in Tables 1 and 2, respectively (4,5,18,19,20).

---

[1]The findings in this report are not to be construed as an official Department of the Army position unless so designated by other authorized documents.

Acrolein, also called acryladehyde or 2-propenal, has been used for about 15 years to control submersed aquatic weeds in irrigation systems in the United States and in other countries where open channels are used to distribute water for crop production. Information on the process was first released in 1958 and 1959 (6,18,19,20). Conclusions of early field investigations conducted on acrolein by the Agricultural Research Service and the Bureau of Reclamation are included in a report prepared in 1963 by Comes, et al. (12). Over the years, methods and equipment used to apply acrolein have been refined and they are described in an up-to-date handbook (18). The nomenclature, use precautions, and biological behavior are summarized in Table 3.

ENVIRONMENTAL EFFECTS

Field observations and laboratory data show that fish vary considerably in their tolerance to acrolein. Carp and thread-fin shad are particularly sensitive, being killed at 1 to 2 ppm. Black bass, blue gill, and lamprey eel larvae appear to tolerate up to 5 ppm.

In a number of canals certain fish have been observed to swim ahead of the main wave and thus avoid destruction. This suggests that trace quantities of the herbicide or repellents released into the stream a few minutes before commencing treatment may be helpful in preventing kill of fish. Fish apparently move out of the wave before the product of concentration and time reaches a toxic level, while in the faster moving streams the wave overruns them.

When treating ponds and lakes, fish kill can be avoided by treating half the area, allowing fish to migrate to the untreated side. After the material has dissipated, approximately 48 hr, treat the other half of the area. Acrolein toxicity to aquatic organisms (1,3,7,8,10,11,13,15,16,17) are summarized in Table 4.

Once the effectiveness of acrolein for aquatic weed control in irrigation systems was established, it was necessary to determine the effects of acrolein-treated irrigation water on crops. Crop tolerance studies conducted at Agricultural Research Service stations in Washington, Montana, and Arizona were reported on by Bruns, Yeo and Arle (9). They concluded that, although many field and garden crops are sensitive to relatively high concentrations of acrolein, crops may be flood-, furrow-, or sprinkler-irrigated with water containing less than 15 ppmv (parts per million by volume) without any serious adverse effects.

Early attempts to determine residues of acrolein in irrigation water were relatively unsuccessful, especially at the very low applications levels, due to the inconsistency of results achieved with the 2,4-dinitrophenylhydrazine colorometric method described by the Shell

Chemical Company (20). The fluorometric method described by Alarcon in 1963 (2) appeared to have good possibilities. Laboratory and field studies were conducted using this procedure. The method proved to be satisfactory and was adaptable to field laboratory use.

The availability of a more reliable analytical method provided the opportunity to determine the residues of acrolein in irrigation water resulting from routine field applications for aquatic weed control. Also, because information was not available on the concentration of acrolein considered safe to fish in those situations where the treated water may return to a natural aquatic ecosystem, studies were necessary to determine concentrations of acrolein nonlethal to fish.

Residue Studies of Acrolein in Irrigation Water.   The commercially available acrolein formulation used in these studies contains 92 percent by weight of acrolein, ai (active ingredient). The density of this formulation is 7.068 lb/gal (0.847 kg/l) at 60°F (15.6°); therefore a gallon of the product contains 6.5 lb of acrolein (1 liter contains 0.78 kg). All concentrations referred to in this report are computed on the basis of the weight of the acrolein per weight of water treated. The acrolein formulatiuon is packaged in 53-gallon (200. 6-1) steel cylinders and 350-gallon (1,325-1) skid tanks. Nitrogen gas is used to pressurize the containers. Through the use of proper pressures, valves, and metering orifices, a uniform rate of acrolein can be injected into the irrigation water.

Canals and laterals of varying capacities and lengths on the Quinch, East and South Columbia Basin Irrigation Districts of the Columbia Basin Project, (CBP) Wash., were studied for acrolein residues during treatments made for aquatic weed control. Generally, field treatments were made by applying a predetermined quantity of acrolein to the water at a rate dependent on the desired concentration and on the rate of flow in the canal. On the CBP treatments were made by adding the required volume of the acrolein formulation over a time period of 48 hours to provide a computed concentration of about 0.1 ppm (parts per million), or by adding the same quantity of acrolein over a shorter time period of 4 to 8 hours resulting in a concentration of approximately 1.0 ppm. In canals where weed control is needed over great distances, treatments in addition to the initial one are made to maintain the acrolein at an effective herbicidal level. These are referred to as booster applications.

Acrolein controls aquatic weeds by destroying the vegetation existing above the bottom soil of the channel at the time of treatment. Treatments on the CBP were started early in the irrigation season when the aquatic vegetation was only a few inches long and susceptible to the low rates applied. During the first half of the season, treatments were spaced about 3 weeks apart because of the rapid growth of aquatic vegetation. As the growth rate decreased, the treatments were spaced further apart so that, toward the end of the season, 4 to 5 weeks elapsed between acrolein applications. During the 1973 and 1974 irrigation seasons 20 acrolein treatments were monitored. Eight of these treatments were made for periods of about 48 hours and with acrolein concentrations of about 0.1 ppm, while the remainder were made over relatively short time periods with computed concentrations ranging from 0.7 to 1.8 ppm.

Acrolein Tests on Rainbow Trout. The Bureau of Reclamation's Aquatic Weed Control Test Station at Carter Lake, Colo., about 7 miles west of Berthoud, Colo., was used for this study (10). The main part of the facility consists of two flumes and one bypass channel that are 750 feet (229 m) in length. Each channel consists of five 150-foot-long (46-m) sections, with a drop structure at the end of each section where water can be diverted from either flume into the bypass channel or it may be allowed to continue down the next section of the flume. A constand flow of water moves through each flume section at all times, and the rate of flow is measured at the head box or at the outlet from the pipeline that delivers water directly to the head of each flume section.

Several applications of computed concentrations of acrolein were made for 4.8- and 48-hour periods to represent practices used in the field for aquatic weed control. Applications for both periods of time were made by dripping a 10 percent aqueous solution of acrolein from a mariotte bottle through tubing fitted with a No. 22 hypodermic needle. Feeding rates to obtain the desired concentrations were maintained by altering the relative distance between the bottom of the air tube and the position of the needle. The bottles were covered with boxes during the treatment to protect them from sudden changes in the ambient temperature.

The fish were exposed to computed acrolein concentrations of 0.01, 0.05, and 0.10 ppm for 48 hours and 0.10, 0.25, 0.40, 0.5, and 0.8 ppm for 4.8 hours. The treated water was sampled during several periods and analyzed for acrolein by the fluorometric procedure cited earlier in the text. Concentrations found by analysis of the treated water are given in Table 5.

The trout showed definite responses to the higher concentrations of acrolein within the first hour of exposure. They assumed a somewhat vertical position in the water and moved to the surface in an attempt to get air, a sign of suffocation. The fish showed some stress, although not as severe, at the intermediate concentrations, and there were no apparent signs of stress at the lowest levels. None of the trout that exhibited a stressed condition recovered after the acrolein treatments were ended.

Residues of Acrolein in Crops. Acrolein concentrations were determined in crops following the application of this herbicide through irrigation water. Acrolein was applied at rates of 0.1, 0.6, 1.5, and 60 ppm in 2 acre inches of water to plots of soybeans, corn, and sugar beets by both furrow and sprinkler application methods. No acrolein was found in the treated crop samples collected at harvest time.

Irrigation Hazard of Acrolein Residues. In a study conducted to determine the tolerance of certain crops to aquatic herbicides in irrigation water it was found that crops irrigated with acrolein treated water showed no yield reduction at 20 ppm for the most sensitive crop tested and the level of no effect was higher for most crops. These results along with the study finding no acrolein residues in crops indicate that acrolein when used at the low levels of 0.1 to 5 ppm concentration do not present a significant hazard to crop production and utilization (5,6,9,12,15,16,21,22).

HEALTH EFFECTS

The acute toxicity of acrolein to various species of animals is given below:

Species	Route	LD_{50} values, mg/kg
Rats	Oral	46
Rats	Subcutaneous	50
Mice	Subcutaneous	30
Rabbits	Oral	7.1

Skin contact with the liquid is the chief occupational hazard (may cause chemical burns). 1 ppm of acrolein in air produces detectable eye and nose irritation in 2 to 3 min and is intolerable in 5 min.

The symptoms of poisoning by oral ingestion are gastrointestinal distress, with pulmonary congestion and edema. From inhalation of the fumes there is irritation of the respiratory system, headaches and eye irritation. Pulmonary edema may develop. Symptoms may be slow in appearing. It is advisable to keep persons who have been exposed to acrolein under observation for 24 hr following exposure. Contact causes dermal, severe irritation of the skin, vesiculation and a chemical burn if not removed immediately. A physician should be called immediately in all cases of suspected poisoning.

If the material has been swallowed, induce vomiting immediately. This may be done by introducing a finger into the throat or by giving warm salt water (1 tablespoon of salt to a glass of water). Repeat until vomit fluid is clear. Never give anything by mouth to an unconscious person. Keep patient prone and quiet. If inhaled, get victim into fresh air immediately and give artificial respiration if breathing has stopped. If spilled on the skin, remove all contaminated clothing and wash skin with soap and running water. If the material gets into the eyes, wash immediately with running water for at least 15 min. For eyes get medical attention. (8,18,19,20).

SUMMARY AND CONCLUSIONS

The findings of this study show that the fluorometric analytical procedure is an accurate and reliable method for determining acrolein concentrations of residues in irrigation water. These residue data are useful in defining application levels effective for aquatic weed control and the downstream points at which booster applications are needed. Similarly, the fish toxicity studies demonstrate the maximum concentrations of acrolein that fish can tolerate in treated water.

Routine acrolein treatments for aquatic weed control in canals on the Columbia Basin Project were monitored at several downstream sampling stations to determine the residues of acrolein in irrigation water. Generally, the concentrations found by analysis of water samples collected near the treatment site agreed closely with the computed levels determined from the total quantity of acrolein applied, the time period of application, and the flow rate of water in the canal. The level of acrolein dissipated gradually with distance from the application site.

Acrolein concentrations dissipate at a moderate rate as the treated water moves through irrigation canals. A low rate-long application period (0.1 ppm for 48 hours) with one booster application requires a distance of 30 to 40 miles (48.3 to 64.4 km) for the acrolein concentration to decrease to the 0.02 ppm level.

Rainbow trout are sensitive to low levels of acrolein and the concentrations applied for aquatic weed control will kill the trout. Reasonably safe levels for rainbow trout appear to be in the range of 0.2 and 0.02 ppm for 4.8- and 48-hour exposures, respectively.

REFERENCES

1. Alabaster, J.S. 1969. Survival of fish in 164 herbicides, insecticides, fungicides, wetting agents, and miscellaneous substances. Int. Pest Control 2:29-35.
2. Alarcon, R.A. 1968. Fluorometric Determination of Acroelin and Related Compounds with M-Amino-phenol. Anal. Chem. 40, 1704.
3. Applegate, V.C., J.H. Howell, A.E. Hall and M.A. Smith. 1957. Toxicity of 4,346 chemicals to larval lampreys and fish. U.S. Fish Wildl. Serv. Spec. Sci. Rep. Fish. 207. 157 pp.
4. Bartley, T.R., J.G. Armstrong, and P.A. Frank. 1974. Some Effects of Xylene and acrolein on rainbow trout. WSSA Abstracts No. 90.

Abstracts of the 1974 meeting of the Weed Science Society of America, Las Vegas, Nevada.

5. Bartley, T.R. and E.O. Gangstad. 1974. Environmental aspects of aquatic plant control. Jour. of the Irrigation and Drainage Division ASCE. Sept. 1974. pp 231-244.

6. Blondeau, Rene. 1959. The control of submersed aquatic weeds with Aqualin herbicide. West. Weed Control Conf. Res Prog. Rpt. 1959. 72-73.

7. Bohmont, B.L. 1967. Toxicity of herbicides to livestock, fish, honeybees, and wildlife. Proc. West. Weed Conf. 21:25-27.

8. Bond, C.E., R.H. Lewis, and J.L. Fryer. 1960. Toxicity of various herbicidal materials to fishers. Pages 96-101 in C.M. Tarzwell, ed. Biological problems in water pollution. Trans. 1959 Semin., Robert A. Taft Sanit. Eng. Cent. Tech. Rep. W60-3.

9. Bruns, V.F., R.R. Yeo, and H.F. Arle. 1964. Tolerance of Certain Crops to Several Aquatic Herbicides in Irrigation Water. U.S. Dept. Agr. Tech. Bull. 1299, 22 p.

10. Burdick, G.E. H.J. Dean, and E.J. Harris. 1964. Toxicity of Aqualin to fingerling brown trout and bluegills, N.Y. Fish Game J. 11:106-114.

11. Butler, P.A. 1965. Effects of herbicides on estuarine fauna. Proc. South. Weed Conf. 18:576-580.

12. Comes, R.D., R.Y. Yeo, V.F. Bruns, J.M. Hodgson, and others. 1963. Chemical Control of Submersed Waterweeds in Western Irrigation and Drainage Canals. U.S. Dept. of Agr., Agr. Res. Serv., ARS 34-57, 14p. (Joint Rpt. of U.S. Dept. of Agr. and U.S. Dept. Int.)

13. Folmar, L.C. 1976. Overt avoidance reactions of rainbow trout fry to nine herbicides. Bull. Environ. Contam. Toxicol. 15(5):509-514.

14. Folmar, C. 1977. Acrolein, dalapon, dichlobenil, diquat and endothall. U.S. Fish and Wildlife Service. Tech. Report No. 88. USDI. Washington, D.C.

15. Furgeson, F.F., E.K. Dawood, and R. Blondeau. 1965. Preliminary field trials of acrolein in the Sudan. W.H.O. Bull. 32:243-248.

16. Hansen, G.W., F.E. Oliver and N.E. Otto. 1983. Herbicide Manual, a Water Resources Technical Publication. U.S. Government Printing Office, Washington, D.C.

17. Louder, D.F., and E.G. McCoy. 1965. Preliminary investigations of the use of aqualin for collecting fishes. Proc. Annu. Conf. Southeast. Assoc. Game Fish Comm. 16:240-242.

18. Magna Corporation. 1973. Magnacide "H" Herbicide Process Handbook, ACD 65-153, Copyright Shell Chemical Company— 1972, U.S. Patent No. 2,959,476.

19. Shell Development Company. 1958. Process for Controlling Aquatic Vegetation with F-98 Aquatic Herbicide. ARD-58-7.

20. Shell Chemical Company. 1965. Aquatic Biocide Process Handbook—Revision 1. ACD 65-154.
21. St. Amant, J.A., W.C. Johnson, and M.J. Whales. 1964. Aqualin as a fish toxicant. Prog. Fish-Cult. 27:84-88.
22. Unrau, G.O., M. Farooq, K. Dawood, L. Miguel, and B. Sazo. 1965. Field trials in Egypt with acrolein herbicide. W.H.O. Bull. 32:249-260.

Table 1.   USDA Registered Use of Acrolein (Acryladehyde)[1]

TYPE PESTICIDE: Herbicide, Alagecide PRINCIPAL FORMULA-
TIONS: L

GENERAL INFORMATION: Explosive, difficult to handle; effectiveness is temperature dependent (dosage
at 60 degrees F must be double that
used at 80 degrees F); toxic to fish at
normal application rates.

TIME REQUIRED FOR CONTROL: Disruption of physiological processes within minutes of con-
tact; disintegration of plants
within a few hours.

PHYTOTOXICITY TO TARGET WEEDS: Flacidity; disruption of plant
integrity.

MODE OF ACTION: Disruption of cell membranes; disruption of
enzymes.

AQUATIC WEEDS CONTROLLED:

coontails	*Potomageton crispus*	watercress
Elodea canadensis	*P. foliosus*	waterhyacinth
horned pondweed	*P. illinoiensis*	waterstargrass
Naja spp. (naiads)	*P. nodosus*	waterstarwort
	P. obtusifolius	
	P. pectinatus var. *interruptus*	
	P. richardsonni	

ALGAE CONTROLLED:

Chara spp.	*Hydrodictyon reticulatum*
Cladophora spp.	*Spirogyra* spp.
C. glomerata	

NOTES AND LIMITATIONS: Do not use more than 15 ppm of product. Do not permit dairy animals to drink treated water. Do not use
where water will flow into, or transfer via underground streams to potential sources of drinking water. Do not release treated water for 6
days after application into any fish bearing waters or where it will drain
into them. Do not apply to water drainage areas where runoff or flooding will contaminate ponds, lakes, streams, tidal marshes and
estuaries.

From: EPA Compendium of Registered Pesticides. 1979.

Table 2.   Registered Sites, Dosage, Tolerance and Use- Limitations of ACROLEIN

Sites and Dosage	Tolerance, Use and Limitations
AQUATIC AREAS	
Industrial: *pulp and paper mill systems*	NF Initial starting rates must be low enough to avoid exceeding 2.0-3.0 ppm., which may cause irritation to machine operators.
0.4-0.6 ppm. (in white water)	Apply by metering as prescribed in manufacturers' handbook.
Moving water: *irrigation canals drainage ditches*	NF Treated water reaching crops must not exceed 13.8 ppm. Do not use where treated water flows or transfers to potential sources of drinking water.
0.9-13.8 ppm	Apply by direct pumping and meter into water at rates prescribed in manufacturers' handbook.

From: EPA Compendium of Registered Pesticides. 1979.

Table 3.   Nomenclature, Use, Precautions and Biological Behavior of ACROLEIN (2-propenal).

A. Nomenclature, Chemical and Physical Properties of the Pure Chemical[1]
  1. Common name: acrolein (ANSI, WSSA)
  2. Product name and manufacturer:
     AQUALIN Herbicide — Shell
  3. Structural formula: H   H
     $$H_2C = C\text{-}\text{-}C = O$$
  4. Molecular formula: C_3H_4O
  5. Wiswesser line notation: VH1U1
  6. Molecular weight: 56.1
  7. Physical state, color, and odor: Liquid, colorless, pungent and very irritating to the eyes at less than 1 ppm.
  8. Specific gravity, C:0.841 20/4
  9. Melting point:--86.95 C
  10. Boiling point: 52.69C
  11. Decomposition temperature: See Flammability.
  13. Vapor pressure, mm Hg, at 10,20,30,50 C: 135.71, 210, 325.70, 692.15.
  14. Solubility: Completely miscible in lower alcohols, either, hydrocarbons, acetone, and benzene. Moderately soluble in water (at 68 F); saturated solution contains approximately 25% acrolein.
B. Herbicidal Use
  1. General: For control of submerged weeds (Potamogeton, Najas, Zannichellia, Ceratophyllum, Spirogyra, and others) and floating weeds (water cress, waterhyacinth and water primrose) in irrigation canals, ditches, drains and ponds. It is also an algicide. Not phytotoxic to common field crops when used as directed by product label.
  2. Application method: Applied directly to the water under supervision of trained personnel of licensed applicators.
  3. Rates: Applied at full strength (92% acrolein). Not to exceed 15 ppm at any time during application.
  4. Usual carrier: Used directly in water.
C. Use Precautions
  1. Flammability: Flash point (TCC) --25C
  2. Possible incompatibilities: Soluble in water. Do not contaminate with any foreign material at any time. To avoid the possibility of polymerization, keep under oxygen-free nitrogen only.
  3. Corrosiveness: Iron and low carbon steel are unaffected at room temperature. Slight corrosion might occur under more severe conditions of temperature. Can be stored under oxy-

gen-free nitrogen in dark glass bottles, in cylinders, or in black iron drums.

4. Recommended method of cleaning glassware and spray equipment: Use large volumes of water.

5. Storage stability: Highly reactive chemically and readily forms polymers. In closed systems, this polymerization can proceed with explosive violence in the presence of alkaline materials and strong acids. It will polymerize slowly in the presence of air, forming an insoluble white precipitate. For this reason, it is shipped under an oxygen-free atmosphere and is inhibited with hydroquinone. However, hydroquinone does not inhibit the polymerization catalyzed by alkalies and strong acids. Therefore, contamination with any foreign materials should be avoided.

D. Physiological and Biochemical Behavior

1. Absorption characteristics: Poorly absorbed by plant.

2. Mechanism of action: Acrolein is a general cell toxicant and kills through its sulfhydryl reactivity, which destroys vital enzyme systems in the plant cells. The dead plant tissues disintegrate and float downstream.

3. Biological properties other than herbicidal: General biocide.

E. Behavior In or On Soils

4. Resulant average persistence at recommended rates: Acrolein will remain in the water for 2 to 3 days depending upon water temperature. One application will usually keep a canal clean through out the season.

From: Herbicide Handbook. WSSA. 1979.

Table 4. Acrolein toxicity to aquatic organisms.

Organism	Type of test	Experimental conditions	Toxicity	Reference
Physa spp.	FR	—	25.0 K (4 h)	Unrau et al. (1965)
Biomphalaria alexandrina	FR	—	25.0 K (4 h)	Unrau et al. (1965)
B. alexandrina	FR	—	25.0 K (3.5 h)	Furgeson et al. (1965)
Bulinus truncatus	FR	—	25.0 K (4 h)	Unrau et al. (1965)
B. truncatus	FR	—	25.0 K (3.5 h)	Furgeson et al. (1965)
Crassostrea virginica	L,CFT,A	—	0.05 EC$_{50}$ (96 h)	Butler (1965)
Penaeus aztecus	L,CFT,A	—	0.10 T (48 h)	Butler (1965)
Pimephales promelas	L,ST,A	a,b,c,d,e	0.15 T (24 h) 0.115 T (48 h)	Louder and McCoy (1965)
Fundulus similis	L,CFT,A	—	0.24 T (24 h)	Butler (1965)
Gambusia affinis	L,ST,A	a,b,c,d,e	0.149 T (24 h) 0.061 T (48 h)	Louder and McCoy (1965)
Rasbora heteromorpha	L,ST,A	a,b,c,d,e	0.13 T (48 h)	Alabaster (1969)
Amia calva (fry)	L,ST,A	a,b,c,d,e	0.062 T (24 h)	Louder and McCoy (1965)
Carassius auratus	FP	—	2.0 T (24 h)	Jordan et al. (1962)
C. auratus	L,ST,A	—	1.0 K (3 h)	St. Amant et al. (1964)
Salmo trutta (fingerlings)	L,CFT,A	a,d	0.046 T (24 H)	Burdick et al. (1964)

Table 4. Acrolein toxicity to aquatic organisms. (cont.)

Organism	Type of test	Experimental conditions	Toxicity	Reference
Lepomis macrochirus (fingerlings)	L,CFT,A	a,d	0.079 T (24 h)	Burdick et al. (1964)
L. macrochirus	FP	—	2.0 T (24 h)	Jordan et al. (1962)
L. macrochirus	L,ST,A	a,b,c,e,d,e	0.14 T (24 h) 0.125 T (48 h) 0.1 T (72 h)	Louder and McCoy (1965)
Micropterus salmoides	L,ST,A	a,b,c,d,e	0.183 T (24 h) 0.163 T (48 h) 0.16 T (72 h) 0.16 T (96 h)	Louder and McCoy (1965)
Salmo gairdneri	L,CFT,A	a,b,c,d,e	0.1 SB avoidance	Folmar (1976)

From: Folmar, L.C. Technical report NO 88, U.S. Fish and Wildlife Service, U.S. Department of the Interior, Washington, D.C. 1977.

Table 5.   Response of rainbow trout on exposure to acrolein.

Acrolein concentration p/m	Exposure period, hours	Mortality, percent
0.08	4.8	0
.09	4.8	0
.24	4.8	10
.41	4.8	70
.50	4.8	100
.90	4.8	100
.008	48	0
.048	48	32
.096	48	100

From: Bartley & Haltrup. 1975. Acrolein residues in irrigation water and effects on rainbow trout. Tech. Report. REC-ERC-75-8. United States Department of the Interior. Denver, Colorado.

PART II

EVALUATION OF SELECTED AQUATIC HERBICIDES

Chapter 5

HERBICIDAL, ENVIRONMENTAL AND HEALTH EFFECTS OF AROMATIC SOLVENTS (XYLENE)[1]

INTRODUCTION

Aromatic solvents are mixtures of cyclic hydrocarbons of petroleum of coal tar origin. Grade B xylene (dimethyl benzene) is an aromatic solvent of the most common xylol type, which is used for controlling submersed aquatic weeds, and meets specifications developed by the U.S. Bureau of Reclamation Laboratories, Denver, Colo., as follows:

Flash point (tag closed cup), not less than .... 80 F
Distillation range, ASTM: D86-54°F at 760 mm pressure:
    Initial boiling point not less than .... 240 F
    Not more than 10% at .... 265 F
    Not less than 50% at .... 320 F
    Not less than 90% at .... 380 F
    End point, not higher than .... 420 F
Aromatic content, ASTM: D 1319-55T, not less than .... 85 %
Water content, not greater than.......................... 0.2 %

Grade B xylenes that have been used by many irrigation projects or districts to control submersed aquatics usually meet the following Bureau of Reclamation specifications:

Flash point (tag closed cup), not less than .... 75 F
Distillation range (°F at 760 mm pressure):
    Initial boiling point, not less than .... 253 F
    Not more than 5% by volume below .... 266 F
    Not less than 90% by volume below .... 293 F
    Dry point, not more than .... 311 F
Specific gravity at 60°/60 F, not less than 0.850
                          not more than 0.870

A number of field and greenhouse experiments have been conducted to determine the effect of aromatic solvent or xylene-treated water on various crops when applied by furrow- or flood-type irrigation

---

[1]The findings in this report are not to be construed as an official Department of the Army position unless so designated by other authorized documents.

(1,3,5,6,8). Such experiments showed that the aromatic solvents applied at rates necessary to control submersed aquatic weeds caused no economically important injury to a wide variety of field crops unless seedlings or foliage were submerged during flood irrigation with treated water.

HERBICIDAL EFFECTS

Emulsified xylene products of various manufacturers are used quite extensively for control of aquatic vegetation. The liquid product is metered out into the irrigation system according to the rate of flow of the water. Two to four treatments are generally required per season. Growth of submersed vegetation is suppressed by destruction of the chlorophyll and disentigration of the plant tissue on contact, but the herbicide does not translocate in the system and regrowth usually occurs in 4 weeks-6 weeks. This application invariably kills fish that may be in the canal as it moves with the flow of water downstream. It dissipates rapidly as it moves through the canal. Booster applications are necessary to maintain an effective concentration if the canal is more than a few miles long. Xylene is exempt from the requirement of a tolerance when used as an aquatic herbicide applied to irrigation and conveyance systems not to exceed an initial rate of 750 ppm.

Xylene is exempt from the requirement of a tolerance when used as an inert ingredient of a pesticide on food crops. The USDA Summary of Registered Agricultural Pesticide Chemical Uses, 2nd Edition, July 1, 1964, shows xylene as an inert ingredient as a solvent or diluent for pesticides. The amount of xylene that would be applied with recommended rates of pesticide application ranges from a low of 2.0 pounds per acre actual for vegetable crops to a high of 7.5 pounds per acre for tree fruits. The amount of xylene contacting the foliage of crops as a result of aquatic weed control treatments would be expected to be considerably less than the amounts that result from its use as an inert ingredient in pesticides (7).

This herbicide is injected under pressure beneath the water surface over a period of 2 hours to 2 days to form a wave of treated water containing 1 to a maximum of 15 ppm of product. This is restricted. Do not use more than 15 ppm of product. Do not permit dairy animals to drink treated water. Do not use where water will flow into, or transfer via underground streams to potential sources of drinking water. Do not release treated water for 6 days after application into any fish bearing waters or where it will drain into them. Do not apply to water drainage areas where runoff of flooding will contaminate ponds, lakes, streams, tidal marshes and estuaries.

ENVIRONMENTAL EFFECTS

Irrigation Hazard of Xylene Residues. The xylene emulsion at best is only a temporary phase of dispersion. The emulsion breaks and the xylene being an immiscible compound with water and, much less dense than water, rises to the surface. From the surface the material evaporated readily due to the volatility of the compound. Xylene levels in the water are also reduced through absorption by aquatic vegetation and dilution in movement through the canal. The xylene that reaches crop land would volatilize quickly, leaving no lingering residue. To our knowledge crops receiving xylene treated irrigation water have not been analyzed for xylene. We would not expect to find any significant residues in crops where the water is applied by furrow irrigation.

Laboratory and field plot tests conducted over a 3-year period showed that water containing xylene applied by furrow irrigation at concentrations and rates found necessary to control the most resistant submersed aquatic weeds caused no economically important injury to a number of field crops. To obtain significant injury to the crops tested, it was necessary to apply 2 to 3 times the rates found necessary for control of aquatic weeds.

Field Investigations. A field experiment was initiated at the Prosser Irrigation Experiment Station, Prosser, Washington, to determine the effects of xylene on crop plants when applied by sprinkler irrigation methods (4). This study was conducted to obtain experimental data on the effect on certain crops of xylene-treated water applied by sprinklers under controlled field conditions. On June 20, 1972, emulsified grade B xylene (dimenthyl benzene) was applied to alfalfa, tomatoes, dwarf corn, squash, potatoes, and field beans at concentrations of 370 and 740 parts per million by volume (p/mv) in water by sprinkler irrigation. Crops were treated again on July 19 and August 15. The same kinds of crops were treated with the xylene at 1,480 p/mv on July 19 only. The treatments were made during the last 30 minutes of an 8-hour sprinkler irrigation, during which a total of 2 acre-inches of water was applied.

The stages of growth of the crops on the dates of treatment are shown in Table 1.

The crops were harvested for yield determinations as follows:

1. Alfalfa was clipped July 14, August 22, and September 14. The hay was field-cured and weighed after each clipping.
2. Tomato yields were not determined because the stands were too uneven.
3. Corn was picked September 1, air dried until October 30, and then weighted.

4. Squash yields were not determined because the stands were too uneven.
5. Potatoes were dug and weighed August 24.
6. Beans were cut on August 19, field cured until August 31, and then threshed and weighed.

Samples of tomatoes and squash from treated and untreated plots were coded and distributed among 25 individuals who volunteered to taste the fruits in lieu of an expert taste panel.

No detectable symptoms of injury were produced by any of the treatments, even those of concentrations two to four times higher than needed to control submersed aquatic weeds in irrigation channels. Growth and development of crops on treated and untreated plots did not differ visibly. The yields of alfalfa, potatoes, dwarf corn, and field beans did not differ significantly at the 5% level of probability (table 2).

The 25 tasters detected no off-flavors in squash or tomatoes grown on the xylene-treated plots.

HEALTH EFFECTS

Aromatic solvents (xylenes (dimethyl benzenes)) are very toxic to fish, crayfish, and other aquatic animals but have an exceedingly good record of safety to crops and warm-blooded animals. It is common practice for farmers to continue diverting water onto crops during periods when xylene is used for weed control. Because xylene is used primarily in the smaller canals of water distribution systems, there is usually very little waste or return water: all the water is diverted by the time it reaches the end of the system. Because of its volatility and breakdown of the emulsion during the irrigating process, practically no solvent remains in drainage water (usually very small volumes if any) from irrigated fields. Livestock and other animals refuse to drink water containing more than trace amounts of aromatic solvents (9,12).

As a solvent mixture of the ortho, meta, and para isomers, it resembles benzene in many physical and chemical properties, but does not produce the chronic blood diseases characteristic of benzene absorption. Xylene's severe narcotic action is usually noted when concentrations exceed 200 ppm. Repeated skin contact may produce a !dermatitis (11) so that care to limit direct exposure should be exercized when field applications are made, or during the manufacture and handling of the product.

SUMMARY AND CONCLUSIONS

For years, many Pacific Northwest farmers have irrigated a wide variety of crops by furrows or sprinklers with water treated with aromatic solvents to control aquatic weeds in the delivery channels. None have reported observing injury of economic importance. The experimental results reported here add credibility to field observations that water treated with aromatic solvent (xylene range) at concentrations needed to control aquatic weeds will not injure farm crops significantly when applied by sprinkler irrigation.

LITERATURE CITED

1. Arle, H.F. 1950. The effect of aromatic solvents and other aquatic herbicides on crop plants and animals. West. Weed Control Conf. Proc. 12:58-60.
2. Bartley, T.R., and E.O. Gangstad. 1975. Environmental aspects of aquatic plant control. Journ. of the Irrigation and Drainage Division, ASCE. 100:231-244.
3. Bruns, V.F., J.M. Hodgson, H.F. Arle, and F.L. Timmons. 1955. The use of aromatic solvents for control of submersed aquatic weeds in irrigation channels. U.S. Dept. Agr. Cir. 971, 33 p.
4. Bruns, V.F. and A.D. Kelley. 1974. Effect of sprinkler irrigation with xylene-treated water. Bulletin 796. Washington State University. Pullman, Washington.
5. Bruns, V.F., R.R. Yeo, and H.F. Arle. 1964. Tolerance of certain crops to several aquatic herbicides in irrigation water. U.S. Dept. Agr. Tech. Bull. 1299, 22 p.
6. Comes, R.D., R.R. Yeo, V.F. Bruns, J.M. Hodgson, and others. 1963. Chemical control or submersed waterweeds in western irrigation and drainage canals. U.S. Dept. Agr., Agr. Res. Serv., ARS 34-57, 14 p.
7. Gangstad, E.O. 1972. Herbicidal control of aquatic plants. Journal of the Sanitary Engineering Division, ASCE, Vol. 98, No. SA2 Proc. Paper 8851, Apr., 1972, pp.
8. Hansen, G.W., F.E. Oliver and N.E. Otto. 1983. Herbicide Manual, a Water Resource Technical Publication. U.S. Government Printing Office. Washington, D.C.
9. Hazardous Materials Advisory Committee. 1974. *Herbicide Report, Chemistry* and *Analysis, Enviromental Effect* for *Agriculture* and other *applied uses.* EPA-SAB-74-001 Environmental Protection Agency, Washington, D.C. 171 pp.

10. Hesser, E.F., R.W. Lowry, and E.O. Gangstad. "Aquatic Plant Problems in the Walla Walla District," Hyacinth Control Journal, Vol. 11, 1972, pp. 9-13.
11. National Safety Council. 1974. *Accident Prevention Manual for Industrial Operations.* National Safety Council. Chicago, Ill. 1523 pp.
12. Shaw, J.M., AND F.L. Timmons. 1949. Controlling submersed water weeds on irrigation systems with aromatic solvents. U.S. Bur. Reclam., Res. and Geol. Div. Lab. Rpt. CH-97, 10 p.

Table 1. Stages of growth of crops on dates of treatment

Crop	June 20	July 19	August 15
Alfalfa	Parebloom (av. 14 in high)	Regrowth (av. 3 in high)	Early bloom (av. 16 in high)
Tomatoes	Emerging to 8 in high	Prebloom to early fruiting	Fruiting (green)
Dwarf corn	7-leaf (av. 14 in high)	Late silk	Hard dent (mature)
Squash	Cotyledon to 5-leaf	Early Bloom	Fruiting
Potatoes	Prebloom (av. 12 in high)	!Postbloom (av. 16 in high)	Maturing
Field beans	Prebloom (av. 12 in high)	3rd set of pods !developing	Mature

From: Burns and Kelley, Effect of sprinkler irrigation with xylene-treated water 1974.

Table 2.   The effect of 30-minute sprinkler-irrigation treatments with xylene-treated water on the yield of 4 crops

| Dates of treatment xylene concentration | Yield in units per acre[1] | | | | Corn ears bushels | Potatoes cwt | Field beans bushels |
| | Alfalfa | | | | | | |
	July 14 tons	Aug 22 tons	Sept 14 tons	Total tons			
June 20, July 19, August 15: 370 p/mv	2.12	2.88	1.31	6.30	52.4	359.9	65.1
June 20, July 19, August 15: 740 p/mv	2.18	2.57	1.33	6.08	51.6	384.3	76.6
July 19: 1,480 p/mv	1.81	2.67	1.34	5.83	44.3	360.7	71.3
Untreated check	1.88	2.94	1.30	6.11	52.7	420.8	59.5

From: Bruns and Kelley, Effect of sprinkler irrigation with xylene treated water. 1974.

PART II

EVALUATION OF SELECTED AQUATIC HERBICIDES

Chapter 6

HERBICIDAL, ENVIRONMENTAL, AND HEALTH EFFECTS OF COPPER SULFATE AND OTHER COPPER COMPOUNDS[1]

INTRODUCTION

Copper compounds have been used for many years for aquatic plant control. Copper sulfate is the most widely used algaecide in the United States. It is economical to apply and is relatively effective for certain species. It is most effective under slightly acid or neutral conditions. It is precipitated out of solution under alkaline conditions. This effect is magnified as the alkalinity of the water increases. Basic copper carbonate or a loosely complexed form of copper are recommended for alkaline waters. Organic acids such as citric are sometimes used with copper in these conditions to keep the copper in an active form. Basic copper carbonate is used in static situations where the slow rate of dissolution of this compound makes it practical to use. Several factors are described that must be considered in achieving effectiveness with copper sulfate pentahydrate (CSP) as a control agent. Data included in this chapter were gathered from diverse sources, such as the cooperative program at Denver, cooperative programs with Bureau regional and irrigation district personnel, and information supplied by the Bureau's regional offices and State agencies (19,25).

Aquatic Weed Problems. Submersed aquatic weeds, both algae and rooted types, are common to irrigation canals, drains, and storage reservoirs. These aquatic growths are particularly troublesome to the operation of irrigation projects and cause a multitude of problems, such as impeding waterflow; clogging screens, siphon tubes, and other structures; causing taste and odor problems; increasing the biochemical oxygen demand (BOD) because of organic loading; and harboring disease-carrying organisms. Control measures must be applied to these growths so that the systems can carry the design flow.

The most common algae that cause problems on irrigation systems are the filamentous green types. Some of the genera include **Cladophora** Kutzing, **Ulothrix** Kutzing, **Oedogonium** Link, and **Stigeoclonium** Kutzing. These algae grow attached to concrete canal lin-

---

[1]The findings in this report are not to be construed as an official Department of the Army position unless so designated by other authorized documents.

ings and produce long filaments that extend into the water. In unlined canals filamentous green algae will grow as free floaters and lodge in rooted aquatics and canal structures. Good control of this type of algae is normally achieved with CSP treatments.

The mat-producing filamentous blue-green algae are another group that attach to concrete-lined irrigation canals. These algae, including the commonly found genera of Oscillatoria Vaucher and Phormidium Kutzing, are usually found growing in association with diatoms. Once established, these gelatinous algal mats are resistant to CSP. Fortunately these algae are not as prevalent nor do they restrict waterflow as much as the filamentous green algae.

Several small, free floating or planktonic algae occur in reservoirs and low velocity distribution systems. A prolific algal growth in these waters is referred to as an algal "bloom." Most of these growths are readily controlled by CSP treatments.

There are many species of rooted aquatic plants found on irrigation projects. The group referred to as pondweeds (**Potamogeton** spp) is the most prevalent: sago pondweed (**Potamogeton pectinatus** L.) is one of the most common aquatic weeds found in irrigation distribution systems.

A Bureau of Reclamation guide (19) having colored illustrations of aquatics common to irrigation projects of the Western United States is suggested for identification of a particular aquatic pest. Other publications listed in the bibliography will aid in plant identification. Determining whether the aquatic weed is an algal or a rooted aquatic is most important because of the difference in the amount of CSP required to control the two types.

Copper Sulfate as an Aquatic Herbicide. Copper Sulfate (CSP) is probably the most widely used algaecide in all types of water resource programs, and is extensively used for algae control on irrigation projects. CSP has been used for algae control in municipal waters of the United States since 1905 when it was first recommended by the U.S. Department of Agriculture (22). It has been used for algae control on irrigation projects in the 17 Western States for many years. In 1967, Nielsen described a CSP method of controlling algae in irrigation canals of the Central Valley project, Calif. (24). A technique of using a very low continuous feed rate of CSP to control algae on irrigation canals was described in a progress report (5). Although CSP has been used for algae control for many years, its use for control of submersed aquatic weeds has been limited. Some investigators (12,13) found copper to be toxic to be submersed aquatics and have reported varying degrees of success in using different application techniques and concentrations. Through a number of field experiments, it has been found that continuous application technique of applying CSP are effective for control of pondweeds and algae in irrigation canals. Details of some of these studies are included in papers and progress reports (3,4,5,6).

Slug Application. The "slug" technique involves applying CSP in one of three ways: (1) dumping CSP crystals directly into the water, (2) placing crystals in a bag and suspending it in the flowing water to dissolve them, or (3) pumping a concentrated aqueous solution of CSP into the canal or lateral for a short period of time. In flowing water this results in a treated slug or segment of moving water. The slug application is most frequently made by dumping CSP crystals from containers or a dump truck directly into the flowing water.

Cloth sacks, preferably nylon, loaded with large CSP crystals and partially submerged in the flowing water are sometimes used to apply a slug of CSP. This technique provides a longer dissolution period than the dump method. While the slug technique requires a minimum of equipment for application, the technique may elevate the copper level more than required and there is little control of the rate of dissolution.

Continuous Application. This type of application involves a continuously or intermittently regulated dispensing of CSP crystals. An auger-type volumetric feeder provides a uniform dispensing rate. The feeders are equipped with timers to control the time of application and changeable gear ratios to provide different rates of dispensing. Through knowledge of the volume of waterflow and the amount of CSP needed per day to control a particular aquatic plant, the timer on the feeder can be set to dispense the needed quantity of CSP. This type of feeder is also available in a variable feed-rate model, which provides a near-constant level of copper in fluctuating waterflows. The auger-type feeder, is commercially available.

The controlled dispensing devices have an advantage over the slug application in that the concentrations of copper in the water can be controlled to varying degrees and the amount can be kept to the minimum required to provide control. Also, the very low controlled levels of copper achieved by this technique reduce the impact of undesirable effects that may occur. The commercially available feeders and other equipment needed for this type dispensing are more costly than for the slug method.

Rate of Application. The particular aquatic weed causing the problem should be identified to determine optimum treatment required. Filamentous green algae attached to concrete canal linings or growing in unlined canal systems and reservoirs can be controlled readily with CSP. The filamentous blue-green algae, although not as prevalent as green algae on irrigation projects, are somewhat resistant to CSP treatments. Once these algae have developed into a mat, CSP has limited effectiveness. Therefore, as a preventive measure, it is suggested that low level treatments on a continuous of intermittent daily basis be started before the blue-green algae have developed into heavy mats. Recommended dosage rates are given in Table 1.

Other aquatic herbicides, such as emulsified xylene and acrolein, are commonly used on irrigation projects to control rooted submersed aquatic weeds after they become established. These herbicides, though generally more economical than CSP, are often considered undesirable in water used for nonirrigation purposes. In most instances, CSP may be used for weed control in domestic water supplies and fisheries.

Copper Sulfate Pentahydrate Specifications.   The copper content of a CSP product, the particle size, and uniformity of particle size are important considerations when purchasing CSP. Since copper is the active ingredient in CSP for vegetation control, the percent of metallic copper present should be specified when purchasing copper sulfate. Most CSP products have a 25-percent or slightly higher content of metallic copper. The label on CSP products generally reads as follows:

	Percent
Active Ingredient:	
Copper Sulfate Pentahydrate	99
Inert Ingredient:	1
Copper expresses as metallic.	25.0 or 25.2

When the CSP will be bag or dump applied, it is generally considered more appropriate to use a large particle size product to extend the dissolution time and to maintain the copper content of the water at a lower level. The large CSP crystals having a minimum particle size of three-fourths of an inch are recommended for this type application. Some CSP products are manufactured in the form of a nugget or briquette about the shape and size of an almond. This form would also be desirable for slug application. Smaller size crystals may be used where they are found to give better results and the higher level of copper does not exceed the tolerance set in the registration.

When using the auger-type feeder to dispense CSP crystals directly into the water, a uniform, small crystal size that will flow readily and dissolve quickly is needed. If the CSP product contains a significant quantity of dust size particles, it may bridge over in the feeder hopper, causing an interruption in the dispensing. CSP products are available that consist of a uniform, small particle size with a very low percentage of fines meeting both the feeder and the rapid dissolution requirements. There are suitable CSP products commercially available.

Canal Characteristics.   The velocity of the canal water will affect the distance of effectiveness of a CSP application. The distance of effectiveness increases with the velocity of the waterflow due to the reduced time available for sorption of copper to the canal perimeter.

The type of canal lining also affects the distance of effectiveness. Greater distance of effectiveness is achieved in a concrete-lined canal than an earthen canal because of the greater velocity and less removal due to fewer sorption sites for the copper. The length of the canal should be considered in selecting the application method and dosage rate.

Quite often, the amount of aquatic plant growth in a canal is related to the area of the wetted perimeter. However, in a trapezoidal shaped canal, the wetted perimeter does not increase proportionally with the flow. Hence, the aquatic weed growth does not increase directly with flow; therefore, there is some decrease in sorption sites for the copper as the flow is increased. This indicates that the amount of CSP applied per cubic foot per second of flow can usually be reduced slightly when treating larger flows with the same velocity. The specific amount for each situation will have to be determined experimentally.

Water Quality. Alkalinity, suspended matter, and water temperature are the three major water quality parameters that affect the performance of CSP. Alkalinity of the water is the principal factor that reduces the effectiveness of CSP. Copper ions react with bicarbonate and carbonate ions and the water to form insoluble complexes that precipitate from solution and reduce the amount of biologically active copper. Once the copper is removed from the ionized form, it is no longer effective for aquatic weed control. The waters of western irrigation projects are generally alkaline, although the range in concentration may vary and differs geographically.

Good results are usually achieved in waters of the lower alkalinity range if other important factors are considered in formulating control procedures. As water becomes more alkaline, the loss in weed control effectiveness can be compensated for by the additional larger quantities of CSP. The amount of increased dosage required can best be determined through experience gained by considering the alkalinity level, plant species, and the other factors influencing special situations. In waters of greater than 150 ppm alkalinity CSP would not normally be recommended, particularly where large volumes of water and many miles of canal are involved. If other control methods are not suitable for the situation and low volumes and short distances are involved, CSP may still be considered but its limitation in high alkaline waters should be recognized.

Suspended sediment and other particulate matter afford sites for the sorption of copper, thereby reducing the amount of biologically active copper in the water. The amount of copper sorbed is related to the amount and type of particulate matter in the water. Organic material, both living and dead, represents the greatest sorptive sink for copper. Suspended sediment load another factor influencing the loss of copper for uptake by the target plants. Nelson, Bruns, Coutant and Carlile

(23), found that copper was sorbed by suspended sediment during treatment of the Roza Main Canal with CSP.

Water temperature is a factor in the phytoxicity of copper, particularly in canals operated throughout the year. When the water temperature declines to the lower 50° F (10° C) range, algae do not respond to CSP treatments as they do at a higher water temperatures. Generally higher CSP rates are needed in water below 50° F (10° C). The amount of CSP increase required can best be determined through results obtained from gradual increases in dosage rate.

ENVIRONMENTAL EFFECTS

Residues of Copper in Irrigation Water. When copper sulfate (CSP) is dispensed continuously for algae control the applied quantity is in the 5 to 10 ppb range as copper. Daily feeding of CSP, either on an intermittent or continuous basis, can be used to control submersed aquatic weeds in an irrigation canal. Generally the copper concentration required to control this type of vegetation amounts to ten to twenty times that level needed to control algae. The concentration of copper found in water samples collected at sampling stations over a three year experiment on the Farmers Ditch near Loveland, Colorado is included in Table 2. These data show that the copper concentration (2) diminished gradually as the treated water moved through the canal. These levels of copper give excellent control of leafy (**Potamogeton folisus** Raf.) and sago (**P. pectinatus** L.) pondweed throughout the 9-mile length of the canal.

Several factors influence the amount of copper needed to be applied to control submersed aquatic vegetation and the degree of success of the treatment. These include type and quantity of aquatic plants, alkalinity of the water, ratio of wetted perimeter to volume of flow, length of the canal needing control, turbidity of the water, nature of canal lining, velocity of water and water temperature (3,4,5,6,7).

Residues of Copper in Aquatic Plants, Hydrosoils and Agricultural Soils. Soil and aquatic weed samples were collected for copper residue determinations in conjunction with the 3-year field experiment conducted to determine the effectiveness of copper on submersed aquatics in the Farmers Ditch. The amount of copper found in ditchbottom soil samples is presented in Table 3. These data indicate that much of the copper accumulated in the ditchbottom.

In Table 4 the amount of copper found in treated and untreated aquatic vegetation is given. These data reflect the high levels of copper that the aquatic plants can accumulate from a very low level in the water when exposed for long periods of time. The quantity of copper found in the agricultural soils is shown in Table 5. Sampling Stations were located 4, 4.5, and 6.5 miles respectively downstream from the CSP feeding station. These copper determinations showed no increase over the back ground copper throughout the study.

Irrigation Hazard of Copper Residues. The copper residues shown in Table 5 for agricultural soils collected at the start and end of each irrigation season represent a situation where the maximum quantity of copper is used on an irrigation system. These data show no increase in copper of the soil above the background level through one season or over the 3-year study period. In Table 3 on hydrosoil analysis it is evident that much of the copper applied remained in the ditchbottom soil. On the basis of these data it was estimated that 60 percent of the copper remained in the ditchbottom. On an average the quantity of CSP applied to the Farmers Ditch per season does not exceed 6,000 pounds or 1,500 pounds of copper. If 40 percent of the copper gets to the crop land that would amount to a total of 600 pounds per season applied over 3,000 acres or the equivalent of 0.2 pounds of copper per acre. Assuming this quantity of copper would be distributed throughout the top 6 inches of soil it would amount to the addition of about 0.1 ppm copper per season. This low level of copper addition would not be excepted to be a hazard to crop production since copper is essential to crops.

In those canals where a potable water source is being delivered, any copper sulfate treatments made to the system are carried out in a manner to assure a copper content of less than 1 ppm copper in the water delivered to the municipality. This is done to meet the 1 ppm limit of copper established for drinking water standards. Those concentrations of copper resulting from aquatic weed control practices in irrigation systems would not be considered hazardous to livestock and wildlife drinking the irrigation water (7,8,9,10,11,14,15,16).

HEALTH EFFECTS

CSP used cautiously for algae and pondweed control has a minimum adverse effect on nontarget organisms. Trace quantities of ionic copper may be beneficial or even essential for the growth of organisms, but excessive quantities have been found to be toxic to a wide variety of aquatic life (18,19,20).

Fish and Other Aquatic Life. Fish are perhaps the most commonly observed aquatic life that can be adversely affected by CSP applications. The toxicity of copper to aquatic organisms varies significantly, not only with the species but also with the physical and chemical characteristics of the water, such as temperature, hardness, turbidity, and carbon dioxide content.

McKim and Benoit (21) found that the maximum acceptable toxicant concentration (MATC) for brook trout exposed to copper in water with a hardness of 45 mg/l as $CaCO_3$ and a ph of 7.5 ranged between 9.5 and 17.4 ppb (parts per billion) of copper using survival, growth, and reproduction as criteria to evaluate effects. Mount and Stephan (19) found that the MATC of copper for the fathead minnow (**Pimephales promelas,** Rafinesque) in water with a hardness of 30 mg/l as $CaCO_3$ ranged between 10.6 and 18.4 ppb using survival, growth, and reproduction to evaluate effect. Hazel and Meith (20) found, in bioassays of 25-day-old eyed king salmon eggs and fry exposed continuously to copper solutions adjusted to a pH of 6.8 to 7.2 for a 27-day period, that eggs are more resistant to the toxic effects of copper than are fry. Copper concentrations of 80 ppb did not noticeably affect the hatching success of eyed eggs, but concentrations as great as 40 ppb were acutely toxic to fry, and a concentration of 20 ppb caused increased mortality and inhibited growth. These data indicate that the acceptable level of copper in waters involving a fishery is very low, and each system should be considered on its own relationship. The copper concentrations resulting from the continuous application recommendations for algae control would apparently be safe levels according to the findings of the above three citations.

Observations have been made of fish and other aquatic life in irrigation canals where CSP is used to control algae and/or pondweeds. Continuous application of a very low rate of CSP, 2 to 5 ppb as copper, into the Charles Hansen Feeder Canal of the Colorado-Big Thompson project in Colorado, throughout the year over a period of several years for algae control apparently has not adversely affected the rainbow trout that have escaped into the concrete-lined canal.

The Farmers Ditch near Loveland, Colo., was observed for fish and other aquatic life at the end of each irrigation season. Yellow perch, minnows, carp, and a few trout found in the CSP-treated reaches were in good condition. Other aquatic life such as crayfish, mayfly, and midgefly larvae also appeared to be healthy. These organisms were exposed to the maximum level (0.2 ppm) of copper that will occur during continuous applications of CSP for pondweed control.

Livestock and Wildlife. Trace quantities of copper are generally considered essential to the good health of these animals. Cunningham (9) found that cattle can tolerate 5 g of copper sulfate per day for at least 18 months without toxic effects; however, doses of 1.5 to 2.0 g daily are fatal within 30 days for British breeds of sheep, and a single dose of 2.5 g is said to be near the toxic level for small ewes. Daily copper doses of 2 to 4 mg have been harmless to rats; but doses of 6 to 9 mg per day have been harmful, and doses amounting to more than 1 mg per kg of body weight for 5 days are injurious to growth (25). Hale (18) has reported that 1 g daily of soluble copper is safe for dogs, but more can be fatal. It is not likely that animals would drink sufficient quantities of CSP-treated irrigation water to receive harmful dosages of copper, especially where a continuous application is made and the maximum copper level would be in the 0.1 ppm range. For example, an animal would receive a dose of 1 mg of copper by ingesting 10 liters of treated water.

Humans. Copper is an essential and beneficial element in human metabolism (17). Small quantities are considered nontoxic, but large doses cause adverse effects. Copper is not considered a hazard in drinking water because levels high enough to be dangerous to human beings impart a disagreeable to the water. The recommended limit for copper set in the Drinking Water Standards is 1 mg/l.

Registration of Copper Sulfate. The Environmental Protection Agency (EPA), in reaponse to petitions for the registration of CSP for alsae and pondweed control in various aquatic situations, including irrigation distribution systems, set a tolerance (the upper permissible limit) of 1 ppm copper in potable water (1). Copper was exempted by EPA (2) from the requirement of a tolerance in eggs, fish, meat, milk, irrigated crops, and shellfish when it resulted from the use of CSP as an algaecide or herbicide in irrigation projects conveyance systems, lakes, ponds, reservoirs, or bodies of water in which fish or shellfish are cultivated. CSP products are now labeled through the EPA for use in controlling algae and pondweeds by slug and continuous application methods on irrigation projects and for use in other aquatic situations. To comply with current Federal requirements, CSP products properly labeled for the intended use must be selected.

SUMMARY AND CONCLUSIONS

Copper sulfate when used properly and with full consideration of all aspects of the environment is one of the safest of the aquatic weed herbicides. It is a very important tool to the operator who must deliver water and maintain a high quality. In response to petitions filed with the EPA by the Bureau of Reclamation and others on the use of copper sulfate for aquatic vegetation control, the EPA granted an exemption from a requirement of tolerance for copper in eggs, fish, meat, milk, irrigated crops and shellfish, and the FDA established a tolerance of 1.0 ppm copper in potable water.

REFERENCES

1. Anon., Part 180. 1972. Tolerances and Exemptions from Tolerances for Pesticide Chemicals in or on Raw Agricultural Commod-

ities, Subpart D, Paragraph 180.1021, Copper; Exemption from the Requirements of a Tolerance Federal Register. 37: 3352-53.

2. Anon., Part 121. 1972. Food Additives, Subpart D—Food Additives Permitted in Food For Human Consumption—Cooper. Federal Register. 37: 21991.

3. Bartley, T.R. 1967. Progress report on evaluation of copper for aquatic weed control and herbicide residues on irrigation systems. USDI, Bureau of Reclamation, Report No. WC-32.

4. Bartly, T.R. and N.E. Otto. 1967. Progress report of antifouling materials for algae prevention. USDI, Bureau of Reclamation, Report No. WC—30.

5. Bartley, T.R. 1969. Algae control on irrigation canals by continouous low rate feed of copper sulfate. Research Progress Report, Western Society of Weed Science. 1969.

6. Bartly, T.R. 1969. Copper residue on irrigation canal. Abstract No. 98, 1969 meeting of Weed Science Society of America.

7. Bartley, T.R. and E.O. Gangstad. 1973. Environmental aspects of aquatic plant control. Invitational paper prepared for the National Meetings of The American Society of Civil Engineers, January 1973. Washington, D.C.

8. Blackburn, R.D. and L.W. Weldon. 1969. Control of **Hydrilla verticillata** (Abstr). Proceedings, Southern Weed Control Conference. 22:317.

9. Cummings, J.C. 1975. Residue tolerances for aquatic herbicides. J. Aquatic Plant Manage. 14:4-6.

10. Domogalla, B.P. 1926. Treatment of algae and weeds in lakes at Madison, Wis. Engineering News-Record. 97:950-954.

11. Domogalla, B.P. 1935. Eleven years of chemical treatment of the Madison lakes: its effects on fish and fish foods. Trans. Amer. Fish. Soc. 65:115-120.

12. Derby, R.L. and D.W. Graham. 1953. Control of aquatic growths in reservoirs by copper sulfate and secondary effects of such treatments. Proceedings of the American Society of Civil Engineers, Vol. 79, Separate No. 203, 15 pp.

13. El Din, H.S. and K.W. Jones. 1954. Copper sulfate as an aquatic herbicide. Nature, No. 4421, p. 187.

14. Gangstad, E.O. 1971. Aquatic plant control program. Hyacinth Contr. J. 9:46-48.

15. Gangstad, E.O. 1972. Herbicidal control of aquatic plants. J. of the Sanitary Engineering Division, ASC. 98:397-406.

16. Gelfand, Max. 1946. "Algaecide." United States Patent No. 2,400, 863.

17. Gilbert, Frank A. 1952. Copper in nutrition. **Advances in Agronomy**. IV 147-177.

18. Hale, F.E. 1942. Relation of copper and brass pipe to health. Water Works Engineering. Vol. 95.
19. Hanson, G.W., F.E. Oliver and N.E. Otto. 1983. Herbicide manual, a Water Resources Technical Publication. U.S. Government Printing Office, Washington, D.C. 346 pp.
20. Hazel, Charles and Stephen J. Meith. 1970. **Bioassay of King Salmon Eggs and Sac Fry in Copper Solutions.** California Fish and Game. 56:121-124.
21. McKim, J.M. and D.A. Benoit. 1971. Effects of long term exposures to copper on survival, growth, and reproduction of brook trout (Salvelinus frontinalis). Journal of the Fisheries Research Board of Canda. 28:655-662.
22. Moore, G.T. and K.F. Kellerman. 1905. Copper as an algicide and disinfectant in water supplies. USDA, Bureau of Plant Industry, Bull. No. 76.
23. Nelson, J.L., V.F. Bruns, C.C. Coutant, and B.L. Carlile. 1969. Behavior and reactions of copper sulfate in an irrigation canal. Pesticide Monitoring Journal. 3:186-189.
24. Nielsen, Geoffrey D. 1967. Practical method of controlling algae in irrigation canals. USDI, Bureau of Reclamation. A paper presented at the ASCE Water Resources Conference. October 1967.
25. Otto, N.E. and T.R. Bartley. 1965. **Aquatic Pests on Irrigation Systems: Identification Guide."** A Water Resources Technical Publication. USDI, Bureau of Reclamation.

Table 1. Dosage rate of CSP required to control aquatic weeds by different application techniques where alkalinity of the water is less than 150 p/m as CaCO₃.

Aquatic site	Aquatic weed	Application technique	Treatment frequency	Dosage rates of CSP	Approximate range of maximum copper concentration, p/m
Flowing water	Algae	Slug	approx. 14 days	1/4 to 2 lb/ft³/s/treatment	0.5 to 15*
canals, laterals and drains	Algae	Continuous	Daily	0.1 to 0.2 lb/ft³/s/day	0.005 to 0.01
	Pondweed	Continuous	Daily	1.6 to 2.4 lb/ft³/s/day	0.07 to 0.11
Static water	Algae	Slug	As needed	1 to 4 lb/acre-ft	0.1 to 0.4
Reservoirs	Algae	Continuous	Daily	0.05 to 0.20 lb/acre-ft/day	0.005 to 0.02
Reservoirs	Pondweed	Continuous	Daily	0.5 to 1.0 lb/acre-ft/day	0.05 to 0.10

*These concentrations cover a wide range due to a variable dissolution rate depending upon size of CSP crystal, velocity and temperature of water, method and time of application, and amount of CSP added.
From Bartley and Gangstad, 1973. With permission.

Table 2.   Total Copper Content of Water Samples* Collected From Farmers Ditch During the 3 Year Study

Date Sampled	Miles Downstream	Water Flow, cfs	Duplicate a	PPM copper samples b	Average	
6-15-66	0.00	-	0.00	0.00	0.00	
5-24-67	0.00	34	0.00	0.00	0.00	0.00
7-11-68	0.00	24	0.00	0.00	0.00	
6-15-66	0.25	-	0.09	0.09	0.09	
5-24-67	0.25	34	0.05	0.05	0.05	0.21
7-11-68	0.25	24	0.50	0.50	0.50	
6-15-66	0.30	-	0.10	0.10	0.10	
5-24-67	0.30	34	0.02	0.02	0.02	0.20
7-11-68	0.30	24	0.47	0.47	0.47	
6-15-66	1.10	-	0.07	0.07	0.07	
5-24-67	1.10	34	0.02	0.02	0.02	0.16
7-11-68	1.10	24	0.04	0.40	0.40	
6-15-66	2.50	-	0.07	0.07	0.07	
5-27-67	2.50	34	0.02	0.02	0.02	0.15
7-11-68	2.50	24	0.35	0.35	0.35	
6-15-66	3.80	-	0.06	0.06	0.06	
5-24-67	3.80	34	0.02	0.02	0.02	0.13
7-11-68	3.80	24	0.31	0.31	0.31	
6-15-66	4.40	-	0.04	0.04	0.04	
5-24-67	4.40	34	0.02	0.02	0.02	0.11
7-11-68	4.40	24	0.26	0.26	0.26	
6-15-66	6.30	-	0.03	0.03	0.03	
5-24-67	6.30	34	0.02	0.02	0.02	0.08
7-11-68	6.30	24	0.19	0.19	0.19	
6-15-66	7.50	-	0.01	0.01	0.01	
5-27-67	7.50	34	0.02	0.02	0.02	0.07
7-11-68	7.50	24	0.17	0.17	0.17	
6-15-66	9.00	-	0.01	0.01	0.01	
5-24-67	9.00	34	0.02	0.02	0.02	0.03
7-11-68	9.00	24	0.07	0.07	0.07	

* All samples except the first three were collected in copper sulfate treated water.
From Bartley and Gangstad. 1973.

**Table 3. Total Copper Content of Hydrosoils* Collected From
Farmers Ditch During the 3 Year Study**

| Date Sampled | Miles Downstream | PPM copper - Air dried basis | | |
		Duplicate samples a	b	Average
05-17-67	0.00	24	24	24	
05-07-68	0.00	22	23	22.5	21.5
09-28-67	0.00	21	22	21.5	
10-29-68	0.00	18	18	18.0	
05-17-67	0.25	44	36	40.0	61.0
05-07-68	0.25	92	72	82.0	
09-28-67	0.25	39	48	43.5	47.0
10-29-68	0.25	44	57	50.5	
05-17-67	0.30	96	137	116.5	90.8
05-06-68	0.30	44	86	65.0	
09-28-67	0.30	123	124	123.5	110.0
10-29-68	0.30	87	106	96.5	
05-17-67	1.11	64	40	52.0	54.0
05-07-68	1.11	62	50	56.0	
09-28-67	1.11	66	352	209.0	151.0
10-29-68	1.11	98	97	93.0	
05-17-67	3.80	45	40	42.5	46.0
05-06-68	3.80	44	55	49.5	
09-28-67	3.80	62	56	59.0	62.5
10-29-68	3.80	65	67	66.0	
05-17-67	6.30	26	24	25.0	32.0
05-07-68	6.30	30	48	39.0	
09-28-67	6.30	30	38	34.0	43.0
10-29-68	6.30	54	50	52.0	
05-17-67	9.00	54	78	66.0	63.0
05-07-68	9.00	50	70	60.0	
09-28-67	9.00	38	39	38.5	71.3
10-29-68	9.00	107	101	104.0	

* All soil samples except those collected from Station No. 1 were exposed to copper sulfate treated water.
From Bartley and Gangstad. 1973.

Table 4. Total Copper Content of Aquatic Vegetation* Collected From Farmers Ditch During the 3 Year Study

Date Sampled	Miles Downstream	Aquatic Weed	PPM copper - Ovendried basis				
			Duplicate samples			Average	
			a	b	c		
07-07-66	0.00	LPW 1	20	20	20	20	
08-23-66	0.00	LPW	18	24	20	20.7	17.9
08-01-67	0.00	LPW	18	16		17.0	
08-27-67	0.00	LPW	14	14		14.0	
07-07-66	0.00	EL 2	20	20	20	20.0	
08-23-66	0.00	EL	20	21	25	22.0	21.5
08-01-67	0.00	EL	25	23		24.0	
08-24-67	0.00	EL	20	20		20.0	
05-07-68	0.25	LPW+HPW 3	51	51		51.0	43.8
05-07-68	0.25	Algae	37	36		36.5	
07-07-66	0.30	LPW	4010	4010	4820	4280	
06-15-67	0.30	LPW	470	470		470	2120.0
08-01-67	0.30	LPW+HPW	1600	1620		1610	
05-17-67	0.30	HPW	42	39		40.5	
05-17-67	0.30	Algae	143	128		135.	89.5
05-07-68	0.30	LPW+HPW	125	60		92.5	
05-07-68	1.10	EL	56	56		56	49.5
05-07-68	1.10	Algae	47	39		43	
07-07-66	3.80	SPW 4	1430	1440	1570	1480	

Table 4. Total Copper Content of Aquatic Vegetation* Collected From Farmers Ditch During the 3 Year Study (cont.)

Date Sampled	Miles Downstream	Aquatic Weed	PPM copper - Ovendried basis			
			Duplicate samples			Average
			a	b	c	
08-23-66	3.80	SPW	2510	2450	2660	2542	1770.0
09-29-66	3.80	SPW	1290	1290		1290
08-01-67	4.40	SPW	340	260		350	350.0
08-26-68	7.00	SPW	340	380		360	360.0
07-07-66	9.00	SPW	420	380	360	386.7	386.7

* Samples collected from Station No. 0 were never exposed to copper sulfate, samples collected were taken before treatment started and remainder of samples were collected during treatment
[1] Leafy pondweed
[2] Elodea
[3] Horned pondweed
[4] Sago pondweed
From Bartley and Gangstad. 1973.

PART II

EVALUATION OF SELECTED AQUATIC HERBICIDES

CHAPTER 7. HERBICIDAL, ENVIRONMENTAL AND HEALTH EFFECTS OF DALAPON

Chapter 7

HERBICIDAL, ENVIRONMENTAL AND HEALTH EFFECTS OF DALAPON[1]

INTRODUCTION

Dalapon is 2,2-dichloropropionic acid and is mostly sold as the sodium salt. It is a water-soluble powder applied in solution for a foliage spray. A typical commercial product contains 85 percent of the salt of 74 percent of the acid equivalent. An improved formulation contains magnesium and sodium salts. The acute oral toxicity is low. It is not absorbed through unbroken skin. The powder may cause skin irritation after prolonged contact, but spray concentrations are not irritating. The powder or concentrated solutions can cause painful irritation of the eyes.

Dalapon is used principally to control grasses, but it is also effective against cattails; jack pine; phragmites; rushes; and white-cedar. It is a growth-regulator type of herbicide that is translocated from leaves to roots and rhizomes of perennial grasses. For general weed control, it is mixed with a broadleaved weedkiller such as 2,4-D. Dalapon disappears from the soil most rapidly in warm and humid regions. It persists longer in dry cool solid where microbial activity is low. (1,2,8,9).

Most broad-leaved weeds are tolerant or resistant. Among the resistant species are: algae; bracken; euonymus; American-lotus; wild onion; and waterlily.

HERBICIDAL EFFECTS

Although dalapon is often referred to as a chlorinated or salt substituted aliphatic acid, it is almost exclusively used as the sodium, and/or mixtures with the magnesium salt. Herbicidal effects are summarized in Table 1. The most important application of this herbicide is the use of dalapon as a foliar treatment to control perennial grasses in certain crops and on non-cropped land. Although dalapon is one of the best herbicides available for this purpose, success depends upon a systematic retreatment program. For most perennial grass species, the best control is obtained when the first application is made relatively

---

[1]The findings in this report are not to be construed as an official Department of the Army position unless so designated by other authorized documents.

early in the growing season when leaves are mature and the seed heads have started to form. Subsequent retreatments are required about every five weeks throughout the growing season; the actual time between retreatments depends on the species and the environmental conditions; significant regrowth should have occurred. It may be necessary to make these repeated applications for more than one year for complete control. It must be emphasized that a program as outlined above is essential for the control of most perennial grasses; a single application is only of temporary value. (15,16,17,18).

The phytoxic symptoms of the chlorinated aliphatic acid herbicides are growth inhibition, leaf chlorosis and formative effects, especially at the shoot apex. Rapid foliar necrosis, and contact injury, may occur with high concentrations of dalapon. Root growth inhibition is first detectable, four hours after dalapon treatment and growth cease within twelve hours. Sublethal rates of dalapon progressively reduced the growth rates of *Lemna minor* and *Salvinia natans*. This growth reduction is correlated with the rate of leaf or frond formation and mean leaf or frond area. Meyer and Buchholtz (34) reported that dalapon inhibits the growth of shoots from isolated quackgrass (*Agropyron repens*) rhizomes and buds.

Prasad and Blackman (37,38,39) reported that the primary effect of dalapon on roots of several species studied was an interference with the meristematic activity of the root tip and that mitotic activity was arrested at prophase.

Absorption and translocation of dalapon has been investigated in considerable detail. Most of this research utilized dalapon which was labeled with the radioactive atoms ^{14}C or ^{36}Cl. However, it is particularly interesting to note that the conclusions reached by Santelmann and Willard (44), before the labeled compounds were available, were essentially correct. Using phytoxicity symptoms as the criteria they found it was absorbed by leaves and roots and was translocated throughout the plants. They also determined that dalapon was translocated with the photosynthate by movement in the symplast but that this was not the only means of translocation. This was determined by depleting the leaves of photosynthate, placing the plants in the dark, prior to the application of dalapon to the leaves, and finding a reduction in translocation.

However, the refined technique of using either ^{14}C or ^{36}Cl labeled dalapon in subsequent studies by numerous investigators, has confirmed the finding of Santelmann and Willard (44).

Dalapon appears to be taken up by two different mechanisms. In studies with *Lemna minor*, Prasad and Blackman (38) reported that ^{36}C-dalapon entered both fronds and roots initially at a rapid rate and later at a slow but steady rate. The initial rapid rate was probably primarily an adsorption phenomenon. Foy (10,11,12,13,14) reported a small but significant amount of dalapon absorbed within 15 to 20 seconds by leaves of maize. Subsequent uptake of dalapon by *L. minor* was curvilinear and related to the herbicide concentration and temperature; it was inhibited by metabolic inhibitors such as dinitrophenol, arsenate, azide, iodoacetate, and phenyl mercuri acetate (38). The inhibition by the latter was reversed by glutathione or cysteine and it was concluded that the slow continuous uptake was a metabolic process involving thiol groups.

The rate of absorption and translocation of dalapon is influenced by a number of factors including age of plant, surfactant, temperature, light intensity, and relative humidity. Wilkinson (48,49) reported that leaves from barley plants up to 2 weeks of age translocated dalapon whereas movement from leaves of 3-week old plants could not be detected. Studies on dalapon transport in quackgrass showed that shaded leaves translocated more dalapon than unshaded leaves and the investigators suggested that this was the result of reduced water flow in the xylem which in turn reduced the movement of dalapon from the phloem to the xylem. (43). However, subsequent research by McIntyre (31) with quackgrass showed no influence of a 50% reduction in light on transpiration, but placing plants in the dark following treatment resulted in a 90% reduction in transpiration and an increase in the amount of dalapon translocated to the roots and tillers. In addition, various parts of a treated shoot were placed in the darkness and from these experiments concluded that the influence of darkness on the translocation of dalapon was within the treated leaf itself and not an influence of transpiration as suggested by Sagar (43). It was suggested that in the light a natural metabolite may be formed which complexes with dalapon and inhibits its translocation from the treated leaf. Prasad and Blackman (39) reported that the uptake of dalapon was not influenced by light intensity in the range of 300 to 900 foot-candles in studies with Lemna minor and Salvinia natans; however increases in temperature between 20° and 30°C did increase uptake. Relative humidity has also been implicated in the rate of dalapon absorption and translocation by leaves of barley, bean, zebrina, coleus, and nasturtium (40). They found that the amount of dalapon absorbed and translocated was greater at high relative humidities, 88%, than at the lower relative humidities of 60 or 28%. Pretreatment of the plants at high relative humidity (95%) also increased dalapon absorption and translocation, compared to low relative humidity (28%), when the plants were placed in the same relative humidity (95%) following treatment. They concluded that ontogeny and the degree of cuticle hydration are involved. The increased absorption at high relative humidities is also related to the decreased rate of drying of the applied herbicide drop. They also reported greater absorption and translocation of dalapon in bean leaves at 43°C than at 26°C.

Plant Metabolism: There are numerous reports in the literature of various biochemical events or metabolites. To date, these have not yielded a comprehensive understanding of how these herbicides kill higher plants at the molecular level. (4,5,15).

Several reports suggest that dalapon has some influence on carbohydrate metabolism (44,45,46). McWhorter (32,33) found that dalapon caused a general reduction of glucose with a corresponding increase in sucrose in johnsongrass (*Sorghum halepense*). Bourke et al. (6) studied the effect of dalapon on glucose metabolism in peas and reported that it interfered with glycolysis. Ross (42) using bean leaf disks, having fed ^{14}C-1-glucose and ^{14}C-6-glucose, found no difference in the C_6/C_1 ratio or $^{14}CO_2$ release due to the dalapon treatment. They concluded that dalapon did not affect the total glucose utilization or shift the pathway of glucose metabolism via the pentose phosphate or Krebs cycle pathways. However, they did conclude: (a) the pentose phosphate pathway was not involved as a distinctly exclusive route of glucose utilization, (b) dalapon interfered with glucose utilization (ethanol extract: ethanol-insoluble residue ratio), and (c) partial inhibition may occur at initiation of the glycolytic pathway and within the Krebs cycle.

Lipid metabolism or deposition of wax in the cuticle of the plant is affected by dalapon. Prasad and Blackman (38) observed that when *Salvinia natans* was treated with dalapon many leaves became submerged in the culture solution. Although they attributed this to a reduction in epidermal hairs, modification of the cuticle may also have been involved.

Nitrogen metabolism is also modified by the aliphatic acid herbicides. Mashtakov and Moshchuk (28) reported that dalapon increased the amount of asparagin and glutamine in a resistant variety of *Lupinus lutens.* They also noted a slight increase in protein and B-alanine and no change in the amount of free ammonia. However, in a sensitive variety, they reported a decrease in amides and B-alanine with an increase in free ammonia and protein. They concluded that the action of the herbicide was an inhibition of the enzymes which are involved in the conversion of ammonia to amides, thereby allowing the accumulation of toxic levels of free ammonia. Andersen et al. (11,21) observed that dalapon caused an increase in the degradation of protein to amino acids and an increase in amides. Further breakdown of the free amino acids with the liberation of ammonia was indicated. The amides appeared to act in ammonia detoxication by serving as storage sites for the released ammonia. In sugarbeets the amide was glutamine whereas in yellow foxtail, the amide was asparagine. After some period of time the amide and amino acids returned to normal levels in the resistant species sugarbeets, but this did not occur in the susceptible species, yellow foxtail.

Dalapon was reported to be a protein precipitant by Redemann and Hamaker (41) and concentrations as low as about 200 ppm produced a visible precipitate from egg yolk and egg white protein. This is still a relatively high concentration. However, an aspect of the effect of the aliphatic acid herbicides which has not been investigated but warrants serious study is the effect of these compounds on conformational changes in proteins, including enzymes. Foy (14) notes that halogenated acetates and propionates are theoretically able to alkylate the sulfhydryl or amino groups in enxymes.

Several chlorinated aliphatic acids interfere with the biosynthesis of pantothenic acid in certain microorganisms (19,20,47). Pantoic acid and B-alanine are precursors of pantothenic acid. Pantothenic acid is a precursor of the universally required coenzyme A. Since coenzyme A is required for several essential biochemical reactions in higher plants as well as microorganisms, this would appear to be a likely site of action of dalapon. Hilton et al. (19) reported that the isolated pantothenate synthesizing enzyme from Escherichia coli was inhibited by dalapon competing with pantoate for a site on the enzymes and both pantoate and pantothenate caused significant reduction in the abnormal tiller development on barley plants which resulted from application of sublethal concentrations of dalapon. Pantothenate was more effective than pantoate, but even pantothenate was not effective in overcoming dalapon inhibition of total growth.

The acute toxicity of dalapon sodium aquatic organisms in static water is shown in Table 2. The LC_{50} for all of these species was greater than 100 ppm of dalapon which represents a low order of toxicity. In tests with four species of fish eggs (embryo) were not affected by j50 ppm of dalapon. An acute toxicity test with dalapon in flowing water also showed a similar low order of toxicity to large-mouth bass.

Dalapon sodium salt has been tested on a number of species of insects and other crustaceans, both in fresh water and in salt water in short-exposure tests. Such tests have also been conducted on snails, oysters, and marine phytoplankton. The no-effect level of dalapon for snails, dragonflies, stoneflies, and several crustaceans is at least 200 ppm. Daphnids are more sensitive, being "immobilized" at 11 to 16 ppm. Shrimp are "immobilized" 40 percent at 0.9 ppm.

The highest concentrations of chemicals which were tested (7) in estuaries were shrimp, oysters, and crabs grow are at low ppm concentrations since even ppb are not likely to occur after herbicidal use because of dilution.

ENVIRONMENTAL EFFECTS

Herbicide Residues: Dalapon, as used commercially in the form of the sodium or magnesium salt, is a solid with a low vapor pressure and high water solubility. In the aqueous phase it exists principally as the ionic form. Dalapon or its salts partitions in aqueous-organic media preferentially to the aqueous system. Dalapon is hydrolyzed slowly or photolyzed principally to pyruvic acid, carbon dioxide, chloride ion, and acetaldehyde.

Dalapon, though not readily metabolized in animals, is a highly water-soluble compound readily excreted in the urine. All of the known degradation products from water or microorganisms are also water soluble, such as the chloride, chloropropionate, and pyruvate ions. Cows fed dalapon at 300 ppm in their diets did not have residue exceed 2.5 ppm dalapon in the milk during the test period. Dalapon does not partition selectively to fat tissues. Under a continuous feeding regime, dalapon is found mainly in excretory organs such as the kidney and liver, and in blood. All tissue residues in steers decreased rapidly with a halflife of a few days, when withdrawn from a diet containing 100 ppm dalapon. There is no indication of bioconcentration of dalapon in various tissues of animals or birds. (21,22,23).

Dalapon is readily translocated throughout plants, concentrating in young tissues, but is very stable showing little indication of metabolism, although eventual release of ^{36}Cl and incorporation of ^{11}C in other plant components is noted in small quantities. Dalapon appears to be present essentially as dalapon (free acid) in plant tissues, and is water-extractable as such.

Many genera and species of bacteria as well as fungi and other microorganisms in soil are capable of forming the chloride ion and pyruvic acid from dalapon or its salts. Without the presence of microorganisms, dalapon degradation in soil is slow. After an acclimation time of one to several weeks in the presence of soil microorganisms, metabolism of dalapon proceeds at an accelerated speed. Subsequently the original dosage and additional high dosages of dalapon far greater in concentration than those employed for commercial control are subject to rapid degradation. The speed of degradation of dalapon is greatly dependent on soil conditions favorable to the microorganisms and appears to be quite independent of the dosage of dalapon used. Soil conditions favorable to dalapon degradation are temperatures of 20° to 30°, adequate moisture, and a pH range of 5.3 to 7.5, preferably about 6.5. Soil textures with various sandy, loam, clay, and organic matter levels appear to have a minor effect on rates of dalapon degradation. (23,24,25).

Under conditions favorable to growth of microorganisms, dalapon in soil appears to be degraded at a faster rate than it is leached.

Microorganisms are capable of metabolizing and decomposing dalapon in water. In some instances a lag period was observed during which there was slow degradation followed by a period of rapid degradation when the microorganisms became acclimated to use of dalapon as a source of energy.

Mammals tolerate high concentrations of dalapon (and salts) in their diets for months and years in laboratory tests without mortality or other measurable effect. Effects caused by high concentrations are only those of weight loss and slight effects on the kidney.

Field tests with forage vegetation treated with heavy applications of dalapon sodium salt fed upon by cattle, sheep, and swine caused no ill effects with these animals. (21,22,23,24,25).

Irrigation Hazard of Dalapon Residues. Residues of dalapon in crop plants as given in Table 3 result from irrigation water containing concentrations substantially above those found from ditchbank vegetation treatments. (3). The highest level of 65 ppb in Maynard Canal would not produce a serious residue and the possibility of injury from the use of this water in irrigation is remote. The results are consistent with observed effects and experience in the field. These levels are within the tolerance levels of the registered uses and should not result in limitations of the use of the crop irrigated.

HEALTH EFFECTS

Feeding Studies: When fed to animals, dalapon was quickly excreted in the urine (27). Dogs, fed a single dose of 500 mg. of dalapon sodium salt/kg. of body weight excreted approximately 65 to 70 percent of this amount in two days. In repeated daily dietary feeding tests equivalent to doses of 50 and 100 mg. of dalapon sodium salt/kg./day over a 60-day period the excretion of dalapon in the urine ranged from 25 to 53 percent of the total ingested weight of dalapon. The half-life of dalapon in blood appeared to be approximately 12 hours. (21,22).

Human subjects consuming five successive daily oral doses of 0.5 mg. of dalapon sodium salt/kg. (198.3 mg./person) excreted approximately one-half of the administered dose in the urine over an 18-day period.

Redemann and Hamaker (41) reported that only two labeled compounds were found in milk from a cow whose feed contained [36]Cl-labeled dalapon; these were dalapon and the chloride ion. Cows fed 200 ppm of dalapon in their diet produced milk containing 0.7 to 1.0 ppm of dalapon within three to five days. These residue levels did not change appreciably throughout the eight-week feeding period. No significant amount of dalapon was found in fat of milk. The glyceride of dalapon was searched for, but not found (<0.1 ppm).

Paynter et al. (36) analyzed kidney, liver, muscle, brain, fat, and milk tissues of rats maintained for two years on diets containing 100, 300 and 1,000 ppm of dalapon sodium salt. Residues of dalapon in the tissues were approximately proportional to the dose fed and were at most only a small fraction of the level in the diet. At the 1,000 ppm level of feeding the highest residues of dalapon were found in the kidney (28 ppm), milk (19 ppm), and liver (11 ppm). As shown in other studies, dalapon does not concentrate in fat.

Paynter et al. (36) obtained residue data similar to those on rats by using dogs given daily doses, by capsule, of dalapon sodium salt at the rates of 15, 50, and 100 mg./ kg./day, five days a week for one year. This is the equivalent of a high daily dietary consumption of 500, 1,750, and 3,500 ppm. Results of these tests showed residues in all tissues to be quite low in relation to the level administered.

Swine consuming a diet containing dalapon sodium salt at levels of 100 ppm (= 4.7 mg./kg./day) and 200 ppm (= 8.6 mg./kg./day) of dalapon for 28 and 49 days were slaughtered without withdrawal from the feed. Greatest levels of residues of dalapon, averaging 6.9 and 10.4 ppm at the two feeding levels, respectively, were found in kidney, with lesser amounts in liver of 4.4 and 6.8 ppm in lean meat of 3.6 and 5.8 ppm and in fat of 2.2 and 2.4 ppm. No increase in residue was attributed to extending the time of feeding from 28 to 49 days. (36).

Steers were fed a diet containing dalapon at levels of ten, 30, and 100 ppm, for a period of four weeks. Three animals at each level were slaughtered without a withdrawal period. Three animals, after four weeks on the 100 ppm level, were fed four days on untreated feed before slaughter. Residues of dalapon in blood, fat, kidney, liver, and muscle tissues remained far below those in the diet. When the chemical was removed from the diet, tissue residues in animals fed 100 ppm of dalapon decreased at a half-value rate of about two days.

Laying White Rock hens fed 30 to 60 days before sacrifice on diets containing 25 and 50 ppm of dalapon, were analyzed for residues. Residues of dalapon in hens' eggs appeared to reach a fairly constant level after about two weeks of feeding and never exceeded two ppm. For the other tissues average residues for birds fed 50 ppm were highest for blood and kidney tissues (22 ppm); others were considerably less. Residues from hens fed 25 ppm were roughly half those at 50 ppm of dalapon, and 30-day residue values were not significantly different from 60-day values for each concentration tested. (26).

Bioaccumulation: The main purpose of bioconcentration studies is to determine the distribution of residues, selective or otherwise, of a given chemical over time in different organisms and segments of their environmental surroundings which constitute typical or representative ecosystems. It is important to determine whether residues soon reach a maximum concentration or whether residues are often not measured before the application of the chemical to establish background levels from unknown sources, nor immediately afterwards. Because of this deficiency, two sequential phases of residue bioconcentration are not differentiated: (1) physical adsorption to surfaces which occurs almost immediately and which is related to surface area/volume measurements of the organism and (2) long-term organism penetration which is absorption. This differentiation is important since continued build-up of residues in organisms over time is mostly due to absorption and redistribution within the organism and is a function of its metabolism. Adsorption factors may result in residues which constitute a base-line of residues to be subtracted from total (absorbed and adsorbed) residues, thus helping to determine those residues due to penetration of the chemical into the organism over a period of time (bioconcentration because of absorption). (26,27,28,29,30).

Reproduction Studies

A three-generation study showed no effect on reproduction (fertility, gestation, viability) and lactation of rats fed 3,000 ppm of dalapon sodium salt in their diets during the entire test period.

Rats fed high dosages of dalapon (up to 1,500 mg.kg.) daily during gestation suffered no significant change in the number of viable fetuses of fetus resorptions. No major dose-related skeletal or viscera abnormalities were observed in fetuses. Other than reduced pup weights in the high treatment levels, no untoward effects were noted.

Birds can tolerate high concentrations of dalapon in their diet for weeks without mortality. High dosages causing reproductive effects, as measured by egg-hatching success, are not essentially different from those causing lethal effects to breeding birds. There was no effect on hatching success with any of the econcentrations causing sublethal effects or partial lethality to adults.

High dosages (residues) of dalapon injected into bird eggs do not dause teratogenic effects (.5.000 ppm) or mortality (200 ppm.).

Fish can tolerate high concentrations of dalapon (usually at least 200 ppm) for one to four days and at least 50 ppm for 15 to 21 days. Eggs of fish and fry tolerate at least 50 ppm without mortality.

Concentrations of dalapon which are likely to occur in marine waters appear to offer no significant hazard to marine organism. Concentrations of dalapon which are likely to occur in fresh waters appear to offer no significant hazard to fish and most invertebrate organisms.

Dalapon is relatively nontoxic to honey bees. It is relatively non-toxic to soil invertebrates when used at commercial application rates to soil. Effects appear to be related to change in host-plant species resulting from the herbicide treatment, probably not much different from effects caused by soil tillage.

Residues of dalapon which may be encountered by wildlife on treated grass are representative of the highest residues occurring from commercial treatment and could be as much as several thousand parts per million temporarily. Aside from the fact that such treated grass would soon die as expected from dalapon treatments and, therefore, would be inedible for wildlife, residue concentrations from foliar treatments decline rapidly so that the highest concentrations are soon reduced to the several hundred parts-per-million range or less. Mammals and birds consuming from 100 to 1,000 ppm of dalapon in their diets even over periods of weeks, months, or years are not lethal. Residues in mammal and bird tissues from such feeding remained below 100 ppm of dalapon during treatment, and soon fell below 100 ppm when removed from exposure to dalapon. (26).

Dalapon was administered daily by gavage to pregnant rats from day six through 15 of the gestastion in a tolerance study designed to suggest dose levels acceptable for teratogenic studies. Dosages given were 250, 500, 1,000, 1,500, or 2,000 mg./kg./day. The following parameters were examined: maternal body weights and gains, food consumption, number of viable fetuses, fetus resorptions, and corpora lutea, individual pup weights and sex, and gross external examination of pups. As the result of these tests only the following notable observations were made. Clinical signs of toxicity consisted of soft stools and slight appetite depression in dams from the 2,000 mg./kg. dosage group. On rat from the 1,500 mg./kg. group had diarrhea. Weight gains for pregnant dams were lower than controls at 1,500 or 2,000 mg./kg./day. Fetal resorption rate was increased at both the 1,500 and 2,000 mg./kg. dosage levels, but the increase was not significantly different from controls. Pup weights from the 2,000 mg./kg. dosage level were significantly lower than controls. No effects were seen at 1,000 5,000, or 250 mg./kg./day. (26).

Teratological Studies.   Dalapon was administered in distilled water once daily, by gavage, from day six through 15 of gestation (sperm positive vaginal smear = day zero). Four groups of mated females were administered zero, 500, 1,000 or 1,500 mg. of dalapon/kg./day, respectively. They were killed on gestation day 20 and fetuses were removed by cesarean section. The following tests were conducted: clinical observations, maternal body weights on days zero, six, 15 and 20, food consumption on days six, 15 and 20, observations on the number of viable fetuses, resorptions, and corpora lutea, individual fetal weights and sex, external examination, and skeletal (two-thirds) and visceral (one-third) examinations.

All rats treated with dalapon were restless for approximately ten minutes following dosing. Focal alopecia, intermittent staining of rear quarters with urine, and soft stools were observed in some treated rats. Mean weight gains and food consumption for dalapon-treated adult rats during the test interval (days zero to 20) did not differ significantly from the controls. However, mean weight gains (500 and 1,500 mg./kg.day groups) and mean daily food consumption (1,500 mg./kg./day group) were significantly less than the controls for the dalapon treatment interval (gestation period, days six to 15). Mean pup weights were significantly less than controls only in groups given 1,000 or 1,500 mg./kg./day. An increased incidence of minor variants such as retarded ossification of sternebrae was observed in fetuses of treated dams and was associated with decreased fetal weights. Spontaneous major visceral abnormalities consisted of unilateral microphthalmia in one fetus each of the 500 and 1,000 mg./kg./day groups.

No major dose-related skeletal or visceral abnormalities were observed in the fetuses of dams treated with dalapon and other than reduced pup weights in the 1,000 and 1,500 mg./kg./day treatment levels, no untoward effects were detected. (26).

SUMMARY AND CONCLUSIONS

Dalapon has been used throughout the United States and other parts of the world with varying degrees of sucsess as an aquatic herbicide for control of aquatic grasses and grass like plants. It does not have undesirable environmental or health effects that preclude general use.

REFERENCES

1. Anderson, R.N., A.J. Linck, and R. Behrens. 1962. Absorption, translocation and fate of dalapon in sugar beets and yellow foxtail. Weeds 10:1-3.
2. Andersen, R.N., R. Behrens, and A.J. Linck. 1962. Effects of dalapon on some chemical constituents in sugar beets and yellow foxtail. Weeds 10:4-9.
3. Bartley, T.R. and E.O. Gangstad. 1975. Environmental aspects of aquatic plant control. Journ of the Irrigation and Drainage Division, ASCE. 100:231-244.
4. Blanchard, F.A. 1954. Uptake, distribution, and metabolism of carbon-14 labeled TCA in corn and pea plants. Weeds 3:274-278.
5. Blanchard, F.A., U.U. Muelder, and G.N. Smith. 1960. Herbicide uptake and distribution: Synthesis of carbon-14-labeled dalapon and trial applications to soybean and corn plants. J. Agr and Food chem. 8:124-128.
6. Bourke, J.B., J.S. Butts, and A.C. Fang. 1964. Effect of various herbicides on glucose metabolism in root tissue of garden peas. II. Plant growth regulators and other herbicides. Weeds 12:272-279.
7. Butler, P.A. 1965. Effects of herbicides on estuarine fauna. Proc. S. Weed Conf. 18:576-580.

8. Frank, P.A. and Demint, R.J. 1969. "Gas Chromatographic Analysis of Dalapon in Water" Environmental Science and Technology. 3:69-71.

9. Frank, P.A. and Demint, R.J., and Comes, R.D. 1970. Herbicides in Irrigation Water Following Canal-Bank Treatment for Weed Control Weed Science. 18:687-692.

10. Foy, C.L. 1961a. Absorption, distribution, and metabolism of 2,2-dichloropropionic acid in relation to phytotoxicity. I. Penetration and translocation of ^{36}Cl- and ^{14}C-labeled dalapon. Plant Physiol. 36:688-697.

11. Foy, C.L. 1961b. Absorption, distribution, and metabolism of 2,2-dichloropropionic acid in relation to phytotoxicity. II. Distribution and metabolic fate of dalapon in plants. Plant Physiol. 36:698-709.

12. Foy, C.L. 1962a. Penetration and initial translocation of 2,2-dichloropropionic acid (dalapon) in individual leaves of Zea mays L. Weeds 10:35-39.

13. Foy, C.L. 1962b. Absorption and translocation of dalapon2-^{14}C and ^{36}Cl in Tradescantia fluminensis. Weeds 10:97-100.

14. Foy, C.L. 1969. The chlorinated aliphatic acids. pp. 207-253. In P.C. Kearney and D.D. Kaufman, Degradation of Herbicides. Marcel Dekker, Inc., New York.

15. Funderburk, H.H. and D.E. Davis. 1960. Factors affecting the response of Zea mays and Sorgum halepense to sodium 2,2-dichloropropionate. Weeds 8:6-11.

16. Gangstad, Edward O. 1972. Herbicidal Control of Aquatic Plants. Journ of Sanitary Engineering Division, ASCE Vol. 98, No. SA2, Proc. Paper 8851. pp 397-406.

17. Gooch, F.S. and L.W. Erbe. 1967. The effects of monochloracetic acid, dichloracetic acid, and trichloroacetic acid on the stem tissues of Elodea. Proc. 29th Southern Weed Conf. p. 287.

18. Gusio, Francis J., Bartley, Thomas R. and Beck, Arthur N. 1965. Water Resources Problems Generated by Obnoxious Plants, Journal of the Waterways and Harbors Division, ASCE, Vol 91 No WW4, Proc. Paper 4537, pp. 47-60.

19. Hilton, J.L., J.S. Ard, L.L. Jansen, and W.A. Gentner. 1959. The pantothenate synthesizing enzyme, a metabolic site in the herbicidal action of chlorinated aliphatic acids. Weeds 7:381-396.

20. Hilton, J.L., L.L. Jansen, and W.A. Gentner. 1958. Betalanine protection of yeast growth against the inhibitory action of several chlorinated aliphatic acid herbicides. Plant Physiol. 33:43-45

21. Hoerger, F. 1969. The metabolism of dalapon. Blood absorption and urinary excretion patterns in dogs and human subjects. Unpub. rept., The Dow Chemical Company, Midland, Mich.

22. Hoterges, and E.E. Kenaga. 1972. Pesticide residues on plants: Correlation of representative data as a basis for estimation of their

magnitude in the environment. Environ. Qual. and Safety, Vol. I. Stuttgart: Georg Thieme and New York: Academic Press.
23. Holstun, J.T., Jr., and W.E. Loomis. 1956. Leaching and decomposition of 2,2-dichloropropionic acid in several Iowa soils. Weeds 4, 250.
24. Jensen, H.L. 1957. Decomposition of chloro-substituted aliphatic acids by soil bacteria. Can. J. Microbiol. 3, 151.
25. Kaufman, D.D. 1964. Microbial degradation of 2,2-dichloropropionic acid in five soils. Can. J. Microbiol. 10,813.
26. Kenaga, E.E. 1974. Toxicological and residue data useful in the environmental safety evaluation of dalapon. Residue Review. 53:109-151.
27. Leasure, J.K. 1964. The Halogenated Aliphatic Acids. J. Agr. and Food Chem. 12:40-43.
28. Mashtakov, S.M. and P.A. Moshchuk. 1967. The effect of sodium trichloroacetate on the content of nitrogenous substances in varieties of lupin resistant and sensitive to herbicides. Agrokhimiya 9:80-89.
29. Mayer, F. 1957a. Reaction of trichloroacetic acid and other halogen acetates with sulfhydryl and amino groups and also vegetable matter. Biochem. Z. 328:433-442.
30. Mayer, F. 1957b. Effect of trichloroacetate on higher plants. Z. Naturforsch. 12B:336-346.
31. McIntyre, G.I. 1962. Studies on the translocation in Agropyron repens of ^{14}C-labeled 2,2-dichloropropionic acid. Weed Res. 2:165-176.
32. McWhorter, C.G. 1961. Carbohydrate metabolism of Johnsongrass as influenced by seasonal growth and herbicide treatment. Weeds 9:563-568.
33. McWhorter, C.G. 1971. Control of Johnsongrass ecotypes. Weed Sci. 19:229-233.
34. Meyer, R.E. and K.P. Buchholtz. 1963. Effect of chemicals on buds of quackgrass rhizomes. Weeds 11:4-7.
35. Oyolu, C. and R.C. Huffaker. 1964. Effects of 2,2-dichloropropionic acid (dalapon) on organic acid content of wheat (*Triticum vulgare*). Crop Sci. 4:95-96.
36. Paynter, O.E., T.W. Tusing, D.D. McCollister, and V.K. Rowe. 1960. Toxicology of dalapon sodium (2,2-dichloropropionic acid, sodium salt). J. Agr. Food Chem. 8,47.
37. Prasad, R. and G.E. Blackman. 1964. Studies in the physiological action of 2,2-dichloropropionic acid. I. Mechanisms controlling the inhibition of root elongation. J. Exp. Bot. 15:48-66.
38. Prasad, R. and G.E. Blackman. 1965a. Studies on the physiological action of 2,2-dichloropropionic acid. II. The effects of light and temperature on the factors responsible for the inhibitions of growth. J. Exp. Bot. 16: 86-106.

39. Prasad, R. and G.E. Blackman. 1965b. Studies in the physiological action of 2,2-dichloropropionic acid. III. Factors affecting the level of accumulation and mode of action. J. Exp. Bot. 16:545-568.
40. Prasad, R., C.L. Foy, and A.S. Crafts. 1967. Effects of relative humidity on absorption and translocation of foliarly applied dalapon. Weeds 15:149-156.
41. Redemann, C.T. and J. Hamaker. 1957. Dalapon (2,2-dichloropropionic acid) as a protein precipitant. Weeds 3:387-388.
42. Ross, M.A. 1966. Utilization of ^{14}C metabolities, incorporation of ^{32}P and changes in respiration occurring in leaves from dalapon treated beans. WSSA Abstr. p. 50.
43. Sagar, G.R. 1960. An important factor affecting the movement of 2,2-dichloropropionic acid (dalapon) in experimental systems of *Agropyron repens*. Proc. 5th Brit. Weed Control Conf., pp. 271-278.
44. Santelmann, P.W. and C.J. Willard. 1955. The absorption and translocation of dalapon. Proc. 9th Northeast Weed Control Conf. pp. 21-29.
45. Smith, L.W. and P.j. Davies. 1965. The translocation and distribution of three labelled herbicides in *Paspalum distichum*. Weed Res. 5:343-347.
46. Smith, G.N. and D.L. Dyer. 1961. Fate of 2,2-dichloropropionic acid (dalapon) in the cotton plant. J. Agr. and Food Chem. 9:15-160.
47. Van Oorschot, J.L.P. and J.L. Hilton. 1963. Effects of chloro substitutions on al;iphatic acid inhibitors of pantothenic metabolism in *Escherichia coli*. Arch. Biochem. Biophys. 100:289-294.
48. Wilkinson, R.E. 1956. The physiological activity of 2,2-dichloropropionic acid. Ph. D. Dissertation, University of Calif. Davis. p. 148.
49. Wilkinson, R.E. 1962. Growth inhibitions by 2,2-dichloropropionic acid. Weeds 10:275-181.

Table 1.   Dalapon (2,2-dichloropropionic acid)

A. Nomenclature, Chemical and Physical Properties of the Pure Chemical.
  1. Common name: dalapon (ANSI, BSI, WSSA)
  2. Molecular formula: $C_3H_4Cl_2O_2$
  3. Molecular weight: 143
  4. Physical state, color, and odor: Colorless liquid. No odor.
  5. Density, C: 1.389 22.8
  6. Boiling point: 185 to 190 C
  7. Solubility:

Solvent	Approx. solubility
Alkali solvents	Very soluble
Ethanol	Very soluble
Ether	Soluble
Water	Very soluble

  8. Commercial formulations:
     a. Products names and manufacturer:
        DOWPON[R]—the sodium salt of dalapon
        DOWPON M—a mixture of the sodium and magnesium salts of dalapon
        DOWPON C Improved—a mixture of the sodium and magnesium salts of dalapon and sodium salt of TCA
        RADAPON[R] Liquid—a liquid formulation of the sodium salt of dalapon—The Dow Chemical Company
     b. Physical properties of DOWPON M
        1. Contains 72.5% sodium salt and 12.0% magnesium salt of dalapon. This mixture has superior handling properties to that of the sodium salt of dalapon alone.
        2. Physical state and color: Off-white powder.
        3. Melting point: Decomposes before melting.
        4. Decomposition temperature: 167.7C.
        5. Solubility: At 22 C 110 g/100 ml of water having 100 ppm hardness. Very low solubility in most organic solvents.
B. Herbicidal Use
  1. General: For the control of annual and perennial grasses, dalapon is used in sugarcane, sugarbeets, corn, potatoes, asparagus, grapes, flax, new legume spring seedlings, citrus, and deciduous fruit; coffee, certain stone fruits, and nut trees.
  2. Application methods: Can be applied with conventional aerial or ground equipment as a foliage application. Apply prior to crop emergence or postemergence. Addition of wetting agent is usually helpful.

Table 1.   Dalapon (2,2-dichloropropionic acid) (cont.)

3. Rates: Rates range from 0.75 lb/A in flax to 20 lb/A or more on non-cropland. Multiple treatments at lower rates are also used under certain conditions.
4. Usual carrier: Dalapon is used with a water carrier at volumes of 5 to 300 gpa, depending on crop situation, grass species, and method of application and equipment available.

C. Use Precautions
1. Flammability: Nonflammable.
2. Possible incompatibilities: Compatible with hard water and liquid fertilizers.
3. Corrosiveness: Formulations are mildly corrosive to equipment.
4. Cleaning glassware and spray equipment: Rinse thoroughly with water.
5. Storage stability: Stable in dry form; this mixture of sodium and magnesium salts of dalapon is hygroscopic. Keep container tightly closed when not in use.

D. Physiological and Biochemical Behavior
1. Foliar absorption characteristics: Absorbed by both roots and leaves. Easily washed off foliage.
2. Translocation characteristics: Translocates readily throughout the plant. Accumulates in young tissue.
3. Metabolism and persistence in plants: Is not degraded in plants.

From: Weed Science Society of America. Herbicide Handbook. Champaign, Illinois 1979.

Table 2. Dalapon toxicity to aquatic organisms.

Organism	Type of test	Experimental conditions	Toxicity	Reference
Simocephalus serrulatus	L,ST,A	a,b,c,e	$16.0 IC_{50}$ (48 h)	Sanders and Cope(1966)
Daphnia pulex	L,ST,A	a,b,c,e	$11.0 IC_{50}$ (48 6)	Sanders and Cope(1966)
Cardium edule	L,ST,A	—	>100 T (24 h)	Portmann and Wilson(1971)
Crangon crangon	L,ST,A	—	>100 T (24 h)	Portmann and Wilson(1971)
Pimephales promelas	L,ST,A	a,b,c,d,e	Soft water 390 T (96 h) Hard water 290 T (96 h)	Surber and Pickering(1962)
Erimyzon sucetta	L,ST,A	—	50.0 NTE	Hiltibran(1967)
Rasbora heteromorpha	L,ST,A	a,b,c,d,e	44.0 T (48 h)	Alabaster(1969)
Flounder	L,ST,A	—	>100 T (24 h)	Portmann and Wilson(1971)
Lepomis macrochirus (fry)	L,ST,A	—	50.0 NTE (12 d)	Hiltibran(1967)
L. macrochirus	L,ST,A	a,b,c,d,e	Soft water 40.0 T (96 h)	Surber and Pickering(1962)
L. macrochirus	L,ST,A	—	115 T (48 h)	Cope(1965)
L. cyanellus (fry) (fry)	L,ST,A	—	50.0 NTE	Hiltibran(1967)
Micropterus dolomieui	L,ST,A	—	50.0 NTE	Hiltibran(1967)
Trout	—	—	340 T (24 h)	Holden(1964)
Pteronarcys californica	L,CFT,A,	a,b,c,d,e	100 NTE (96 h)[e]	Sanders and Cope(1968)
Crassostrea virginica	L,CFT,A	—	1.0 NTE (96 h)[e]	Butler(1965)

Table 2. Dalapon toxicity to aquatic organisms. (cont.)

Organism	Type of test	Experimental conditions	Toxicity	Reference
Penaeus aztecus	L,CFT,A	—	1.0T (48 h)[a]	Butler(1965)
Fundulus similis	L,CFT,A	—	1.0 NTE (48 h)[a]	Butler(1965)
Cyprinus carpio	F,P	Pathological examination	SB 250, 25, 2.5 (28 d)[a]	Schultz(1971)
Rasbora heteromorpha	L,ST,A	a,b,c,d,e	240 T (48 h)[a]	Alabaster(1969)
Lepomis macrochirus >1,000 T (48 h)	L,ST,A	a,b,c,d,e	>1,000 T (24 h)	Hughes and Davis(1962)
Salmo gairdneri	L,ST,A	a,b,c,d,e	1.0 SB Avoidance[a]	Folmar(1976)
Lepomis macrochirus	L,ST,A	a,b,c,d,e	>1,000 T (24 h)[c] >1,000 T (48 h)	Hughes and Davis(1962)

From: Folmar, L.C. Technical paper NO 88, Fish and Wildlife Service, The U.S. Department of the Interior. Washington, D.C. 1977.

Table 2.   Dalapon toxicity to aquatic organisms. (cont.)

1. Type of test, letters represent:
     T = Toxicity test, used in conjunction with
             ST = static
            CFT = continuous flow
              A = acute
              C = chronic
     L = Laboratory toxicity test
     F = Field study, used in conjunction with
              R = river, stream or creek
              M = marine
              E = estuarine, and
              O = other
2. Experimental conditions. Factors reported in cited articles:
     a = water temperature
     b = pH
     c = alkalinity
     d = dissolved oxygen
     e = dissolved solids
     f = photoperiod
3. Toxicity, active ingredient. All values in mg/l (ppm) unless
   otherwise noted. Letters included with numerical values
   represent:
     T = LC_{50} (also accompanied by a time factor, e.g., 96 h)
     K = Kill
    SB = Sublethal effects
   NTE = No toxic effect

Table 3. Residue in parts per billion for crop plants treated with flood and sprinkler irrigation with water containing known levels of dalapon, as listed.

Crop Plant	Irrigation Type	Plant Maturity	Rate PPB	Residue PPB
Lettuce	Flood	Early	2250	50
Leaf	Sprinkler	Early	2250	550
	Flood	Late	2250	880
	Sprinkler	Late	2250	1130
Carrots	Flood	Early	2250	00
Roots	Sprinkler	Early	2250	00
	Flood	Late	11250	420
	Sprinkler	Late	11250	560
Potato	Floods	Early	2200	1570
Tubers	Sprinkler	Early	2200	90
	Flood	Late	2200	30
	Sprinkler	Late	2200	40
Onion	Flood	Early	2250	430
Bulbs	Sprinkler	Early	2250	70
	Flood	Late	2250	40
	Sprinkler	Late	2250	180
Soybean	Flood	Early	2250	1930
Seed	Sprinkler	Early	2250	1180
	Flood	Late	2250	1050
	Sprinkler	Late	2250	1360
Sorghum	Flood	Early	1125	530
Grain	Sprinkler	Early	1125	200
	Flood	Late	1125	50
	Sprinkler	Late	1125	110

From: Bartley and Gangstad. 1975.

PART II

EVALUATION OF SELECTED AQUATIC HERBICIDES

Chapter 8

HERBICIDAL, ENVIRONMENTAL AND HEALTH EFFECTS OF DICHLOBENIL[1]

INTRODUCTION

Dichlobenil is the common name for 2,6-dichlorobenzonitrile. It is used as a herbicide for controlling weeds and other vegetation in agricultural, forestry and other applications as well as aquatic plants in lakes, ponds, ditches, and to some extent in flowing water. The herbicidal activity of dichlobenil is characterized by a powerful inhibition of plant growth. Dichlobenil is manufactured in granular form as Casoron G-10 by Uniroyal Chemical Company. Dichlobenil is not acutely toxic to fish at herbicidal concentrations. The range of LD_{50} is 10-20 ppm for pumpkin seed (**Lepomis gibbosus**), bluegill (**L. Macrochirus**), redear sunfish (**L. Microlophus**) and largemouth bass (**Micopteris salmoides**).

The cancellation of 2-(2,4,5-trichlorophenoxy) propionic acid (silvex) for control of Eurasian watermilfoil (**Myriophyllum spicatum L.**) and other submersed aquatic plants is expected to reduce the level of control because some species of submersed aquatic plants are resistant or semi-resistant to control with alternative herbicides. Not all alternative herbicides which are available are registered or effective against alligatorweed (**Alternanthera philoxeroides** [Mart.] Griseb). One of the alternatives expected to be used is dichlobenil.

Dichlobenil is readily absorbed by plant roots and is translocated throughout the plant via the xylem, but more slowly than water due to its affinity for plant tissue (10). Pate and Funderburk (13) reported that dichlobenil is absorbed only slightly when applied as a foliar spray; however, it is readily absorbed by the roots. When bean plants were exposed to a saturated atmosphere of dichlobenil vapor, the compound was absorbed by all aerial parts. Price and Putnam (14) found that dichlobenil readily penetrates most plant tissues and is not actively held within cells. The quantity of herbicide emitted from plants in 24 hours was 70-80% of the amount absorbed. Pate and Funderburk (13) reported that bean, alligatorweed and four soil fungi degraded dichlobenil to 2,6-dichlorobenzoic acid. Massini (10) also presented evidence that dichlobenil is metabolized in plants. Verloop and Nimmo (21) found that the concentration of dichlobenil in bean leaves de-

---

[1]The findings in this report are not to be construed as an official Department of the Army position unless so designated by other authorized documents.

creased from about one-fourth (after 1 day) to about one-twentieth (after 5 days) of the root concentration. They postulated that the decrease may be caused by two phenomena: the herbicide evaporates out of the leaves, or it is degraded by the plant.

Sheets *et al.* (15) studied the persistence of dichlobenil in different roles, and found that the herbicide was most persistent in the clay. Small amounts of 2,6-dichlorobenzoic acid, a product of dichlobenil degradation, were detected in soil from greenhouse pot cultures about 9 months after incorporation of dichlobenil. In a field experiment, residues of dichlobenil persisted from one season to the next, but did not build up in soil sprayed annually for 3 years. In the work of Miller *et al.* (12) low concentrations of dichlobenil and traces of 2,6-dichlorobenzoic acid were found in soil samples taken from cranberry bogs approximately one and two years after application. Barnsley and Rosher (2) found that residues of soil-incorporated dichlobenil persisted for at least 105 days. They concluded that volatilization accounted for a rapid loss of the herbicide from the soil surface and that dichlobenil was slowly degraded by soil microorganisms.

Frank and Comes (6) determined herbicide residues in water and hydrosoil in ponds treated with dichlobenil at a concentration of 0.58 ppm. Relatively high concentrations of dichlobenil (10.65 ppm) were present in the upper one inch of the hydrosoil one day after treatment. The herbicide persisted in both water and mud for periods exceeding 160 days. Van Valin (20) and Cope *et al.* (4) studied the persistence of dichlobenil in ponds in Denver, Colorado and Tishomingo, Oklahoma. A 4% granular formulation applied to a farm pond in Denver at the rate of 10 lb/A or 0.6 ppm active ingredient produced highest residues in water and fish about 2 weeks following treatment, whereas pond mud had the highest level in 1 or 2 days. Thereafter, the decline in the herbicide concentration was gradual and the residues were measurable after 168 days. The highest concentration (500 ppm) measured in algae was in the sample taken one day after treatment. With the next 7 days, the residue level in algae dropped to about 25 ppm followed by a gradual drop in herbicide concentration. In Tishomingo ponds treated with a wettable formulation at rates of 10, 20, and 40 ppm, residues in water and fish were highest within 3 days after treatment. Dissipation of the herbicide was rapid, with only about 3% of the herbicide remaining after 11 days; none was found at 85 days. Dichlobenil was present in pond mud after 312 days at Tishomingo and after 166 days at Denver.

HERBICIDAL EFFECTS

Soybeans were noticeably stunted and malformed within 10 days after treatment with dichlobenil in the irrigation waters particularly at concentrations of 1.0 or 10.0 ppmv (3). The concentration of 0.1 ppmw injured soybeans visibly in the 1962 experiment but not in the 1963 experiment. Actually, such treatments appeared to stimulate the foliar growth of soybeans in 1963.

Within 30 days after treatment with dichlobenil at 10.0 ppmw, there was an increase in stunting, malformation, and desiccation, and 2 percent of the plants were dead. At comparable rates of application, dichlobenil injury to soybeans was similar in nature to fenac injury but less severe.

By harvest time, the soybeans had recovered markedly, especially on plots treated with dichlobenil at 0.1 or 1.0 ppmw. Treatments at 0.1 or 1.0 ppmw did not reduce yields in terms of bushels per acre or weight per 100 seeds (table 1). However, maturity was delayed somewhat by such treatments in 1962, and some seeds were wrinkled and discolored. Treatments at 10.0 ppmw significantly reduced quality but not the yield of soybeans.

Corn apparently was more tolerant than soybeans to dichlobenil. Generally, treatments at 1.0 or 10.0 ppmw caused only slight stunting of corn. A few plants, scattered throughout the plots, were more severely injured. Such injury was characterized by a pronounced crimpling of the leaf blades, a discoloration (yellow to dark blue or purple), a curling or rolling of the leaf apices at the onset of desiccation, or twisting of the leaves into rather compact rolls. No plants were killed, and injured plants recovered rapidly. None of the treatments reduced the quality or yield of shelled corn (table 1).

Sugarbeets treated at 0.1 or 1.0 ppmw were not visibly injured and were not reduced.

Difficulties were encountered in attempting to analyze residues of dichlobenil in soybean samples, and no reliable residue data for soybeans were obtained. Within the limits of detection, no dichlobenil or 2,6-DCBA residues were found in any of the corn of sugarbeet samples from the treated and untreated plots.

Alfalfa appeared less tolerant than sugarbeets in dichlobenil. Although dichlobenil at 0.1 or 1.0 ppmw did not reduce the yields of alfalfa, the treatment at 10.0 ppmv decreased yields considerably in 1963 (table 2). Alfalfa yields were normal on all plots in 1964, the year following the treatment.

In summary, applications of dichlobenil at 0.1 or 1.0 ppmw injured young soybeans and reduced seed quality in at least one experiment, but did not reduce seed yields in either experiment. Similar applications apparently did not affect sugarbeets or field corn. Dichlobenil at 10.0 ppmw killed 2 percent of the plants and reduced the yield of soybeans, but did not reduce the yield of corn.

ENVIRONMENTAL EFFECTS

Uptake and metabolism of ^{14}C-dochlobenil (2,6-dichlorobenzonitrile) by a susceptible aquatic plant alligatorweed **(Alternanthera philoxeroides)** and a tolerant aquatic plant parrotfeather **(Myriophyllum brasiliense)** was investigated (18). Both plants absorbed the herbicide from nutrient solution through the roots and translocated it to the shoots. Maximum absorption of dichlobenil occurred in parrotfeather in the first 48 hours though the plant continued to absorb the herbicide up to 6 days after treatment. After 7 days of uptake, more than 80% of the ^{14}C in parrotfeather was present in the form of dichlobenil metabolites. A major portion of the ^{14}C in the metabolite fraction both in the roots and shoots was in the form of 3-and/or 4-hydroxydichlorobenzonitrile. Small amounts of 2,6-dichlorobenzoic acid and 2,6-dichlorobenzamide were also detected. A significant amount of unknown ^{14}C-compound(s) was present in the aqueous phase remaining after fractional extraction with ether. Neither the ^{14}C-dichlobenil nor its metabolites leaked out of the roots of parrotfeather.

Alligatorweed continued to absorb ^{14}C-dichlobenil from the solution up to 24 hours after treatment after which the concentration of ^{14}C in the plant decreased. Alligatorweed did not appear to metabolize the herbicide. A significant proportion of unaltered ^{14}C-dichlobenil was released from the roots of preloaded alligatorweed indicating that the herbicide had possibly altered the cell permeability. Changes in the cell permeability of alligatorweed in the presence of dichlobenil and its inability to metabolize the herbicide may explain why alligatorweed is more sensitive to dichlobenil than parrotfeather.

Hydroxylated derivatives of dichlobenil have been reported to inhibit photo and oxidative phosphorylation more effectively than the parent herbicide, suggesting that if conjugation of these metabolites is delayed, photo synthesis and respiration are more effectively inhibited (6).

When dichlobenil was applied to water cress **(Rorippa nasturtium-aquaticum** L. Hayek), chromatography indicated the presence of the 3-OH and 4-OH analogs in roots and 2,6-dichlorobenzamide (2,6-BAM) in the stems. The 3-OH and 4-OH compounds seemed to be present in stems and roots of narrowleafed water parsnip **(Berula erecta** Huds. Coville) and 2,6-BAM possibly present in **B. erecta** leaves. The 3-OH and 4-OH metabolites were present in all regions of reedgrass **(Phragmites communis** Trin.) (11).

HEALTH EFFECTS

The acute oral LD_{50} of dichlobenil is 4500 mg/kg for rats, 2100 mg/kg for mice, and 270 mg/kg for rabbits (19). In rats given a lethal dose, the liver and kidneys showed signs of damage. In rabbits the main effect was liver necrosis, and they died at 12 to 24 hours after administration of the chemical (19). When given in the diet of rats for two weeks at 200 ppm, dichlobenil did not induce microsomal drug-metabolizing enzymes in the liver (16).

Ten male and ten female rats were fed dichlobenil at 5000 ppm for 71 days, then half were killed for study and half were put on normal diet. Histopathology and liver function tests returned to normal during eight days on normal diet (19). This means that the maximum tolerated dose for chronic experiments is at least 5000 ppm in the rat.

Dichlobenil is relatively non-toxic to fish and fish-food organisms and is therefore a relatively "safe" aquatic herbicide from the standpoint of aquatic ecology. The acute toxicity as summarized in table 3, ranges from a tolerance of 10 to 6000 ppm per liter.

Dichlobenil is rapidly absorbed in animals and is mostly excreted in the urine within four days, entirely in the form of metabolites.

The metabolites found in hydrolyzed rat urine include:

(a) 2,6-dichloro-3-hydroxybenzonitrile
(b) 2,6-dichloro-4-hydroxybenzonitrile
(c) 2,6-dichlorobenzamide (BAM)
(d) 2,6-dichlorobenzoic acid
(e) 2,6-dichloro-3-hydroxybenzoic acid
(f) 2,6-dichloro-4-hydroxybenzoic acid
(g) six polar constituents of which two are sulfur-containing amino acids

In agreement with the known behavior of other arylnitriles, no evidence was found for the formation of hydrogen cyanide from dichlobenil (7).

Dichlobenil is highly lipophilic and insoluble in water (23). From a water suspension of dichlobenil fed to rats, 50% was found in the feces, demonstrating that lipid is necessary for the absorption of the chemical.

Metabolites (a) 32-hydroxydichlobenil and (b) 4-hydroxydichlobenil which constitute over 40% of excreted dichlobenil, are phenols related to the well-known uncoupler of oxidative phosphorylation, 2/4dinitrophenol, and are expected to have a similar effect on mitochondria. The 3-hydroxy compound, to which over 40% of the herbicide is metabolized, is only 1/3 as active in as is the 4-hydroxy analogue (18). It was reported that the LD_{50} of these metabolites is about 1400 mg/kg.

Dichlobenil was tested for its ability to induce point mutations (base substitution, deletion, or addition) in three different microbial systems: reversion of eight different histidine mutants of **Salmonella typhimurium**, forward mutation of phage T_4, and reversion of rII mutants of T_4. It was negative in all of these assays (1). Another series of microbial tests, in three different species of bacteria, was also negative (13).

Dichlobenil and its metabolites (c, BAM) and (d) are not uncoupling agents (24). The metabolite called BAM has been most extensively tested, although it is a minor metabolite. Its oral LD_{50} for rats if 1470 mg/kg for males and 2330 mg/kg for females. A 90-day feeding experiment in rats at 50, 180, 600, and 2300 ppm showed toxic effects at the two highest doses. BAM was fed to rats at 60, 100, and 180 ppm for three generations. 180 ppm produced toxic effects (no data and no description) while the lower doses produced effects of doubtful significance. BAM was fed to rats for two years at 60, 100, 180, and 500 ppm. The highest level was associated with marginal toxic effects not including tumor formation. A similar two-year experiment using dogs gave similar results.

SUMMARY AND CONCLUSIONS

Dichlobenil is a nonselective herbicide that controls both annual and perennial grass, and broadleaf weeds—is absorbed by the seeds and epidermis of the shoots. It is a powerful inhibitor of germination and of actively dividing meristems, and acts primarily on growing points and root tips. The chemical is useful for aquatic weed control, ornamental bermuda grass, ornamental plants and trees, and shelterbelts. It should not be used if the air temperature is expected to go above 70° F. within a week. It is long lasting, and seeding or transplanting in treated soil should be delayed for 24 months after treatment.

Dichlobenil (Casoron G-10^R granules should be applied at a rate 7-10 lb. ai (70-100 lb. G-10)/surface A in the early spring before weeds start growing. Weeds controlled are Elodea, northern watermilfoil, naiad, coontail, Chara, pondweeds (*Potamogeton spp.*) and alligatorweed (**Alternanthera philoxeroides**).

REFERENCES

1. Andersen, Kenneth J., Edith G. Leighty, and Mark T. Takahashi. 1972. Evaluation of herbicides for possible mutagenic properties. J. Agr. Food Chem. *20,* 649-656.
2. Barnsley, G.E. and P.H. Rosher. 1961. The relationship between the herbicidal effect of 2,6-dichlorobenzonitrile and its persistence in the soil. Weed Res. 1:147-158.

3. Bruns, V.F., J.M. Hodson and H.F. Arle. 1972. Technical Bulletin No. 1461, U.S. Dept. of Agriculture.

4. Cope, Oliver B., J.P. McCraren and L. Eller. 1969. Effects of dichlobenil on two fish pond environments. 17:158-165.

5. Folmar, L.C. 1977. 1977 Technical paper NO 88, U.S. Fish and Wildlife Service, Denver, Colorado.

6. Frank, P.A. and R.D. Comes. 1967. Herbicide residues in pond water and hydrosoil. Weeds 15:210-213.

7. Griffiths, M.H., Moss, J.A., Rose, J.A., and Hathway, D.E. 1966. The Comparative metabolism of 2,6-Dichlorothiobenzamide (BAM) and 2,6-Dichlorobenzonitrile in the Dog and Rat. Biochem. J. *98*, 770-781.

8. Hatzios, K.K. and Donald Penner. 1982. Metabolism of Herbicides in Higher Plants. Burgess Publishing Co., Minneapolis, Minnesota.

9. Kearney, P.C. and D.D. Kanfman (Ed.). 1969. Degradation of herbicides. Marcel Dekker, Inc., New York 294 p.

10. Massini, P. 1961. Movement of 2,6-dichlorobenzonitrile in soils and in plants in relation to its physical properties. Weed Res. 1:142-146.

11. Mottley, J., and R.C. Kirkwood. 1978. The uptake, translocation and metabolism of dichlobenil in selected aquatic species. Weed Res., 18:187-198.

12. Miller, C.W., L.E. Demoranville, and A.J. Charig. 1966. Persistence of dichlobenil in cranberry bogs. Weeds 14:296-298.

13. Pate, D.A. and H.H. Funderburk. 1966. Absorption, translocation and metabolism of ¹⁴C-labeled dichlobenil. Proc. Symp. Use Isotopes Weed Res., Vienna, 17-25.

14. Price, H.C. and A.R. Putnam. 1969. Efflux of dichlobenil from shoots and roots. J. Ag. Food Chem. 17:135-137.

15. Sheets, T.J., C.L. Harris and J.W. Smith. 1968. Persistence of dichlobenil and SD-7961 in soil. Weed Sci. 16:245-249.

16. Shirasu, Y., M. Moriya, Y. Kato, A. Furuhashi and T. Kada. 1976. Mutagenicity Screening of Pesticides in the Microbial System. Mutation Research *40*, 19-30.

17. Siebert, D. and E. Lemperle. 1974. Genetic effects of herbicide: induction of mitotic gene conversion in **Saccharomyces cerevisiae.** Mutation Research *22*, 111-120.

18. Sikka, H.C., Robert S. Lynch and Margaret Lindburger. 1974. Uptake and metabolism of dichlobenil by emersed aquatic plants. J. Agr. Food Chem. 22:230-234.

19. Van Genderen, H., and G.J. Van Esch. 1968. Toxicology of the herbicide dichlobenil (2,6-Dichlorobenzonitrile) and its main metabolites. Fd. Cosmet. Toxicol. *6*, 261-269.

20. Van Valin, Charles C. 1966. Persistence of 2,6-dichlorobenzonitrile in aquatic environments. Adv. in Chem. Series 60:271-279.

21. Verloop, A. and W.B. Nimmo. 1966. Proc. Symp. use of isotopes on weed research. Vienna. SM 69/12.
22. Walker, Charles R. 1964. Dichlobenil as a herbicide in fish habitats. Weeds 12:267-269.
23. Wit, J.G. and H. Van Genderen. 1966b. Metabolism of the Herbicide 2,6-Dichlorobenzonitrile in Rabbits and Rats. Biochem J. *101*, 898-706.
24. Wit, J.G. and H. Van Genderen. 1966b. The monophenolic metabolites of the herbicide 2,6-Dichlorobenzonitrile in animals as uncouplers of oxidative phosphorylation. Biochem. J. *101*, 707-710.

Table 1. Effect on yields of soybeans, field corn, and sugarbeets of applying dichlobenil in irrigation water in Washington.

Date and dichlobenil concentration(1)	Soybeans (2)			Field Corn	Sugarbeets (2)	
	Seed yield per acre	Weight per 100 seeds	Seed Quality	Seed yield per acre(2)	Roots per acre	Root yield per acre
	Bushels	Grams		Bushels	Number	Tons
June 18-19, 1962:						
No chemical (check)	39.1ab	15.2a	Good	100.2a	...	...
0.1 p.p.m.w. (0.045 lb./acre)	45.9a	14.6ab	Fair	96.8a	...	...
1.0 p.p.m.w. (0.45 lb./acre)	37.4ab	15.5a	Fair	86.0a	...	...
10.0 p.p.m.w. (4.5 lb./acre)	29.1 b	13.5 b	Fair	100.6a	...	...
June 12-14, 1963:						
No chemical (check)	37.3a	......	Good	177.5a	28,520a	30.4a
0.1 p.p.m.w. (0.045 lb./acre)	37.8a	......	Good	201.9a	27,430a	30.8a
1.0 p.p.m.w. (0.45 lb./acre)	33.3a	......	Good	171.5a	25,980a	27.8a

[1] Applied in 2 acre-inches of water by furrow irrigation at Prosser, Wash., during 1962 and 1963. See table 1 for stage of growth of various crops on given dates.

[2] Any 2 figures in the same column and year that are not followed by the same letter are significantly different at the 5-percent level of probability, as determined by Duncan's multiple-range test.

From: Bruns, V.F., J.M. Hodson and H.F. Arle. 1972. Technical Bulletin No. 1461, U.S. Dept. of Agriculture.

Table 2. Effect on yields of alfalfa of applying sodium salt of fenac, dichlobenil, or disodium salt of endothall in irrigation water in Montana

Chemical (1)	Application data		Yield of alfalfa per acre(2)	
	Concentra- tion	Rate per acre	1963	1964
	p.p.m.w.	Pounds	Tons	
None			1.82a	3.53a
Fenac.....	0.1	0.04	1.77a	3.58a
Do......	1.0	0.45	1.55 b	3.27a
Do......	10.0	4.56	.81 d	1.22 b
Dichlobenil	0.1	0.04	1.68ab	3.58a
Do......	1.0	0.45	1.73ab	3.49a
Do......	10.0	4.56	1.33 c	3.67a
Endothall .	10.0	4.56	1.72ab	3.64a

[1] Applied in 1.79 acre-inches of water by furrow irrigation at Bozeman, Mont., on July 12, 1963, when plants averaged 8 leaves each.
[2] Any two figures that are not followed by the same letter are significantly different at the 5-percent level of probability, as determined by Duncan's multiple-range test.
From: Bruns, V.F., J.M. Hodson and H.F. Arle. 1972. Technical Bulletin No. 1461, U.S. Dept. of Agriculture.

Table 3. Dicholbenil: toxicity to aquatic organisms.

Organism	Type of test	Experimental conditions	Toxicity	Reference
Simocephalus serrulatus	L,ST,A	a,b,c,e	$5,800 IC_{50}$(48 h)	Sanders and Cope (1966)
S. Serrulatus	L,ST,A	a	$5,800 EC_{50}$(48 h)	Cope (1966)
Tendipedidae	L,ST,A	a,b,c,d,e	15.7 T(24 h)	Wilson and Bond (1969)
			12.5 T(48 h)	
			7.8 T(96 H)	
Pteronarcys californica	L,ST,A	a	$8,400 EC_{50}$(48 h)	Cope (1966)
Daphnia magna	L,ST,A	a,b,c,d,e,f	$9.8 IC_{50}$(26 h)	Crosby and Tucker (166)
D. pulex	L,ST,A	a,b,c,d,e	$3,700 IC_{50}$(48 h)	Sanders and Cope (1966)
D. pulex	L,ST,A	a	$3,700 EC_{50}$(48 h)	Cope (1966)
Cardium edule	L,ST,A	—	7,100 T(24 h)	Portmann and Wilson (1961)
Carcinus maenas	L,ST,A	—	10.0 T(2424 h)	Portmann and Wilson (1971)
Crangon crangon	L,ST,A	—	3.3-10.0 T(24 h)	Portmann and Wilson (1971)
Rasbora heteromorpha	L,ST,A	a,b,c,d,e	7.2 T(24 h)	Alabaster (1969)
			6.0 T(48 h)	
R. heteromorpha	L,ST,A	a,b,c,d,e	14.5 T(24 h)	Tooby(1971)
			12.3 T(48 h)	
Lepomis macrochirus	L,ST,A	a,b,c,d,e,f	20.0 T(48 h)	Crosby and Tucker (1966)
L. macrochirus	L,ST,A	a	$20,000 EC_{50}$(48)	Cope(1966)
Lepomis spp.	L,ST,A	a,b,c,d,e	10,20.0 T(96 h)	Walker(1964)
Morone saxatilis	L,ST,A	a,b,c,d,e	6,200 T(96 h)	Wellborn(1971)

Table 3. Dicholbenil: toxicity to aquatic organisms. (cont.)

Organism	Type of test	Experimental conditions	Toxicity	Reference
Salmo gairdneri	L,ST,A	a	22,000 EC$_{50}$(48 h)	Cope(1966)
S. gairdneri	L,ST,A	a,b,c,d,e,f	22.0 T(48 h)	Crosby and Tucker(1966)
Pteronarcys californica	L,ST,A	a,b,c,d,e	42.0 T(24 h)[a]	Sanders and Cope(1968)
			8.4 T(48 h)	
			7.0 T(96 h)	
Limnephilus spp.	L,ST,A	a,b,c,d,e	28.2 T(24 h)[e]	Wilson and Bond (1969)
			23.3 T(48 h)	
			13.0 T(96 h)	
Callibaetis spp.	L,ST,A	a,b,c,d,e	19.2 T(24 h)[e]	Wilson and Bond(1969)
			15.2 T(48 h)	
			10.3 T(96 h)	
Daphnia magna	—	—	10.0 T[a]	Taylor(1966 a,b)
Enallagma spp.	L,ST,A	a,b,c,d,e	25.5 T(24 h)[e]	Wilson and Bond(1969)
			24.2 T(48 h)	
			20.7 T(96 h)	
Libellula spp.	L,ST,A	a,b,c,d,e	<100 T(24 h)[e]	Wilson and Bond(1969)
			<100 T(48 h)	
			<100 T(96 h)	

Table 3. Dicholbenil: toxicity to aquatic organisms. (cont.)

Organism	Type of test	Experimental conditions	Toxicity	Reference
Hyalella azeteca	L,ST,A	a,b,c,e	18.8 T(24 h)[a] 12.5 T(48 h) 8.5 T(96 h)	Wilson and Bond(1969)
Unnamed fish	—	—	15-30.0 T(96 h)[a]	Taylor(1966 a,b)
Lepomis macrochirus (fry)	L,ST,A	—	10.0 NTE (12 d)[a]	Hiltibran(1967)
L. macrochirus	L,ST,A	a,b,c,e	37.0 T(24 h)[a] 30.0 T(48 h)	Hughes and Davis(1965)
L. cyanellus	L,ST,A	—	25.0 NTE (12 d)[a]	Hiltibran(1967)
Micropterus dolomieui (fry)	L,ST,A	—	25.0 NTE (12 d)[a]	Hiltibran(1967)
Orconectes nais	L,ST,A	a,b,c,d,e	22.0 T(48 h)[b]	Sanders(1970)
Cypridopsis vidua	L,ST,A	a,b,c,d,e	7.8 T(48 h)[b]	Sanders(1970)
Asellus brevicaudus	L,ST,A	a,b,c,d,e	34.0 T(48 h)[b]	Sanders(1970)
Daphnia magna	L,ST,A	a,b,c,d,e	10.0 T(48 h)[b]	Sanders(1970)
Gammarus lacustris	L,ST,A	a,b,c,d,e	16,000 T(24 h)[b] 15,000 T(48 h) 11,000 T(96 h)	Sanders(1969)
G. fasciatus	L,ST,A	a,b,c,d,e	18.0 T(48 h)[b]	Sanders(1970)
Palamonetes kadiakensis	L,ST,A	a,b,c,d,e	9.0 T(48 h)[b]	Sanders (1970)
Lepomis macrochirus	FO	a,b,c,d,e	20.0-40.0 SB[b]	Cope et al.(1969)

Table 3. Dicholbenil: toxicity to aquatic organisms. (cont.)

Organism	Type of test	Experimental conditions	Toxicity	Reference
L. macrochirus	L,ST,A	a,b,c,de	17.0 T(24 h)[b] 17.0 T(48 h)	Hughes and Davis(1962)
L. macrochirus	L,ST,A	a,b,c,d,e	17.0 T(24 h)[c] 17.0 T(48 h)	Hughes and Davis (1965)

From: Folmar, L.C. 1977. Technical paper NO 88, U.S. Fish and Wildlife Service, Denver, Colorado.

Table 3. Dicholbenil: toxicity to aquatic organisms. (cont.)

1. Type of test, letters represent:
   T = Toxicity test, used in conjunction with
      ST = static
     CFT = continuous flow
       A = acute
       C = chronic
   L = Laboratory toxicity test
   F = Field study, used in conjunction with
       R = river, stream, or creek
       M = marine
       E = estuarine, and
       O = other
2. Experimental conditions. Factors reported in cited articles:
   a = water temperature
   b = pH
   c = alkalinity
   d = dissolved oxygen
   e = dissolved solids
   f = photoperiod
3. Toxicity, active ingredient. All values in mg/l (ppm) unless
   otherwise noted. Letters included with numerical values
   represent:
      T = LC_{50} (also accompanied by a time factor, e.g., 96 h)
      K = Kill
    SB = Sublethal effects
   NTE = No toxic effect
      a = Granular formulation
      b = Wettable power formulation
      c = Liquid formulation

PART II

EVALUATION OF SELECTED AQUATIC HERBICIDES

CHAPTER 9. HERBICIDAL, ENVIRONMENTAL AND HEALTH EFFECTS OF 2,4-D

Chapter 9

HERBICIDAL, ENVIRONMENTAL AND HEALTH EFFECTS OF 2,4-D[1]

INTRODUCTION

The herbicide 2,4-D was prepared in 1941 by the interaction of 2,4-dichlorophenol, monochloroacetic acid and sodium hydroxide, and a similar process is used in its commercial production. 2,4-D is a systemic herbicide widely used for control of broadleaf weeds in cereal crops and sugar cane, and on turf, pastures and non-cropland. It is also used to control the ripening of bananas and cirtus fruits, and to delay preharvest dropping of some fruits and to control aquatic weeds in ponds, lakes, reservoirs, marshes, bayous, drainage ditches, canals, rivers and streams that are quiescent or slow moving.

The herbicides 2,4-D is predominantly toxic to green plants and are much less toxic to mammals, birds, fish, reptiles, shellfish, insects, worms, fungi and bacteria. When properly used, it does not persist in the environment at levels harmful to animals and aquatic organisms. It does not concentrate in food chains and is detectable only rarely in food. and then only in insignificant amounts.

The principal hazard in the use of the 2,4-D is to crops and other valuable plants either within the treated area or nearby. Treated crops can be injured through accidental overdosing, improper timing of treatments, unusual weather conditions and other causes. Injury to nearby crops and ornamentals can result from drift of droplets or vapors of the spray. Such losses are largely preventable through the use of proper formulations and spray equipment and the exercise of good judgment. Commercial products of American manufacture have had excellent quality control due to special "secrets of the trade".

HERBICIDAL EFFECTS

Various derivatives of 2,4-dichlorophenoxyacetic acid (2,4-D) are used to control aquatic vegetation. The most commonly used derivatives are esters, such as the butoxyethanol and isooctyl esters. Less frequently used are the sodium potassium and lithium salts of 2,4-D

---

[1] The findings in this report are not to be construed as an official Department of the Army position unless so designated by other authorized documents.

and the amine salts, such as the dimethylamine salt are most frequently used. Granular or pelleted formulations of 2,4-D esters are distributed uniformly over the water surface with little or no drift effects. Detailed studies have been made on the efficacy of 2,4-D application for control of aquatic weeds (6,7,9,10,27,28,38,41). Weed species controlled are given in Table 1.

ENVIRONMENTAL EFFECTS

The toxicity of 2,4-D to fish is variable. The ester derivatives as a group are the most toxic. However, the formulating components are an important factor in acute toxicity to fish. Under field conditions, toxicity at maximum recommended rates has seldom if ever been observed and can be avoided with proper precautions. Any adverse effects on the aquatic environment are primarily the result of habitat modification.

Aquatic Weed Control in Ponds

The widespread occurrence and uncontrolled growth of various aquatic plants, especially in the southeastern United States, has caused many proglems including interference with navigation, obstructed water flow, lowered real estate values, reduced fishing success, and impaired recreational use. Experiments were designed to determine the residue levels and rate of dissipation of the dimethylamine salt of 2,4-D in water, hydrosoil, and fish from ponds treated at 2.24, 4.48, or 8.96 kg 2,4-D acid equivalent per ha (2,4, or 8 lb acid equivalent per acre for control of waterhyacinth (54,55,56).

These applications are one-half, one and two times the recommended treatment rate. Ponds were located in two widely separated geographical locations to study the effects that different physical and chemical characteristics of the aquatic environment might have on the uptake and dissipation of the herbicide. The results of these studies of ponds in Florida and Georgia and the summary of treatment means for rates of applications and days after treatment are given in Table 2.

The effect of the 2,4-D application on waterhyacinth in the Florida and Georgia ponds was assessed by visual observation. Seven days after spraying, nearly all of the waterhyacinth in all ponds were brown and decomposing. An estimated 98% of the plants were killed by the herbicide application, with no differences in kill noted among the different treatment levels. Since all three treatment levels of the herbicide were equally effective, it would be best to use the lowest effective concentration (2.24 kg *ae*/ha) although retreatment may be necessary in some spots to prevent reinfestation.

The highest amount of 2,4-D residue in Florida pond water was 0.345 mg/l found 3 days after treatment in the pond treated at 8.96 kg/ha (8 lb/A). Residue levels of 2,4-D found in Florida ponds decreased to 0.005 mg/l within 14 days after treatment. In Georgia pond water the highest detectable residue was 0.692 mg/l 3 days after treatment at 9.96 kg/ha. Only trace levels or no residues were detected 14 days after treatment. The highest 2,4-D residue detected in hydrosoil from Florida ponds was 0.046 mg/kg found 3 days after treatment at 8.96 kg/ha. In the Georgia ponds, the highest residue found was 0.042 mg/kg on the seventh day after treatment at 8.96 kg/ha. The highest residues found in any fish were samples from the 1-day harvest from ponds in Florida. These fish had an average of 0.029 mg/kg (ppm) of 2,4-D (54,55,56).

Aquatic Weed Control in St. Johns River, Florida

The St. Johns River originates in an extensive marsh near Vero Beach, Florida and flows northward approximately 312 miles (502 km) through a series of lakes to Jacksonville and then eastward to the Atlantic Ocean. The topographic drainage area of the river is 9,430 mi^2 (24,424 km^2) of which the flood plain contains an open water area of more than 300 mi^2 (777 km^2) during seasonal low water periods.

The Jacksonville District along with various State and local agencies conducts waterhyacinth control operations throughout the St. Johns River Basin, using the most economical and efficient method of control available which is chemical spray treatment with the dimethylamine salt of 2,4-D.

Prior to the registration of 2,4-D for use in flowing and potable waters by the Environmental Protection Agency (EPA), public concern was expressed over environmental effects resulting from its use in the St. Johns River. As a result, on 4 December 1973, the EPA directed the U.S. Army Corps of Engineers to discontinue the use of any product containing 2,4-D which was not specifically labeled for use in flowing waters. All waterhyacinth control operations in the St. Johns River ceased since none of the available 2,4-D products were specifically registered by EPA for use in flowing waters. In the absence of control operations, plant populations increased to problem proportions. In order to preclude major economic and environmental damage attributable to massive hyacinth infestations the Corps requested a specific exemption from EPA so that control efforts could resume. EPA granted such an exemption on 2 May 1974 and control operations began shortly thereafter.

During chemical control operations on waterhyacinth water samples and blue crabs (**Callinectes sapidus** Rathbun) were collected along the river course. The herbicide residues in water and blue crabs are summarized in Table 3. Levels of 2,4-D observed were well below established tolerance limits and exhibited no apparent accumulation from the amount of 2,4-D applied during routine waterhyacinth control operations in flowing waters (42).

Weed Control in Robert S. Kerr Reservoir

In 1977, the U.S. Department of the Army, Corps of Engineers (COE), Tulsa District, requested the Oklahoma Water Resources Board (OWRB) to conduct a chemical monitoring program on Robert S. Kerr Reservoir in conjunction with their Aquatic Plant Control Program. The COE is concerned about the infestations of an aquatic plant, Eurasian watermilfoil (**Myriophyllum spicatum** L.), in the Reservoir due to the problems this plant causes for the Tennessee Valley Authority (58,61). The main purpose of OWRB's involvement in 1977 was to detect any violation of water quality standards from the herbicide butoxyethanol ester of 2,4-dichlorophenoxy acetic acid (BEE 2,4-D).

The OWRB's Water Quality Division performed the chemical monitoring in 1977 and submitted a report to the COE. In 1977 five sites were treated, approximately 158.1 ha, with BEE 2,4-D. At these sites temperature, dissolved oxygen, pH, conductivity, two forms of nitrogen and phosphorus, and BEE 2,4-D were monitored. From 39 water samples collected, the herbicide was detected only once in the Little San Bois Creek area.

The program was expanded in 1978 involved monitoring ten sites, two of which were controls. The objectives were to compare water quality data (mainly nutrients) collected from the treated areas with that of the controls, and the pretreatment data compared to post treatment data. Since this reservoir is shallow and is considered generally homothermic, the water quality of the coves and associated drainages were assumed to be closely related.

The major results included significant increases in total phosphorus concentrations at three sites and a significant decrease in ammonia nitrogen at one site after treatment. 2,4-dichlorophenol which was of major concern in the study was never detected. In summary, Oklahoma's Water Quality Standards were not violated (48).

Metabolism of 2,4-D in Fish

Schultz (54) demonstrated that fish exposed to the dimethylamine salt of uniformly ring-labeled 2,4-dichloro [^{14}C]phenoxyacetic acid (DMA-^{14}C-2,4-D) in plastic pools contained ^{14}C residues in their tissues. Further, these ^{14}C residues increased throughout the 12-week exposure and did not appear to reach an asymptote. Yet, gas chromatographic (GC) analyses of these tissues revealed only negligible amounts of 2,4-D and he suggested that metabolism or degradation of 2,4-D had occurred. Also, 2,4-D residues in water and hydrosoil from the plastic pools decreased rapidly during the exposure period. Microbial degradation of 2,4-D in water and hydrosoil was presumed to be a primary factor in the disappearance of the parent molecule.

The objectives of the present investigation were to confirm the existence of [^{14}C]2,4-D degradation products in fish and in water and identify and ^{14}C residues in fish tissues. Two plastic lined pools with and without fish, were used in the study (59).

Water Analysis.   Radioactivity in the two pools declined during the 84 days after treatment, but at different rates. After 84 days, the pool without fish contained only 16% of the original radioactivity applied, and 89% of this activity was ^{14}CO$_2$. Water in the pool with fish had 49% of the initial radioactivity after 84 days, but did not contain detectable ^{14}CO$_2$. Examination of non-CO$_2$ radioactivity in water from both pools by GC-RAM, GC-MS, GC-MS, and TLC during the exposure revealed only [^{14}C]2,4-D (59).

During the latter part of the test period, the pool with the fish contained a heavy algal bloom which was not present in the control pool. The pH of 84-day water samples from the control pool and the pool with fish averaged 8.4 and 9.8, respectively. Presence of the algal bloom in the pool with fish was probably responsible for the observed high pH. Since biological and chemical differences existed in the two pools, the populations of microorganisms established were probable different.

Tissues Analysis.   Radioactive residues were accumulated in both head-viscera and fillets, a finding which concurred with that of Schultz (54). The ^{14}C residues in head-viscera and fillets continued to increase throughout the duration of the experiment. However, we did not detect [^{14}C]2,4-D (detection limit 0.1 ug/g) in fish tissues. More ^{14}C residues were found in samples of head and viscera than in fillets.

The incorporation of ^{14}C in fatty acids hydrolyzed neutral lipids was confirmed by using the GC-TRAP. A 84-day head-viscera sample, which contained 2200 cpm/g of tissue (total activity), was selected for analysis by this method. Significant radioactivity (924 cpm/g of tissue) was extractable with 1% phosphoric acid in methanol. The neutral lipid fraction represented 16% of the total radioactivity in the sample. The percentage of radioactivity detected in individual methyl esters of fatty acids liberated from the neutral lipids ranged from 12 to 31% of all the activity present in neutral lipid fractions. Radioactivity was detected in all methyl esters, however, C16:0-C16:1 and C18:0-C18:1 eluted as ester pairs.

Methyl linolenate (C18:3) had the highest specific activity and contained 31% of the activity found in the original neutral lipid fraction, but this ester constituted only 4% of all the esters, based on GC-FID relative peak height. The radioactivity associated with all the methyl esters from neutral lipids was 13 cpm/mg.

In addition, ^{14}C was detected in hlycogen, which was isolated from a fish liver extract. The biochemical synthesis of ^{14}C amino acids and their subsequent incorporation into proteins is inferred. The incorporation of ^{14}C in fatty acids, glycogen, and protein materials accounted for 85% of the ^{14}C activity in the samples. Also, $^{14}CO_2$ was identified as a degradation product of ring-labeled DMA-^{14}C-2,4-D in a similarly treated plastic pool containing no fish (59). These results were confirmed by Sikka, et al. (57).

Effect of 2,4-D in Irrigation Water on Crops

2,4-dichlorophenoxyacetic acid (2,4-D) undoubtedly is used more widely for broadleaved weed control along irrigation and drainage systems and around lakes and reservoirs than any other herbicide. It is extremely difficult to spray weeds on the banks of such systems and impoundments with 2,4-D without introducing some of the material into the water. The use of such water to irrigate crops then poses two major questions: (A) What effect will the 2,4-D in irrigation water, far beyond those which might reach farm lands through waters from ditchbank spraying, and (B) would it injure young grapes to any degree. According to Frank, Demint, and Comes (37), treatment of canal banks with 2,4-D at 2.24 to 3.36 ac kg/ha resulted in maximum concentrations of only 0.025 to 0.061 ppm in the water.

Investigations of herbicides in water and crops irrigated with water containing herbicides were conducted at the Stanford Research Institute. During the course of the investigation, six herbicides and six crops were studied under carefully controlled greenhouse conditions to determine the extent to which edible portions of these crops accumulated residues of herbicides and their metabolities. The dimethylamine salt of 2,4-D was included in the studies and applied at two different rates at two different stages of crop maturity. All crops were kept frozen at approximately 0°F between the time they were harvested and analyzed for residues. Crop materials analyzed were potato tubers, sorghum heads, soybeans, Romaine lettuce, carrot roots, and onion bulbs.

In general, residues were highest in Romaine lettuce, very low in sorghum and potatoes, and insignificant in soybeans, carrots and onions. Average maximum concentrations (ppm) of 2,4-D residues in the various crops irrigated with water containing the highest concentrations were as follows: potatoes—0.03 to 0.12; grain sorghum—<0.05 TO 0.12; soybeans—<0.05; carrots—0.02 to 0.06; Romaine lettuce—0.11 to 0.33; and onions—<0.01. Thus, maximum residues of 2,4-D in each crop were either non-detectable or insignificant or were much lower than FDA tolerances for several foods crops. The results were of further significance because the highest concentrations of 2,4-D applied were much greater than those found in water after normal applications for weed control along irrigation and drainage systems (9,10,15,16,17,18,19,20).

Effect of 2,4-D on Furrow-Irrigated Beans

The response of Red Mexican beans to field applications of 2,4-D at 2 and 6 pounds per acre in 3 acre-inches or irrigation water (2.21 and 6.63 ppmw, respectively) during the seedling and bloom stages of growth was studied (16).

The responses of bean plants to 2,4-D in this experiment were notably different from those normally obtained from foliage applications. The types and degrees of injury noted were: (a) leaf chlorosis; (b) dwarfing of the leaves, especially terminal leaves; (c) only minor distortion or curling of the leaves; (d) discoloration of the leaf veins; (e) thickening of the interveinal tissue with the development of leather-like texture; (f) purple pigmentation in the lower leaves; (g) severe damage to the terminal growing points; (h) excessive enlargement of stems and nodes, especially near the growing points; (i) severe injury to the root systems followed by the development of abnormal clublike adventitious roots; and, (j) general stunting of plant growth.

The application of 2.24 *ae* kg/ha of 2,4-D in irrigation water during the seedling stage caused pronounced injury to the top-growth and roots of the bean plants. Within 16 days after the application, plants began to recover and no significant reduction in yield resulted.

The rate of 6.72 *ae* kg/ha 2,4-D during the seedling stage caused severe damage to the top-growth and destroyed nearly all of the root systems of the plants. Amazingly, within 3 weeks, a number of plants began to recover with the development of club-like adventitious roots, particularly those injured less severely during the initial stages. Even though maturity was delayed, these plots yielded only 40 percent less beans than untreated checks. Laboratory and greenhouse tests exhibited no carry-over effects of 2,4-D in bean seeds harvested from treated plots.

Effect of 2,4-D on Furrow-Irrigated Sugar Beets

Applications of 2,4-D at rates of 2.24 and 6.72 *ae* kg/ha in 3 acre-inches of irrigation water (2.21 and 6.63 ppm, respectively) were lethal to a high percentage of sugar beet plants when applied at the seedling stage (17).

Only a few small plants severely injured by the initial applications of 2.24 *ae* of 2,4-D during the 1-inch diameter stage were visibly affected by a re-treatment approximately 4 weeks later. Chemical analyses of leaf and petiole samples collected during the season indicated a higher level of nitrate-nitrogen in treated than in untreated tissue beginning 6 to 12 days after treatment. The mean weight per beet and the sucrose content at harvest time were highly correlated with the final stand. These correlations as well as the observed nitrate-nitrogen differences indicate that stand differences resulting from the 2,4-D treatments were important. Wilting, chlorosis, prostration, and desiccation were the principal symptoms of 2,4-D damage. Malformation of topgrowth, a typical reaction of many species of plants to foliage applications of 2,4-D, was observed in only a few plants.

Effect of 2,4-D on Furrow-Irrigated Grapes

The rates of 2.24, 8.96, 17.92 and 35.84 ae kg/ha 13, 33, 65, and 54 percent of the plants, respectively, whereas lesser rates caused no death of plants. Roots systems of injured plants were partially or completely destroyed. Remaining portions or fragments showed varying degrees of discoloration and of tip enlargement. Depth, distribution, and development of the root systems at time of treatment apparently was an important factor in the experiment.

Herbicide Effects on Irrigated Crops

2,4-D was applied at 0.1, 0.5, and 2.5 lb/A in 2 acre-inches of water (0.22, 1.10, and 5.51 ppmw, respectively), on August 7-9 by furrow irrigation over 1 1/4-hour periods to sugar beets 3 to 5 inches in diameter, to sweet corn in the early-milk stage, and to soybeans that were about 65 percent podded (6). On August 11-17, 2,4-D was applied at 0.01, 0.1, and 1.0 lb/A in 2 acre-inches of water (0.02, 0.22, and 2.21 ppmw, respectively) by sprinkler irrigation over 8-hour periods to sugar beets 3 to 5 inches in diameter, to dwarf corn in the late-milk stage, and to soybeans that were 65 percent podded.

Effect on furrow-irrigated sugar beets. 2,4-D caused some abnormal curvature of petioles, some wilting and slumping, and some chlorosis or necrosis in sugar beets. Yields of tops or roots were not decreased significantly by any of the treatments.

Effect on furrow-irrigated soybeans. Leaf chlorosis in soybeans ranged from about 5 to 20 percent on plots furrow-irrigated with 2,4-D-treated water. However, none of the treatments decreased seed yields significantly.

Effect on furrow-irrigated sweet corn. The higher rates of 2,4-D tended to enhance the desiccation of the lower leaves of sweet corn, but none of the treatments decreased the yields of fodder or shelled corn.

Effect on sprinkler-irrigated sugar beets. 2,4-D caused only temporary drooping and wilting of the beets. Fresh weight and root yields of sugar beets were increased. Limited analyses for sugar content indicated that the 2,4-D treatments reduced percent sugar somewhat but still increased the gross sugar yields.

Effect on sprinkler-irrigated soybeans. 2,4-D suppressed growth temporarily and caused some early chlorosis. None of the other treatments injured the plants noticeably. Seed yields and quality were not reduced by any of the treatments.

Effect on sprinkler-irrigated dwarf corn. None of the 2,4-D sprinkler treatments visibly injured dwarf corn or significantly reduced the fodder or shelled corn yields.

2,4-D concentrations in furrow-irrigated soil. Apparently no significant amounts of 2,4-D were lost from the first 6 inches of soil within 7 days after treatment. The concentrations in the soil were about 10%, or less, of the concentrations applied in the water.

2,4-D concentrations in sprinkler-irrigated soil. No 2,4-D was detected in the first 6-inch layer of soil after sprinkler treatment at 0.01 lb/A (0.02 ppmw). Less than 15% of the applied concentration in water was recovered from the soil on plots treated at 0.1 and 1.0 lb/A (0.22 and 2.21 ppmw).

2,4-D residues in furrow-irrigated sugar beets. Residues were detected in beet roots 7 days after treatment at 0.5 (1.10 ppmw) and 2.5 lb/A, but none in roots from plots treated at 0.1 lb/A (0.22 ppmw).

2,4-D residues in furrow-irrigated soybeans. Seven days after treatment, soybean roots, foliage, and pods contained no detectable residues of 2,4-D on plots treated at 0.1 or 0.5 lb/A. Low levels of residues (0.009 to 0.05 ppm) were detected in such plant parts from plots treated at the high rate. At harvest time, no 2,4-D residues were detected in any plant parts except 0.09 ppm in roots (not edible) from plots treated at the high rate.

2,4-D residues in furrow-irrigated sweet corn. Detectable residues of 2,4-D accumulated in roots of corn 7 days after treatment and were still present at very low levels (0.009 to 0.07 ppm) at harvest time. The only residue detected in corn foliage was 0.08 ppm 7 days after treatment at 2.5 lb/A. No 2,4-D residues were detected in the grain at either 7 days after treatment (roasting ear stage) or at harvest time (mature, hard kernel stage).

2,4-D residues in sprinkler-irrigated sugar beets. 2,4-D residues were detected in both foliage and roots 2 days after sprinkler treatments at 0.01, 0.1, and 1.0 lb/A (0.02, 0.22, and 2.21 ppwm, respectively). The maximum concentration was 3.80 ppm in roots from plots treated at 1.0 lb/A. A residue of 0.009 ppm was still detected in roots from those plots at harvest time. However, none of the other beet foliage or roots contained detectable amounts of 2,4-D at harvest time.

2,4-D residues in sprinkler-irrigated soybeans. Some 2,4-D (0.008 to 0.52 ppm) was detected in roots, foliage, and pods of soybeans 2 days after sprinkler treatments at 0.1 and 1.0 lb/A. At the same time, only foliage contained a detectable amount of 2,4-D (0.009 ppm) after treatment at 0.01 lb/A. No 2,4-D residues were detected in any of the plant parts at harvest time except 0.02 ppm in the roots (not edible) from plots treated at 1.0 lb/A.

2,4-D residues in sprinkler-irrigated dwarf corn. 2,4-D residues in dwarf corn were similar to those in soybeans. Accumulations (0.008 to 0.51 ppm) were found in the roots, foliage, and grain 2 days after sprinkler treatment at 0.1 and 1.0 lb/A (0.22 and 2.21 ppmw). However, only the foliage contained detectable residues (0.008 ppm) 2 days after treatment at 0.01 lb/A (0.02 ppmw). No 2,4-D residues were found in any of the plant parts at harvest time except 0.04 ppm in the roots (not edible) from plots treated at 1.0 lb/A.

Effect of 2,4-D on Flood-Irrigated Cotton

Uniform experiments were conducted in 1953, 1954, 1955, and 1956 on the effect of 2,4-D in irrigation water on flood-irrigated cotton (Acala 44). Each year, the amine sale of 2,4-D (triethanolamine in 1953-54 and alkanolamine in 1955-56) was applied during the first irrigation after emergence (June 1-4) at rates of 0, 0.67 1.12 1.79 and 2.24 *ae* kg/ha. At this time, cotton usually was 8 to 10 inches high and had developed five to seven true leaves. The application of 2,4-D at 0.6 *ae* kg/ha caused slight or no injury to the cotton and no decreases in yields. The 2,4-D treatments at 1.12 *ae* kg/ha usually malformed some of the foliage and interfered somewhat with the normal development of early squares and bloom. Total yields of cotton, however, were not reduced by the 1.12 *ae* kg/ha. In fact, yields tended to be higher on the treated than on the untreated plots, and these yield differences were significant in 1955.

The results would indicate that cotton is remarkably tolerant to 2,4-D when applied at herbicidal dosages in irrigation water, particularly when compared with its susceptibility to minute quantities applied to the foliage.

HEALTH EFFECTS

Acute and Chronic Toxicity to Animals

Bucher (21) in 1946 was among the first to report the results of experiments with small animals using 2,4-D. Temporary myotonia lasting from eight to twenty-four hours or more following a single injection of 150 to 250 mg/kg was observed in mice, rats, rabbits and dogs. Florsheim and Velcoff (36) reported a decrease in both thyroid and body weights in male rats given single subcutaneous injections of 2,4-D at 100 mg/kg.

Baker *et al* (8) administered 112 grams of grass mixed with hor-semeat and dog meal divided over three consecutive meals to two healthy one-year-old mongrel dogs. The dogs readily ate the food and no ill effects were observed during the following 96 hours. Each animal was then treated with 500 mg/kg 2.4-D in a single oral dose. No deleterious effects were seen in the next 96 hours of observation. One animal, killed and necroposied at 96 hours post administration, failed to reveal any macroscopic lesions and the other animal remained healthy for 82 days following the second treatment, at which time the experiment was terminated.

In dogs, Drill and Hiratzka (29) found that toxic symptoms were often delayed up to six hours following a single oral administration of lethal doses of 100, 250 and 400 mg/kg 2.4-D. The deaths were delayed and occurred two to nine days after the compounds were administered. The acute oral Ld_{50} for (98.5 percent purity) 2,4-D was in the range of 100 mg/kg or higher. Death appeared to be due in most cases to hepatic congestion or pneumonia. Pathological changes were limited to the gastrointestinal tract, lungs and liver, and followed the development of anorexia, weight loss and myotonia.

Rowe and Hymas (51) noted that the Ld_{50} of 2,4-D for cattle ranged between 500 and 2000 mg/kg body weight while a single dose of 1000 mg/kg may not cause illness. Radeleff (50) cited a report in which cattle given one dose of 250 mg/kg 2,4-D showed signs of toxicity. In calves six to eight weeks old, Bjorklund and Erne (13) found that single doses of 100 to 200 mg/kg 2,4-D produced reversible signs of toxicity.

Toxic symptoms summarized by Rowe and Hymas (51) included the following general observations in animals treated with acute toxic doses of 2,4-D: loss of appetite, loss of weight, depression, roughness of coat, general tenseness and muscular weakness particularly of the posterior quarters. Post mortem findings usually included irritation of the stomach of small animals and of the abomasum of ruminants, minor evidence of liver and kidney injury and in some instances congestion of the lungs.

Analyses of data from the available studies supported the conclusion that the dog may be slightly more susceptible to oral doses of 2,4-D than other animals. Monkeys, sheep and cattle appeared to somewhat more tolerant. Administration of various salts and esters of 2,4-D as pure chemicals and as commercial preparations do not show significant differences in the toxicity of the salt and ester forms of 2,4-D when compared to the free acid (46,47).

No drastic damaging effects were noted when male Long-Evans rats were given 2,4-D equivalent to 2-5 g/kg over a 4 to 7-week feeding period. Response to herbicide treatment was dependent on animal age and on the duration of time that the chemical was fed. Little or no effect was noted on liver weight. Herbicide-induced enlargement of the liver was associated with increases in most of the major cellular components on a per liver basis. Isolated liver nuclei were 20-30 percent more active in the in-vitro RNA synthesis than in the control nuclei (6).

Schwetz et al (53) found that oral doses of 12.5 to 87.5 mg/kg 2,4-D did not adversely affect the weight gain of rats during pregnancy. In a preliminary study, non-pregnant rats tolerated 75 mg/kg 2,4-D for 10 days while 100 mg/kg killed two rats and produced overt signs of toxicity in three survivors.

Hansen et al (40) conducted a study with rats starting at 3 weeks of age, using groups of 25 female and 25 male animals, fed 0, 5, 25, 125, 625 or 1,250 mg 2,4-D/kg of diet for 2 years. During the study no significant differences in survival rates between controls and test animals were noted. The mean body weights of the different groups of males and females and the organ-to-body weight ratios for liver, kidney, heart, spleen and tests were not significantly different (P>0.025). The only exceptions were in two male rats, one at 625 mg/kg, and a second at 125 mg/kg dosage level in the diet. These two animals had slightly enlarged spleens. Mean values for hemoglobin, hematocrit, and total white blood cell count of controls and of rats at each dose level, at the same time interval, were similar and within normal range. The maximum no effect level for the rats in this study was greater than 1,250 mg 2,4-D/kg of diet.

Hansen et al (40) in another study fed 0, 100, 500 or 1,500 mg 2,4-D/kg of diet to groups of 20 male and 20 female rats. No effect was observed at the 100 and 500 mg/kg of diet levels. At the 1,500 mg/kg level, there was no effect on fertility nor on the average number of pups per litter; however, significant effects on the average number of pups weaned and also on their weaning weights were noted. The no effect level is at least 500 mg/kg but less than 1,500 mg/kg of 2,4-D in the diet.

Mitchell et al (47) fed a cow 5.5 g of 2,4-D acid daily for 106 days with no apparent harmful effects on the health or milking performance. Post mortem examinations revealed no pathological changes in the liver, kidneys or body fat. By biological responses following exposure to the dimethylamine salt of 2,4-D. 2,4-D is lipid soluble and is rapidly and completely absorbed through all normal routes of exposure. Its butyl ester, and therefore probably all of its esters, is hydrolized before absorption from the gastrointestinal tract. It is not metabolized in animals, but rapidly penetrates the placenta (44).

Developmental Toxicity

Schwetz et al (52) feed 2,4-D to rats as oral doses at 8.5 to 12.5 mg/kg/day during organogenesis and found skeletal abnormalities including edema and growth retardation. Konstantinova et al (45) of the Scientific Institute of Rural Hygiene in Saratov, USSR, tested 2,4-D and found developmental toxicity in the form of internal hemorrhages after 50 mg/kg/day of 2.4-D and after 1 mg/kg/day of 2,4-dichlorophenol and also after a mixture of 0.1. Akeksashina (2) of the Byelorussian Scientific Research Institute of Sanitation and Hygiene in Minsk, USSR, did two different experiments. One used intraperitoneal doses of 0.1 or 0.5 mg/kg/day throughout pregnancy and found growth retardation and hemorrhaging into the abdominal cavity at the higher dose and vascular distention at both doses. The other experiment tested single doses of $1/2$ LD_{50} given intraperitoneally on various days of gestation, and found increased resorption of fetuses with reduced litter size, growth reduction with increased size of brain ventricles, and hemorrhaging into the abdominal cavity. A test for developmental toxicity in hamsters was done by Collins and Williams of the U.S. Food and Drug Administration (26). They used oral doses of 20 to 100 mg/kg/day during organogenesis and found a dose-dependent increase in fused ribs at 60mg/kg/day and above which was significant only if repeats were pooled.

Effects on Reproduction and Fertility

Bionetics Research Laboratories (12) reported that either the acid, or the isopropyl, butyl and isooctyl esters of 2,4-D, administered orally or subcutaneously at days 6-14 of gestation, increased the incidence of anaomalous fetuses among BL6, AKR and C3H strains of mice but not among B6AK and ALHa strains. No single strain showed a positive response to all formulations. No single formulation caused response among all strains of mice. Thus, the reported effects were highly strain-specific. In addition, the Bionetics study involved parenteral administration using dimethyl sulphoxide (DMSO) has been shown to be a teratogen in several species of laboratory animals when administered by the route used in the Bionetics study.

Starting with rats three weeks of age, groups of 25 female and 25 male animals were fed for two years either 0, 5, 25, 125, 625 or 1,250 mg 2,4-D/kg of diet. No significant effects on growth rate, survival rate, organ weights or hematologic values were noted. Hansen et al (39) noted in a three generation, six litter rat reproduction study, no deleterious effect of dietary 2,4-D, while apparently affecting neither fertility of either six nor litter size, sharply reduced the percent of pups born surviving to weaning and the weights of weanlings.

In studies by Schwetz et al (53), the acid of 2,4-D, the propylene glycol butyl ether ester of 2,4-D and the isooctyl ester of 2,4-D were evaluated for effects on fetal development, neonatal growth and survival when administered at 12.5, 25, 50, 75 and 87.5 mg/kg orally to pregnant Sprague-Dawley (Spartan strain) rats during organogenesis (days 6-15 of gestation). Fetuses were delivered by Caesarean section on day 20 of gestation and were examined grossly, measured and weighed. Fetotoxic responses seen at high dose levels 50, 75 and 87.5 mg/kg included subcutaneous edema, delayed ossification and wavy ribs. Teratogenic responses were not seen at any dose level. 2,4-D did not affect fertility, gestation, lactation or viability of the newborn. The esters of 2,4-D decreased viability of the newborn and lowered lactation indices (Lactation Index = pups weaned/pups alive on day 4 × 100). In a second part of the experiment in which litters delivered naturally, 2,4-D and its esters had little or no effect on fertility, gestation, viability or lactation indices. There were no observable effects on neonatal growth and development.

Carcinogenic and Tumorigenic Potentials

Carcinogenic properties of 2,4-D in mamalian biological systems were studied by Bionetics Research Laboratories (12). Included in the test compounds were the 2,4-D acid and the isopropyl, butyl and isooctyl esters of 2,4-D. They were given orally, at a daily dosage rate of 46.4 mg/kg. An additional test using the dosage rate of 100 mg/kg for 2.4-D acid was included. These doses were given by stomach tube starting at 7 days of age and continued until the mice were 4 weeks of age. After weaning, the test compounds were mixed directly into the diet and the same dosage rate maintained for approximately 18 months of observation. The tumor incidence in any group or combination of groups in which 2,4-D was not significantly different from that in control animals (13,14).

Groups of male and female mice were given single subcutaneous injections of 215 mg/kg 2,4-D in dimethyl sulphoxide (DMSO) on the 28th day of life and observed up to 78 weeks of age. Tumor incidences in any group or combination of groups were not significantly different from that in controls. No increase in the incidence of tumors was observed in similar groups of mice treated with single subcutaneous injections of 21.5 mg/kg butyl or 100 mg/kg isopropyl esters of 2,4-D, both 99 percent pure. Mice treated with 21.5 mg/kg isooctyl ester of 2,4-D, 97 percent pure, had 5/17 females of one strain developing reticulum-cell sarcomas (15).

Hansen et al (39) studied groups of 25 male and 25 female Osborne-Mendel rats that were fed for two years on diets containing 2,4-D at 0, 5, 25, 125, 625 or 1,250 mg/kg levels. The 2,4-D was 96.7 percent pure and contained no detectable levels of 2,7-dichloro or 2,3,7,8-tetrachlorodibenzo-p-dioxin (limit of sensitivity of method of analysis was 1 mg/kg). No target organ tumors were observed and the individual tumor types were randomly and widely distributed and of the type normally found in aging rats of that strain. Statistical analysis of the randomly distributed tumor types indicated a tendency for the proportion of females with tumors to increase with 2,4-D dosage and a trend toward dose related increases in the proportion of males with malignant tumors. The number of treated rats with malignant tumors over controls was found only in males receiving the highest dosage level.

Mutagenic and Cytogenetic Potentials

Most of the mutagenic studies of 2,4-D have been conducted in bacterial cultures or in plant and animal tissue cultures (3,5). Pilinskaya (49) observed that treatment of cultured human lymphocytes with 2.5 $\times$ 10^{-7} M (0.02 ug/ml) 2,4-D increased the number of chromatid aberrations (single acentric fragments) and, to a lesser extent, the chromosomal aberrations (paired acentric fragments). In mice, toxic concentrations (100-300 mg/kg) of 2,4-D administered as a single oral dose significantly increased the frequency of aberrant metaphases (2-4 fold) with single fragments being the aberration seen. Solutions of 0.001 mM to 1.0 mM 2,4-D with or without rat liver activation in DNA synthesis in SV-40, transformed human fibroblast cells in culture (1).

The significance of chromatid aberrations to human or animal mutations is still an open question. Four manifestations of developmental toxicity have been demonstrated in animals treated with 2,4-D or its esters or amines.

Malformation: skeletal at high dose (60 mg/kg/day or above), peripheral circulatory system distended at low dose (0.1 mg/kg/day) and after single high dose (1/2 LD_{50}, eye anomalies at 100 mg/kg/day (2).

Malfunction: subcutaneous edema at 12.5 mg/kg/day and above, hemorrhage into soft tissues and body cavities from 50 mg/kg/day to 0.5 mg/kg/day (2).

Growth retardation: prenatal at 0.5 mg/kg/day and above. Postnatal after 50b mg/kg/day or when treatment continued during lactation (2).

Lethality: pre-implantation not reported. Post-implantation at 100 mg/kg/day and above, or after a single high dose (1/2 LD_{50}). Postnatal in progeny of rats fed 150 mg/kd/day, or in a pig fed 500 ppm (2).

Different degrees of sodium 2,4-D poisoning were produced by Elo and Tlitalo (31) in adult male Sprague-Dawley rats when 250 mg/kg 2,4-D was administered by subcutaneous injection. After various intervals the concentration of intravenous ^{14}C-2,4-D was compared to the level found in the cerebrospinal fluid (CSF) and brain. At 4.5 hours when the sodium 2,4-D radioactivity in plasma had diminished to 67 percent of control levels, an 11-fold increase in the brain and a 39-fold increase in the CSF were seen compared to a 4.5 fold increase in the liver.

In rats, pigs and calves, 2,4-D administered in doses of 50-100 mg/ kg orally as salts were readily absorbed and eliminated, mainly in the urine, with plasma half-lives varying from 3-12 hours. The rate of 2,4-D elimination in rats was dosage dependent. Following administration of ^{14}C-2,4-D, Khanna and Fang (43) found radioactivity in all organs and tissues examined.

An estimate of the greatest amount that might possibly be ingested can be made from the legal tolerances established by the FDA for 2,4-D in various crops. They are 5 mg/kg on 4 fruit crops (apples, citrus fruits, peas and quinces) and 0.5 mg/kg on 4 grain crops (barley, oats, rye and wheat). If it is assumed that all the crops for which a tolerance exists always carried the maximum amount of 2,4-D permitted, it can be calculated that approximately 0.3 mg/kg of 2,4-D would be contributed to the total diet (fruit crops = 6 percent of the dietary intake of man and grain crops = 9 percent). When the maximum estimated human exposure to 2,4-D via the diet is compared to the dosages given rats in the present study, it is apparent that there is an extremely wide margin of safety between 0.3 mg/kg of diet in man and the 1,250 mg/kg of diet fed to rats (60).

Carcinogenicity and Toxicity

Carcinogenicity and toxicity of 2,4-Dichlorophenoxyacetic acid was recently reviewed by M.D. Reuber (52) and he found that 2,4-Dichlorophenoxyacetic (2,4-D) is carcinogenic in male and female rats and probably also in mice is mutagenic and teratogenic in animals, and causes poisoning in animals and human beings. The toxicology of 2,4-D is well established in the literature from many different sources, but the statistical significance of carcinogenicity, mutagenicity and teratogenicity are open to question. In the statistical analysis cited by Reuber, the controls varied from 0 to 45%, and the treatments from 0 to 83%. It seems more than obvious that the statistical treatment given is in error, and the results are better described as non-significant.

SUMMARY AND CONCLUSIONS

The 2,4-D herbicides were discovered over forty years ago, incidental to research on naturally occurring plant hormones. As the chemical nature of these substances became known, related compounds were synthesized and tested for effects on plant growth. Certain phenoxy acetic acids, including 2,4-D, were found to be plant growth regulators and in due course were discovered independently in the United States and Britain to be active herbicides capable of selectively killing many broadleaved weeds in cereal grains, grasslands and coniferous forests. Further research led to the commercial use of several phenoxy herbicides, including 2,4-D, 2,4,5-T, MCPA and silvex. These pioneer accomplishments have now expanded into a world-wide effort by industry and public research agencies that has discovered a wide array of useful herbicides, most of which are chemically and functionally unrelated to 2,4-D.

Despite the development of many other herbicides 2,4-D remains a major tool in vegetation management. Although replaced by newer materials in some instances, 2,4-D is currently in critically short supply in world commerce. An important development for the tropical nations has been the recent discovery that a wide range of weeds can be prevented in paddy rice by applying 2,4-D to the water three or four days after transplanting. This and other developments forecast expanded usefulness for 2,4-D and related chemicals in the management of such diverse resources as croplands, forests, ranges, waterways, industrial lands, public utility properties, wildlife habitats, urban parks, athletic fields and landscape plantings.

The 2,4-D herbicides are widely used because they are more efficient and usually less hazardous and less injurious to the environment than alternative methods. Use of these chemicals is estimated to reduce the cost of production of the crops on which they are used by about 5% and to reduce overall agricultural production costs in the United States by about 1%. Uses in forests and nonagricultural situations provide additional savings. If 2,4-D was no longer available, the cost of food, forest products, electric power, transportation and governmental services would be higher. These costs would be borne by consumers.

The scientific data on 2,4-D are exhaustive, comprising more than 50,000 scientific papers and technical reports over a 40-year period. The 2,4-D herbicides are relatively old materials in terms of research and accumulated experience in their use. It is possible to assess risks projected on the basis of experimental data and also to confirm or deny these projections on the basis of hazards that have developed or failed to develop from a quarter-century of extensive use throughout the world.

REFERENCES

1. Ahmed, Farid E., Ronald W. Hart, and Neil J. Lewis. 1977. Pesticide induced DNA damage and its repair in cultured human cells. Mutation Research *42*, 161-174.
2. Aleksashina, Z.A., S.Y. Buslovich and V.M. Kolosovskaya. 1973. Embryotoxic action of the diethylamine salt of 2,4-D. Gigiena I Sanitariya *2*, 100-101.

3. Anderson, Kenneth J., Edith G. Leighty and Mart T. Takahashi. 1972. Evaluation of herbicides for possible mutagenic properties. J. Agr. Food Chem. 20, 649-656.
4. Antonenko, T.A. 1977. Experimental data from a study of the permeability of the placental barrier for the herbicide 2,4-D (acid form) and its passage with the mother's milk during feeding. Gog. Aspekty Okhr. Zdorov'ya Naseleniya. 1977. 177-178.
5. Arkhipov, G.N. and I.N. Kozlova. 1974. Study of the carcinogenic properties of the herbicide amine salt of 2,4-D. Voprosy Pitaniya 5, 83-84.
6. Ashton, F.H. and A.S. Crafts. 1973. **Mode of Action of Herbicides.** Wiley & Sons, p. 274.
7. Averitt, W.K. and E.O. Gangstad. 1976. Dissipation of residues of 2,4-D in static water. Journal of Environmental Quality. 5:145-147.
8. Baker, D.L., F.K. Ramsey and E.P. Sylvester. 1953. Suspected poisoning of dogs from eating grasses treated with 2,4-D. North Am. Vet. 24:194.
9. Bartley, T.R. and E.O. Gangstad. Environmental aspects of aquatic plant control. Journ. of the Irrigation and Drainage Division, ASCE. 100:231-244. 1974.
10. Bartley, T.R. and A.R. Hattrup. 1970. 2,4-D contamination and persistence in irrigation water, Proceedings of the Western Society of Weed Science. 23:10-32.
11. Berkley, Mary C. and Kenneth R. Magee. 1963. Neuropathy following exposure to a dimethylamine salt of 2,4-D. Arch of Int. Med. 111, 351-352.
12. Bionetics Research Laboratories, Inc. 1968. Evaluation of carcinogenic, teratogenic and mutagenic activities of selected pesticides and industrial chemicals. Vol. I. Carcinogenic Study. Submitted under contracts PH 43-64-57 and PH 43-67-735 with the National Cancer Institute. Available from National Technical Information Service, Document Number PB-223-159.
13. Bjorklund, N.E. and K. Erne. 1966. Toxicological studies of phenoxyacetic herbicides in animals. Acta Vet. Scand. 7:364-3490.
14. Boutwell, R.K. and Dorothy K. Bosch. 1959. The tumor-promoting action of phenol and related compounds for mouse skin. Cancer Research, 19, 413-424.
15. Bruns, V.F. 1953. The response of concord grapes to 2,4-D in irrigation water. Annual Report, Weed Investigations, Irr. Expt. Sta., Prosser, Wash.
16. Bruns, V.F. 1954. The response of certain crops to 2,4-dichlorophenoxyacetic acid in irrigation water. Part I. Red Mexican Beans. Weeds 3:359-376.

17. Bruns, V.F. 1957. The response of certain crops to 2,4-dichlorophenoxyacetic acid in irrigation water. Part II. Sugar Beets. Weeds 5:250-258.

18. Bruns, V.F. and W.J. Clore. 1958. The response of certain crops to 2,4-dichlorophenoxyacetic acid in irrigation water. Part III. Concord Grapes. Weeds 5-258-270.

19. Bruns, V.F., J.M. Hodgson, and H.F. Arle. 1972. Response of several crops to six herbicides in irrigation water, U.S. Department of Agriculture, Technical Bulletin No. 1461, 1973.

20. Bruns, V.F., B.L. Carlile, and A.D. Kelley. 1973. Responses and residues in sugarbeets, soybeans, and corn irrigated with 2,4-D or silvex-treated water. Technical Bulletin No. 1476, Agricultural Research Service, U.S. Department of Agriculture.

21. Bucher, N.L.R. 1946. Effects of 2,4-dichlorophenoxyacetic acid on experimental animals. Proc. Soc. Exp. Biol. Med. 63:204-205.

22. Burton, Jerry A., Thomas H. Gardiner and Lewis S. Schanker. 1974. Absorption of herbicides from the rat lung. Arch. Environ. Health 29, 31-33.

23. Buslovich, S.Y. and F.D. Koldobskaya. 1972. Activity of hexokinase in skeletal muscles of albino rats in experimental myotonia. Voprosy Meditsinkoi Khimii 18, 403-406.

24. Chang, Hsian-chen, Jack W. Rip and Joe H. Cherry. 1974. Effects of phenoxyacetic acids on rat liver tissues. J. Agr. Food Chem. 22, 62-65.

25. Clark, D.E., J.S. Palmer, R.D. Radeleff, H.R. Crookshank and F.M. Farr. 1975. Residues of chlorophenoxy acid herbicides and their phenolic metabolites in tissues of sheep and cattle. J. Agric. Food Chem. 23(3):573-578.

26. Collins, T.F.X. and C.H. Williams. 1971. Teratogenic studies with 2,4,5-T and 2,4-D in the hamster. Bull. Environ. Contam. Toxicol. 6:559-567.

27. Davis, Frank S. 1974. Toxicology, persistence, and mobility of phenoxy herbicides in the environment. In aquatic use patterns for 2,4-dimethylamine and integrated control. U.S. Army Corps of Engineers Waterways Experiment Station. Technical Report 7, EL-E16.

28. Dinman, B.D. 1972. "Non-concept of no-threshold": Chemicals in the environment. Sci. 175:495-497.

29. Drill, Victor A. and Tomiharu Hiratzka. 1953. Toxicity of 2,4-dichlorophenoxyacetic acid and 2,4,5-trichlorophenoxy-acetic acid. A report on their acute and chronic toxicity in dogs. Industrial Hygiene and Occupational Medicine 7, 61-67.

30. Dudley, Alden W. Jr. and Nirwan T. Thapar. 1972. Fatal human ingestion of 2,4-D, a common herbicide. Arch. Path. 94, 270-275.

242   VEGETATION MANAGEMENT OF FRESHWATER RESOURCES

31. Elo, H. and P. Ylitalo. 1977. Substantial increase in the levels of chlorophenoxyacetic acids in the CNS of rats as a result of severe intoxication. Acta Pharmacol. Toxicol. 41:280-284.
32. Erne, K. 1966. Distribution and elimination of chlorinated phenoxyacetic acids in animals, Acta Vet. Scan. 7:240-256.
33. Erne, K. 1966. Studies on the animal metabolism of phenoxyacetic herbicides. Acta Vet. Scan. 7:264-271.
34. Federal Supply Services. 1958. Federal Specification: Herbicide, 2,4-dichlorophenoxyacetic acid. O-H-200a. U.S. Government Printing Office, Washington, D.C.
35. Fedorova, L.M. and R.S. Belova. 1974. Incorporation of 2,4-dichlorophenoxyacetic acid into the organs of animals: paths and dynamics of its excretion. Gig. I. Sanit. 2:105-107.
36. Florsheim, W.H. and S.M. Velcoff. 1962. Some effects of 2,4-dichlorophenoxyacetic acid on thyroid function in the rat: effects on iodine accumulation. Endocrinology. 71:1-6.
37. Frank, P.A., R.J. Demint, and R.D. Comes. 1970. Herbicides in irrigation water following canal-bank treatment for weed control. Weed Sci. 18:687-692.
38. Gangstad, Edward O. 1982. Dissipation of 2,4-D residues in large reservoirs. J. Aquat. Plant Manage. 20:13-16.
39. Hansen, W.H., M.L. Quaife, R.T. Habermann and O.G. Fitzhugh. 1971. Chronic toxicity of 2,4-dichlorophenoxyacetic acid in rats and dogs. Toxicol. Appl. Pharmacol. 20:122-129.
40. Hemmett, R.B. Jr. and S.D. Faust. 1969. Biodegradation kinetics of 2,4-dichlorophenoxyacetic acid by aquatic microorganisms. Residues Reviews: 29:191-207.
41. Hoeppel, R.E. and H.E. Westerdahl. 1983. Dissipation of 2,4-D DMA and BEE from water, mud and fish at Lake Seminole, Georgia. Water Resources Bulletin. 19:197-204.
42. Joyce, J.C. and H.C. Sikka. 1977. Residual 2,4-D levels in the St. Johns River, Florida. J. Aquatic Plant Manage. 15:76-82.
43. Khanna, S. and S.C. Fang. 1966. Metabolism of C^{14} — labeled 2,4-dichlorophenoxyacetic acid in rats. J. Agric. Food Chem. 14:500-503.
44. Kholi, J.D., R.N. Khanna, B.N. Gupta, M.M. Dhar, J.S. Tandon and K.P. Sircar. 1974. Absorption and excretion of 2,4-dichlorophenoxyacetic acid in man. Xenobiotica 4, 97-100.
45. Konstantinova, T.K., L.P. Ephimenko and T.A. Antonenko. 1976. The embryotropic effect of the dissociation products of herbicides based on 2,4-D. Gigiena I Sanitariya 11, 102-105.
46. McLennan, M.W. 1974. 2,4-D toxicity in dairy cattle. Australian Vet. J. 50(12):578.
47. Mitchell, J.W., R.E. Hodgson and C.F. Gaetjens. 1944. Tolerance of farm animals to feed containing 2,4-D. J. Anim. Sci. 5:226-232.

48. Morris, K. and Ron Jarman. 1981. Evaluation of water quality during herbicide applications to Kerr Lake, Oklahoma. J. Aquatic Plant Manage. 19:15-18.
49. Pilinskaya, M.A. 1974. Cytogenetic effect of the herbicide 2,4-D on human and animal chromosomes. Tsitol. Genet. 8(3):202-206.
50. Radionov, A.D., A.N. Chumachenko and I.D. Kirilenko. 1967. The toxic properties of the herbicide 2,4-D. Hygiene and Sanitation *32*, 116-118.
51. Rowe, V.K. and T.A. Hymas. 1954. Summary of toxicological information of 2,4-D and 2,4,5-T type herbicides and an evaluation of the hazards to livestock associated with their use. Amer. J. Vet. Res. 15:(57)622-629.
52. Reuber, M.D. 1983. Carcinogenicity and toxicity of 2,4-dichlorophenoxyacetic acid. The Science of the Total Environment. 31:203-218.
53. Schwetz, B.A., G.L. Sparschu and P.J. Gehring. 1971. The effect of 2,4-dichlorophenoxyacetic (2,4-D) and esters of 2,4-D on rat embryonal, fetal and neonatal growth and development. Food Cosmet. Toxicol. 9:801-807.
54. Schultz, D.P. 1973. Dynamics of a salt of (2,4-Dichlorophenoxy acetic acid) in fish, water, and hydrosoil. J. Agr. Food Chem. 21:186-192.
55. Schultz, D.P. and P.D. Harman. 1974. Residues of 2,4-D in pond waters, mud and fish. Pestic. Monit. J. 8:173-179.
56. Schultz, D.P. and E.O. Gangstad. 1976. Dissipation of residues of 2,4-D in water, hydrosoil and fish. J. Aquatic Plant Mange. 14:43-45.
57. Sikka, H.C., H.T. Appleton and E.O. Gangstad. 1977. Uptake and metabolism of dimethylamine salt of 2,4-dichlorophenoxy-acetic acid by fish. J. Agric. Food Chem. 25:1030-1033.
58. Smith, G.E., and B.G. Isom. 1967. Investigation of effects of large-scale applications of 2,4-D on aquatic fauna and water quality. Pestic. Monit. J. 1:16-21.
59. Stallings, D.L. and James N. Huchins. 1978. Metabolism of 2,4-dichlorophenoxyacetic acid (2,4-D) in bluegills and water J. Agric. Food Chem. 26:447-452.
60. Young, A.L., J.A. Calcogni, J.W. Thaken and J.W. Trembley. 1978. The toxicology, environment fate and human risk of herbicide orange and its associated dioxin. USAF Occupational and Environmental Health Laboratory. Brooks Air Force Base, Texas.
61. Wojtalik, T.A., T.F. Hall and L.O. Hill. 1971. Monitoring ecological conditions associated with wide-scale applications of DMA 2,4-D to aquatic environments. Pesticides Monitoring Jour. 4(4):18-203.

Table 1.   Susceptibility of common weeds controlled by 2,4-D.

Plant name	Type of plant	Control
Alder (*Alnus* spp.)	Woody	Good
Amaranth:		
Green (*Amaranthus hybridus*)	Annual	Excellent
Palmer (*A. palmeri*)	do	do
Arrowhead:		
Annual (*Sagittaria calycina*)	Annual	Excellent
Aster:		
Many-flowered (*Aster ericoides*)	Perennial	Good
Baccharis, coyote brush (*Baccharis salicina*)	Woody	Excellent
Baileya, desert (*Baileya multiradiata*)	Perennial	Good
Cornflower:		
Batchelor's button (*Centaurea cyanus*)	do	Excellent
Beggartick, devils (*Bidens frondosa*)	do	Excellent
Bindweed:		
Hedge (*C. sepium*)	do	Good
Blackeyed susan (*Rudbeckia serotina*)	Perennial	Good
Bloodweed (*Ambrosia aptera*)	Annual	Excellent
Boxelder (*Acar negundo*)	Woody	Good
Broomweed, common (*Gutierrezia dracunculoides*)	Annual	Good
Broom, Scotch (*Cylisus scoparius*)	Woody	do
Burdock, common (*Arctium minus*)	Biennial	Excellent
Bur-head (*Echinodorus cordifolius*)	Annual	do
Buckbrush (*Symphoricarpos orbiculatus*)	Woody	Good
Bullnettle (*Cnidoscolus stimulosus*)	Perennial	Good
Burroweed (*Haplopappus tenuisectus*)	do	do
Buttercup:		
Corn (*R. arvensis*)	do	Good
Tall (*R. acris*)	do	do
Carpetweed (*Mollugo verticillata*)	Annual	Excellent
Catsear, spotted (*Hypochocris radicata*)	Perennial	Good
Catnip (*Nepeta cataria*)	do	do
Chicory (*Cichorium intybus*)	Perennial	Good
Cinquefoil:		
Common (*P. canadensis*)	do	Good
Rough (*P. norvegica*)	Annual[3]	Excellent
Sulfur (*P recta*)	Perennial	Good
Cocklebur, common (*Xanthium pensylvanicum*)	Annual	Excellent
Coffeeweed (*Daubentonia texana*)	Woody	do

Table 1. Susceptibility of common weeds controlled by 2,4-D. (cont.)

Plant name	Type of plant	Control
Coyote brush (*Baccharis pilularis*)	do	Good
Croton:		
Lindheimer (*Croton lindheimeri*)	Annual	Excellent
Texas (*C. texensis*)	do	do
Wolly (*C. capitatus*)	do	do
Dandelion (*Taraxacum officinale*)	do	Excellent
Deerweed (*Lotus scoparius*)	Woody	Excellent
Devil's claw (*Proboscidea louisianica*)	Annual	do
Dock:		
Broadleaf (*Rumex obtusifolius*)	Perennial	Good
Curly (*R. crispus*)	do	do
Fiddle (*R. pulcher*)	do	Excellent
Pale (*R. altissimus*)	do	Good
Eveningprimrose, common (*Oenothera biennis*)	Biennial	Excellent
Falseflax, smallseeded (*Camelina microcarpa*)	Annual	do
Fennel, dog (*Eupatorium capillifolium*)	do	Good
Filaree, redstem (*Erodium cicutarium*)	Annual[3]	Good
Fireweed (*Epilobium angustifolium*)	Perennial	do
Fleabane:		
Rough (*E. strigosus*)	Annual[3]	Good
Flixweed (*Descurainia sophia*)	do	Excellent
Galinsoga, hairy (*Galinsoga ciliata*)	Annual	Good
Geranium, Carolina (*Geranium carolinianum*)	Annual[3]	Good
Gooseberry, sierra (*Ribes roezli*)	Woody	Excellent
Goosefoot:		
Nettleleaf (*C. murale*)	do	Excellent
Oakleaf (*C. glaucum*)	do	do
Groundcherry:		
Wrights (*P. wrightii*)	Annual	Excellent
Groundsel:		
Cressleaf (*S. glabellus*)	do	Excellent
Riddell (*S. riddellii*)	Perennial	do
Gumweed (*Grindelia squarrosa*)	Perennial	Excellent
Healall (*Prunella vulgaris*)	Perennial	Good
Hellebore, false western (*Veratrum californicum*)	do	do
Hemlock, poison (*Conium maculatum*)	Biennial	do

Table 1.   Susceptibility of common weeds controlled by 2,4-D. (cont.)

Plant name	Type of plant	Control
Hemp (*Cannabis sativa*)	Annual	do
Hogpeanut (*Amphicarpa bracteata*)	Perennial	Excellent
Ironweed, Western (*Vernonia baldwini*)	do	Good
Ivy, English (*Hedera helix*)	do	
Jerusalem-artichoke *Helianthus tuberosus*	do	Good
Jewelweed (*Impatiens pallida*)	Annual	Excellent
Jimsonweed (*Datura stramonium*)	Annual	Good
Knapweed:		
Diffuse (*C. diffusa*)	Biennial	Excellent
Kochia (*Kochia scoparia*)	do	Excellent
Knotweed:		
Sakhalin (*P. sachalinense*)	Perennial	Good
Kudzu (*Pueraria lobata*)	Perennial	do
Lambsquarters, common (*Chenopodium album)*	*Annual*	*Excellent*
Lettuce:		
Wild (*L. scariola*)	Annual	Excellent
Loco, bigbend (*Astragalus earlei*)	Annual[3]	Excellent
London-rocket, annual (*Sisymbrium irio*)	Annual	Excellent
Lupine (*Lupinus rivularis*)	Woody	Excellent
Tailcup (*L. caudatus*)	do	Good
Mallow:		
Venice (*Hibiscus trionum*)	do	Good
Manzanita (*Arctostaphylos* spp.)	Wood	do
Marshelder (*Iva xanthifolia*)	Annual	Excellent
Mexicantea (*Chenopodium ambrosioides*)	Annual	Excellent
Milkweed (*Asclepias curassavica*)	Perennial	Good
Moneywort (*Lysimachia nummularia*)	Perennial	Excellent
Morningglory:		
Common (*Ipomoea purpurea*)	Annual	do
Ivyleaf (*I. hederacea*)	do	do
Woolly (*I. hirsutula*)	do	do
Mountain Mahogany (*Cerocarpus montanus*)	Woody	
Mudplantain (*Heteranthera limosa*)	Annual	Excellent
Mulesears (*Wyethia amplexicaulis*)	Perennial	Good
Mustard:		
Black (*Brassica nigra*)	Annual	Excellent
Haresear (*Conringia orientalis*)	do	Excellent

Table 1.   Susceptibility of common weeds controlled by 2,4-D. (cont.)

Plant name	Type of plant	Control
Hedge (*Sisymbrium officinale*)	do	do
Indian (*Brassica juncea*)	do	do
Tumble (*Sisymbrium altissimum*)	do	do
Wild (*Brassica kaber*)	do	do
Wormseed (*Erysimum cheiranthoides*)	Annual[3]	do
Nettle:		
Stinging (*Urtica dioica*)	Perennial	Good
Tall (*U. procera*)	Annual	do
Niggerhead (*Rudbeckia occidentalis*)	Perennial	do
Nightshade:		
Silverleaf (*S. claegnifolium*)	Perennial	Poor
Parsley, desert (*Lomatium grayi*)	Perennial	Excellent
Parsnip, wild (*Pastinaca sativa*)	Biennial	do
Partridgepea (*Cassia fasciculata*)	Annual	do
Peavine (*Astragalus emoryanus*)	Annual	Good
Pennycress, field (*Thlaspi arvense*)	do	Excellent
Pennywort, lawn (*Hydrocotyle sibthorpioides*	Perennial	Good
Pepperweed:		
Field (*Lepidium campestre*)	Annual	Excellent
Virginia (*L. virginicum*)	Annual	Excellent
Yellowflower (*L. perfoliatum*)	do	do
Texas (*D. texana*)	do	Excellent
Pigweed:		
Prostrate (*Amaranthus graecizans*)	Annual	do
Rough (*A. retroflexus*)	*do*	*do*
Tumble (*A. albus*)	do	do
Plantain:		
Blackseed (*Plantago rugelii*)	Perennial	Excellent
Broadleaf (*P. major*)	do	do
Buckhorn (*P. lanceolata*)	do	do
Ponyfoot (*Dichondra repens*)	do	Excellent
Poorjoe (*Diodia teres*)	Annual	Good
Poppy, Roemer (*Roemeria refracta*)	do	Excellent
Prickly poppy (*Aregemone intermedia*)	Annual	Excellent
Puncturevine (*Tribulus terrestris*)	do	Good
Pusley, Florida (*Richardia scabra*)	*do*	*Excellent*
Radish, wild (*Raphanus raphanistrum*)	Annual	Excellent
Ragweed:		
Common (*Ambrosia artemisiifolia*)	do	do

Table 1.   Susceptibility of common weeds controlled by 2,4-D. (cont.)

Plant name	Type of plant	Control
Giant (*A. trifida*)	do	do
Western (*A. psilostachya*)	Perennial	Good
Rape, Bird (*Brassica rapa*)	Biennial	Excellent
Redbay (*Persea borbonia*)	do	do
Redstem (*Ammannia coccinea*)	Annual	Excellent
Praire (*R. pratincola*)	do	Fair
Rubberweed:		
Bitter (*Hymenoxys odorata*)	Annual	Excellent
Colorado (*H. richardsoni*)	Perennial	Good
Sage:		
Creeping (*Salvia sonomensis*)	do	Good
Purple (*S. leucophylla*)	do	do
White (*S. apiana*)	Perennial	Good
Sagebrush:		
Big (*Artemisia tridentata*)	Woody	do
California (*A. californica*)	do	Excellent
Sand (*A. filifolia*)	do	do
Salsify:		
Common (*Tragopogon porrifolius*)	Biennial	Good
Meadow (*T. pratensis*)	do	do
Sorrel (*Rumex acctosa*)	Perennial	Good
Heartwing (*R. hastatulus*)	do	Excellent
Shepherdspurse (*Capsella bursa-pastoris*)	Annual	Good
Sicklepod, coffeeweed (*Cassia tora*)	do	Excellent
Skunkcabbage (*Symplocarpus foetidus*)	Perennial	Good
Smartweed:		
Ladysthumb (*Polygonum persicaria*)	Annual	do
Pennsylvania (*P. pensylvanicum*)	do	do
Snakeweed:		
Threadleaf (*G. microcephala*)	do	Good
Sneezeweed, bitter (*Helenium tenuifolium*)	Annual	Excellent
Sowthistle:		
Annual (*Sonchus oleraceus*)	do	Excellent
Spiny (*S. asper*)	*Annual*	*Excellent*
Spanishneedles (Bidens bipinnata)	do	do
Sticktight, European (*Lappula echinata*)	do	Good
Sumpweed, rough (*Iva ciliata*)	Annual	Excellent
Sunflower (*Helianthus annuus*)	do	do

Table 1. Susceptibility of common weeds controlled by 2,4-D. (cont.)

Plant name	Type of plant	Control
Sweetclover, annual yellow (*Melilotus indica*)	do	do
Tansymustard (*Descurainia pinnata*)	Annual	Excellent
Thistle:		
Blessed (*Cnicus benedictus*)	do	do
Bull (*Cirsium vulgare*)	do	Excellent
Russian (*Salsola kali*)	Annual	Good
Tickseed (*Coreopsis tinctoria*)	do	do
Toyon (*Heteromeles arbutifolia*)	Woody	Good
Velvet-leaf (*Abutilon theophrasti*)	Annual	Excellent
Vervain:		
Blue (*Verbena hastata*)	Perennial	do
Hoary (*V. stricta*)	do	Good
Prostrate (*V. bracteata*)	do	Excellent
Roadside (*V. bonariensis*)	do	Good
Vetch:		
Narrowleaf (*Vicia angustifolia*)	Annual	Excellent
Milk (*Astragalus* spp.)	Perennial	Good
Two grooved (*A. bisulcatus*)	do	Excellent
Wild (*Vicia* spp.)	Annual	do
Walnut, black (*Juglans nigra*)	Woody	Excellent
Waterhemlock, spotted (*Cicuta maculata*	Perennial	Good
Water-hyacinth (*Eichhornia crassipes*)	do	do
Waterplantain (*Alisma trivale*)	do	Excellent
Willow (*Salix* spp.)	Woody	Good
Witchweed (*Striga asiatica*)	Annual	Excellent
Wormwood, annual (*Artemisia annua*)	Annual	Good
Yellow-rocket (*Barbarea vulgaris*)	Perennial[3]	Good
Yerba-santa (*Eriodictyon californicum*)	Woody	Excellent

From: Klingman, D.L., and Shaw, W.C., 1967. Using Phenoxy Herbicides Safety, U.S. Department of Agriculture Farmers' Bulletin No. 2183, U.S. Government Printing Office, Washington, D.C. With permission.

Table 2. Residues of the dimethylamine salt of 2,4-D in water (mg/l), hydrosoil (mg/kg) and fish (mg/kg) drom ponds in Florida and Georgia treated with 2.24, 4.48 and 8.96 kg 2,4-D ae per hectare.

Pond	Rate kg/ha	Depth m	Temp. C	Time Days	Water mg/1	Hydro-soil mg/kg	Fish mg/kg
Florida	2.24	1.3	34	01	0.025	0.005	0.080
	4.48	1.0	31	01	0.155	0.014	0.048
	8.96	1.2	31	01	0.312	0.033	0.005
Georgia	2.24	1.3	27	01	0.025	0.018	0.005
	4.48	0.9	29	01	0.233	0.024	0.014
	8.96	1.2	30	01	0.657	0.026	0.022
Florida	2.24	1.3	30	03	0.005	0.005	0.005
	4.48	1.0	30	03	0.172	0.014	0.005
	8.96	1.2	31	03	0.345	0.046	0.005
Georgia	2.24	1.3	29	03	0.087	0.008	0.005
	4.48	0.9	32	03	0.390	0.018	0.005
	8.96	1.0	30	03	0.692	0.040	0.005
Florida	2.24	1.3	31	07	0.005	0.005	0.005
	4.48	0.9	31	07	0.048	0.010	0.005
	8.96	1.2	31	07	0.025	0.008	0.005
Georgia	2.24	1.3	26	07	0.059	0.010	0.005
	4.48	0.9	27	07	0.400	0.018	0.005
	8.96	1.0	29	07	0.395	0.042	0.005

Table 2. Residues of the dimethylamine salt of 2,4-D in water (mg/l), hydrosoil (mg/kg) and fish (mg/kg) drom ponds in Florida and Georgia treated with 2.24, 4.48 and 8.96 kg 2,4-D ae per hectare. (cont.)

Pond	Rate kg/ha	Depth m	Temp. C	Time Days	Water mg/l	Hydrosoil mg/kg	Fish mg/kg
Florida	2.24	1.3	32	14	0.005	0.005	0.036
	4.48	1.0	32	14	0.005	0.010	0.005
	8.96	1.2	31	14	0.005	0.013	0.043
Georgia	2.24	1.3	28	14	0.027	0.005	0.005
	4.48	0.9	31	14	0.008	0.005	0.005
	8.96	1.0	30	14	0.050	0.005	0.005
Florida	2.24	1.3	30	28	0.005	0.005	0.005
	4.48	1.0	32	28	0.005	0.007	0.005
	8.96	1.2	30	28	0.005	0.005	0.005
Georgia	2.24	1.3	27	28	0.005	0.006	0.005
	4.48	0.9	31	28	0.005	0.005	0.005
	8.96	1.0	30	28	0.005	0.005	0.010
SUMMARY OF TREATMENT MEANS							
Rates	2.24				0.020	0.006	0.018
	4.48				1.118*	0.010	0.009
	8.96				0.208*	0.018	0.009

Table 2. Residues of the dimethylamine salt of 2,4-D in water (mg/l), hydrosoil (mg/kg) and fish (mg/kg) drom ponds in Florida and Georgia treated with 2.24, 4.48 and 8.96 kg 2,4-D ae per hectare. (cont.)

Pond	Rate kg/ha	Depth m	Temp. C	Time Days	Water mg/l	Hydro-soil mg/kg	Fish mg/kg
				1	0.099	0.018	NS
				3	0.235	0.020	0.029
				7	0.281	0.022	0.005
				14	0.155	0.016	0.005
				28	0.017*	0.007*	0.017
					0.005*	0.006*	0.006
Significant Difference P = 05* Days					0.127	0.008	NS

From: Schultz and Gangstad, 1976. J. Aquatic Plant Manage. 14:43-45. With permission.

Table 3. Residues (ppb) of 2,4-D in water and blue crabs in the St. Johns River, FL.

Station[a]	Date	Water	Blue crabs
	7-22-75	0.61	NA[b]
W-9	8-25-75	1.20	NA
Hwy 192	10- 1-75	0.45	NA
	10-20-75	0.00	NA
	1-28-76	0.04	NA
	7-22-75	0.00	NA
W-8	8-25-75	0.18	NA
Hwy 520	10- 1-75	0.08	NA
	10-20-75	0.08	NA
	1-27-76	0.10	NA
	7-22-75	0.00	NA
W-7	8-25-75	0.20	NA
Hwy 50	10- 1-75	0.06	NA
	10-20-75	0.07	NA
	1-27-76	0.35	NA
	7-22-75	0.25	NA
W-6	8-25-75	0.36	NA
Hwy 46	10- 1-75	1.30	NA
	10-20-75	0.04	NA
	1-27-76	0.04	NA
	7-22-75	1.00	NA
W-5	8-25-75	0.15	NA
DeLand	10- 1-75	0.00	NA
	10-20-75	0.15	NA
	1-27-76	0.00	NA
	5- 1-75	ND[c]	47.80
WC-4	7-22-75	0.15	0.00
Welaka	8-25-75	0.05	0.00
	10- 1-75	0.00	0.00
	10-20-75	0.11	0.00
	1-27-76	0.05	0.00
	5- 1-75	ND	65.10
WC-3	7-22-75	0.18	0.00
Palatka	8-25-75	0.00	0.00
	10- 1-75	00.00	0.00
	10-20-75	0.28	0.00
	1-27-76	0.00	NA

Table 3. Residues (ppb) of 2,4-D in water and blue crabs in the St. Johns River, FL. (cont.)

Station[a]	Date	Water	Blue crabs
	5- 1-75	ND	53.40
WC-2	7-22-75	0.00	0.00
Green Cove Springs	8-25-75	0.02	0.00
	10- 1-75	0.00	0.00
	10-20-75	0.09	0.00
	1-27-76	0.00	NA
	5- 1-75	ND	61.00
WC-1	7-22-75	0.02	0.00
Jacksonville	8-25-75	0.00	0.00
	9-30-75	0.00	0.00
	10-20-75	0.08	0.00
	1-27-76	0.06	0.00
Guano Wildlife Preserve	5-14-75	ND	62.6

[a] Station locations
[b] NA—Not Applicable—Blue crabs not available at these locations
[c] ND—No Data Available

From: Joyce and Sikka. 1977. J. Aquatic Plant Manage. 15:76-82. With permission.

PART II

EVALUATION OF SELECTED AQUATIC HERBICIDES

Chapter 10

HERBICIDAL, ENVIRONMENTAL AND HEALTH EFFECTS OF DIQUAT[1]

INTRODUCTION

Diquat is a quarternary salt of 4,4'-dipyridyl formulated as the dichloride or dibromide salts. Since the discovery of its herbicidal properties in the late 1950's, diquat has been used widely for the control of a broad spectrum of terrestrial and aquatic vegetation. It is a quick-acting contact herbicide and is manufactured by the Ortho Division of Chevron Chemical Company and is marketed as Diquat Water Weed Killer for aquatic uses. Diquat compounds used as herbicides are diquat dibromide and diquat dichloride. Diquat dibromide is very soluble in water, slightly soluble in alcoholic and hydroxylic solvents, and practically insoluble in non-polar organic solvents. It is essentially lipid insoluble and it is stable in acid or neutral solutions and unstable under alkaline conditions. Commercial diquat formulations contain a corrosion inhibitor, and a buffer.

Diquat is absorbed on soils by exchange reactions up to the cation exchange capacity of the soil, and the absorption is essentially irreversible in montmorillonitic clays but partially reversible in kaolinitic clays. Apparently, only a small portion of applied diquat is absorbed by aquatic weeds, and little translocation of diquat occurs. Ultraviolet light rapidly degrades diquat in aqueous solution. Diquat resists biological degradation in aquatic environments, but the presence of sorbents in the water in the form of particulate matter greatly influence diquat persistence in the aquatic environment. Although diquat has been found in muds of pools and ponds 4 years after application, no adverse effects on adult fish such as bluegill were noted at levels of diquat applied for weed control.

HERBICIDAL EFFECTS

Diquat apparently exerts its herbicidal action by formation of a stable free-radical on introduction of an electron, the radical forming reactive hydrogen peroxide radicals on reoxidation. The hydrogen

---

[1]The findings in this report are not to be construed as an official Department of the Army position unless so designated by other authorized documents.

peroxide radicals accumulate and destroy plant cells. Diquat will control most annual and perennial broadleaved weeds and grasses and certain algae and other water weeds.

Chemical Control of Hydrilla

Hydrilla has become a serious aquatic plant problem in Florida, Louisiana, and Texas (3). During the past 10 years, several different herbicides have been studied in the laboratory and the field for control of hydrilla (2,4). These studies indicated that 7-oxabicyclo (2.2.1) heptane-2,3-dicarboxylic acid (endothall) and diquat in combinations with copper provide varying degrees of control of hydrilla. (7,8,9,10,20,27,31,32).

Results and Discussion

Growth Pools.   These tests (Table 1) showed that diquat and copper sulfate are non-toxic to fish at the levels used for weed control.

Field Test.   The effectiveness of the treatments in Inglis Reservoir is shown in Table 2. The combination of diquat plus copper sulfate resulted in a more rapid kill of hydrilla than the diquat plus Cutrine; however, both of the treatments gave 70% to 95% control of hydrilla 82 days after treatment. Regrowth was apparent at 128 days after treatment. Satisfactory control persisted about 9 months.

Residue Levels.   The recovery of copper and diquat in control (spiked) water samples was 100%. Apparently no loss of these chemicals occurred during transit from the treatment area to the laboratory. Data of the study are presented in Table 3. The pretreatment water samples contained 0.001 to 0.011 ppmw of copper. Water samples from stations 3,5,7, and 8 contained concentrations of copper greater than 0.1 ppmw 1 day after treatment. In general, more copper was in the top sample (0.3 m below the surface) than in the bottom sample (0.3 above the hydrosoil). The area treated with copper sulfate pentahydrate (CSP) plus diquat contained 0.129 to 0.102 ppmw of copper 1 day after treatment as compared to 0.035 to 0.036 ppmw for the copper triethanolamine complex (Cutrine) treated area. A rapid dissipation of copper from both areas occurred. The level of diquat in water samples was not detectable 14 days after treatment.

Water Quality.   The results of water quality studies are summarized in Table 4. These observations indicated that ammonia nitrogen increased shortly after spraying and was high during the first month. Nitrate nitrogen dropped slowly. It is assumed that since the dissolved oxygen was low, the nitrate was reduced, yielding oxygen, causing a decrease in nitrate and increase in ammonia. Dissolved oxygen at the surface was not affected to any great extent by the treatment.

Control of Submersed Aquatic Weeds

Six small reservoirs were obtained for studies involving the control of submersed aquatic weeds, dissipation of the herbicides used to control the vegetation, effect of the herbicide-treated water on turf grasses, and effects on fish. (45). The reservoirs were located at the El Macero Golf Course near Davis, California, the Riverbend Golf Course near West Sacramento, California, and the Auburn Valley Golf Course near Auburn, California.

The kinds of aquatic weeds growing in the various reservoirs included horned pondweed (**Zannichellia palustris L.**), curley-leaf pondweed (**Potamogeton crispus L.**), sago pondweed (**P. pectinatus L.**), watermilfoil (**Myriophyllum spicatum** var. **exalbescens** Jep), American elodea (**Elodea canadensis** Michx.), coontail (**Ceratophyllum dermerseum L.**), California waterprimrose **Ludwigia peploides** (HBK) Raven], and chara (**Chara** spp.).

The different kinds of fish inhabiting the reservoirs were green sunfish (**Lepomis cyanellus** Raf.), redear sunfish (**L. microlphus** Gunther), smallmouth bass (**Micropterus dolomieui** Lacepede), golden shiner **Notemigonus crysoleucas** (Mitch.)], mosquitofish **Gambusia affinis** (Baird and Girard)] and common carp (**Cyprinus carpio** L.).

Materials and methods

The locations and dates of applications of mixtures of diquat plus copper sulfate pentahydrate (CSP), hereafter referred to as dicop are given below:

Applications of Diquat Plus CSP	
Location	Dates of Application
El Macero #1	5/9/72, 7/25/72, 8/25/72
Auburn Valley #1	5/8/72, 7/17/72, 8/21/72
Riverbend #1	5/8/72, 7/17/72, 8/25/72

The dicop was applied using 100 ppb of diquat plus 300 ppb copper ion. Alicop was applied at 500 ppb of aliquat 4 plus 500 ppb of copper ion. These applications were made when the initial growths or regrowths were 12-24 in. in height. Each application was made by slowly pouring the liquid mixtures into the water beside the boat and allowing the prop wash of the outboard motor to mix the chemicals. A crisscross pattern of application was used to obtain uniform distribution.

Four 1-qt. samples of water treated with dicop and alicop were collected from different sites in each reservoir 1, 2, 3, and 4 days after application. Samples of dichlobenil-treated water were collected 1, 15, 30, 60, and 90 days after application. The samples were immediately frozen to preserve them for chemical analysis.

To determine the effect on turf grasses 1-, 2-, and 4-gal samples of treated water were also collected on each sampling date and applied to the turf grasses growing at or nearest each location. The grass plots were each 2 by 4 ft. Each irrigation was replicated four times. The following kinds of grasses were irrigated at the different locations: El Macero—creeping bentgrass (**Agrostis stolonifera** L.), bermudagrass (**Cynodon dactylon** L.), and Kentucky bluegrass (**Poa pratensis L.**); Auburn Valley—creeping bentgrass (**A. stolonifera** L.) and colonial bentgrass (**Agrostis tenuis** Huds.); Riverbend-creeping bentgrass (**A. stolonifera** L.) and colonial bentgrass (**A. tenuis** Huds.).

The diquat, aliquat 4, and copper ion were analyzed separately. The diquat analysis was made using a method described by the Chevron Chemical Company. (13). The method involved concentrating the diquat on an exchange resin 25 times, leaching the diquat from the resin, adding sodium dithionite to obtain a color reaction, determining the optical density on a Bausch and Lomb Spectronic 70, and calculating the concentration of diquat from a standard curve. The residue data from the four samples collected from each pond on each sampling date were totaled and averaged.

Results and Discussion

The average of the nine treatments (three treatments at each of three sites) showed the diquat dissipated to near nondetectable levels after 4 days. Two-thirds of the diquat disappeared after 1 day, indicating rapid adsorption by the aquatic vegetation, soil, and detritis. Almost all the diquat dissipated from Riverbend #1 the first day. The water in this reservoir had the highest nutrient levels of the three sites. Consequently, it had more planktonic organisms to adsorb the diquat. This did not alter the effectiveness of the treatment in controlling the aquatic weed growth in each reservoir.

Fifty golden shiners were killed after the second day of the first treatment in the Riverbend Reservoir #1. Subsequent treatments in the same reservoir and at the same rate did not harm the remaining shiners. No other fish showed stress or injury in the other dicop treatments. None of the grasses showed any injury from being irrigated with treated water from the different reservoirs. An average of all nine treatments showed copper ion dissipated to 47 ppb in 4 days. The pattern of dissipation of copper ion was similar to that of diquat; two-thirds of the applied copper disappeared after 1 day.

Aquatic Plant Control in Drainage Ditches

With the completion of McNary Dam in 1954 and the raising of the McNary pool, it was necessary to construct some 21 miles of drainage ditches in the Tri-City area to drain the lowlands behind the levees. Of these 21 miles of ditches, 10 miles are for inland drainage and 11 miles for levee drainage. It was necessary to install 15 pumping plants in the Tri-City area to lift waste water and treated sewage over the protective levees. Maintaining a specific water table evaluation is very critical, when the table gets too high crop damage results; when it gets too low, it may cause well failures. As the mouths of these drainage ditches pool, almost constant pumping is required to lift this water from these ditches, over the dikes, and into the main stem of the Columbia River. (28).

Principal aquatic plants found in this area are sago pondweed (**Potamogeton pectinatus L.**), curly leaf pondweed (**Potamogeton crispis L.**), speedwell (**Veronica** spp.), and common duckweed (**Lemna minor L.**). Mechanical control of these aquatic weeds was inefficient and laborious. Lack of access roads to many of the ditches made maintenance difficult. In areas that were inaccessible for mobile equipment, a team of horses was used to drag a chain down the ditch to tear the weeds loose. The loosened weeds would then float down the ditch to the pumping plant where they were removed with a clamshell bucket, and by hand labor, using pitchforks. Following construction of access roads, a tractor equipped with a side boom was used to drag a chain down the ditch for loosening the weeds. As time progressed, a 20 ft rake was fabricated which was handled by a crane in the same manner as a dragline bucket. This method, too, was slow and expensive due to the labor required.

The mechanical method was improved upon by the use of three-isomer xylene (socal), a liquid aromatic petroleum product administered directly into the water. This chemical had a burning effect on the aquatic growth, causing the portion of the weed above ground to slough off. The root was not affected; therefore, repeated treatments were necessary; about every 4 weeks. The chemical was easy to apply and one man could treat all the ditches in approximately 3 days. A sprayer with a 300 gal tank was used for injecting the chemical into the stream. Socal is refined with the highest aromatic content possible to give optimum kill, and was used successfully for aquatic weed control. However, because this water is pumped into the main stem of the Columbia River, the Washington State Pollution Commission, along with the state and Federal fishery agencies, requested that the Corps of Engineers seek other nontoxic chemicals for treating aquatic vegetation.

Results and Discussion

For this study, drainage ditches 12-1 and 12-2 in the Pasco area were treated with a socal-diquat combination for control of aquatic weeds. Fish (4 to 5-inch rainbow trout) were placed in the ditches approximately 20 ft from the discharge pump intakes 24 hr before the test date. This was to allow the fish to become accustomed to the change in water quality and to eliminate any mortalities before the test.

One and two-tenths miles of drain 12-1 were tested, the application being 2 gal socal per cfs and 1.0 gal of diquat per cfs, the flow of water being 20 cfs. Xylene plus 1.5% of emulsifier (ADH-10) was injected into the water through a small orifice under 75 psi for a period of 30 minutes. Diquat was slowly poured into the water over a period of time. Water temperature at drain 12-1 was 50° F. The water was clear with a moderately heavy growth of aquatic plants. The most prevalent aquatic weeds were sago pondweed and speedwell.

The fish traps in drains 12-1 and 12-2 were examined following the complete discharge (4 hr) of the chemicals from the drainage ditches. All the fish in drain 12-2 were dead, excluding the future use of socal. Drain 12-1 empties into a 10 acre pond before being discharged into the Columbia River. All the fish survived this treatment due to the diluting effect of the ponding area before discharge. The fish were held for a period of 23 hr and were alive after this period and were released.

Eighteen hours after treating ditches 12-1 and 12-2 with the socal-diquat combination, the speedwell had turned brown and was flattened on the ditch bottom. This plant was turning soft and small sections were breaking off and disintegrating in the flowing water. After 3 weeks speedwell and sago pondweed were completely killed.

Drainage ditch 5-D in Kennewick was treated with 1 gal of diquat per cfs (10 cfs flow). The action was slower than with the socal-diquat combination, but the results were very satisfactory. This ditch required only two treatments during the entire summer, demonstrating a slower reaction with diquat alone, but a longer sustained inhibition of plant growth. The amount of chemical used was equal to 26.7 ppm in the flowing water. The fish in the drainage ditch (mainly carp and suckers) would avoid the chemical when possible, but no adverse effects were noted.

The results indicate that diquat can be used directly in the flowing stream or in combination with socal. It can be used in a 2% solution to spray ditchbank weeds and also over water surface to control algae. Spraying for algae must be carried out every 2 weeks during hot weather. Application of diquat to the flowing stream at the rate of 20 to 28 ppm will control all submerged plants in this area for a period of 6 to 8 weeks on each treatment.

Several incomplete experiments point to the possibility of dropping the concentration of diquat to 18 ppm and still obtaining satisfactory plant control. This chemical was not found to be harmful to fish in this experiment in concentrations up to 27 ppm. Diquat controlled the algae during treating for submerged vegetation and no other chemical affected algal growth.

Socal, being highly toxic to aquatic life, could not be used in concentrations above 10 ppm, and the point of injection would have to be at least 2 miles from the discharge, to prevent socal from entering the river system.

ENVIRONMENTAL EFFECTS

Residues in Irrigated Crops

Methods and materials

Six crops were grown in the greenhouse in fertilized loam soil. Except for potatoes, seedlings were thinned to an appropriate stand after emergence of the crops. A random block design was used throughout the experiment. Crops used in the experiment were potatoes, grain sorghum, soybeans, Romaine lettuce, carrots, and onions. (40).

Two irrigation methods were used to apply the herbicides to the crops—simulated overhead sprinkler and soil irrigation. The simulated overhead sprinkler method was developed during this study and was modified as the work progressed. For the potato crop, which was grown first, 10 ml of each herbicide solution was applied directly on the foliage of each plant. However, a new method was developed after the potato crops had been treated. This new method, which was used for all the other crops, was as follows: Every 3 min during a 4-hr period, each plant received drops of water from an overhead sprinkling can such that at the end of the treatment period one acre-in. of solution had been applied. Because of the frequency of the relatively small individual applications, the plants were wet throughout the treatment period. It is felt that this method closely simulates the type of irrigation achieved with a Rainbird^R sprinkler.

In the simulated soil irrigation method of herbicide application, the irrigation solution in an amount sufficient to provide 1 acre-in. of water was applied to each crock. The dimensions of the crocks were such that 1 lb per crock provided 1 acre-in.

Treatment of crops

Crops used in this experiment were treated as follows:

a. Potatoes—White potatoes were grown from seed pieces in 5 gal glazed crocks. The early application of the herbicides was made 117 days after planting when tubers were just beginning to develop. The potatoes were harvested 10 days after treatment (127 days after planting). Considerable variability in tuber size was observed. Another group of potato plants, grown at the same time, was treated with the herbicide solutions 158 days after planting. The potatoes treated at the more mature stage were harvested 168 days after planting. Considerable variability in tuber size was also observed in these potatoes.

b. Grain Sorghum—An early-maturing, dwarf variety of grain sorghum (NK-22) was selected for green house planting. Seeds were planted in fertilized soil in 2-gal glazed crocks. A single plant was grown in each crock. The early application of the herbicide was made 55 days after planting, i.e., the point in plant development when the most advanced grain in the developing panicle was in the milk stage. Most of the sorghum plants had two or more tillers, some of which were considered to be in the early boot stage. The late application of the same herbicide was made on another group of sorghum plants 77 days after planting, the point in plant development when the most advanced grain in the panicle was in the firm-to-hard dough stage. All sorghum plants were harvested 87 days after planting. Harvesting consisted of severing all plants at the crown and separately weighing and bagging the grain and chopped foliage. Both foliage and grain samples were immediately frozen after collection and weighing.

c. Soybeans—The Hawkey 63 variety of soybeans was selected for greenhouse planting. Seeds were planted in fertilized soil in 2-gal crocks. A single plant was grown in each crock. The early application of the herbicide was made 44 days after planting during what would be considered the early pod stage, i.e., when the most advanced inflorescences had set fruit. Upper portions of the soybean plants were still flowering profusely. The late application of the same herbicide was made on another group of soybean plants 92 days after planting during what would be considered the mature pod stage, i.e., when pods on the lower portions of the plants were turning yellow. Even though the lower leaves had begun to change color, most of the foliage and upper pods were still green. Early soybean plants were harvested 107 and late plants 118 days after planting. Beans were shelled and kept frozen at approximately 0°F until analyzed.

d. Romaine Lettuce—Romaine lettuce was cultured in 2-gal glazed crocks. Each crock contained three plants. Treatments at the early stage of plant development was made 42 days after planting when the leaves had begun to cup. Treatment at the mature stage of growth was made 55 days after planting when leaves were densely cupped. Both early- and late-treated Romaine lettuce plants were harvested, bagged, weighed, and frozen 60 days after planting.

e. Six carrot plants (var. Imperator) were grown in each 2-gal glazed crock. The group of carrots selected for the early application of herbicide solution was treated 56 days after seeding. Before the group of mature carrot plants was treated, an evaluation of herbicidal concentrations was made. Subsequent treatment concentrations were increased to five times that used on previous crops. These higher concentrations were applied to the mature carrot plants 89 days after seeding. All carrot plants were harvested 103 days after seeding.

f.   Onions—White, sweet Spanish onions (Burpee-5274) were planted in 2-gal glazed crocks. Each crock had at least three vigorous plants and the herbicidal solution was applied to the group of plants considered to be in an early stage of development 78 days after planting. Bulbs were beginning to swell and were approximately 1/4-1/2 in. in diameter. Herbicidal solution was applied to the group of plants considered to be in a mature stage of development 115 days after planting. Bulbs were well developed at this stage (approximately 1/2 in. in diameter) but were not considered to be "drying-off." Concentrations of the herbicides were identical with those applied to the carrots at the mature stage of development. All onions were harvested 125 days after seeding. The foliage was weighed and discarded along with the roots. The bulbs were washed to remove residual soil, weighed, and placed in polyethylene bags for freezer storage until analysis.

Residue analysis

Methods of analysis.   The methods of analysis for residues of the diquat included in this study were based largely on methods previously reported in the literature. (13). It was necessary to modify or adapt these methods to the crop-herbicide combination involved in our studies before reliable results could be achieved.

Results of analysis.   Diquat residue results are summarized in Table 5. No diquat was detected in any of the crops studied within the limits of the sensitivity of the method.

Response to Aerobic Community Metabolism

The success of an aquatic plant management program depends not only on control of the nuisance macrophyte, but also on avoidance of detrimental side-effects. Fish mortality and degraded aesthetics caused by dissolved oxygen depletion sometimes follow chemical treatment of dense stands of submersed macrophytes. Dissolved oxygen problems occur when the aerobic metabolism of an aquatic community becomes severely unbalanced. The response of aerobic community metabolism, the relationship between all photosynthetic production and total aerobic respiration, is an important consideration in evaluating an aquatic plant management program. (4,5,6).

The contribution of the phytoplankton assemblage to total aerobic community metabolism was measured in the top meter of the water column with DO based light and dark bottles. The bottles were exposed during the entire period of community net production indicated by the diurnal DO curves. Nighttime respiration (extrapolated from the rate of DO consumption in the dark bottles) was subtracted from net production (DO accumulation in the light bottles during exposure) to give a 24-hr oxygen budget for the phytoplankton assemblage. At the moderate-growth station duplicate series of bottles were set and the results averaged. During the comparisons of the treated and untreated bays a set was run in each bay.

Results and Discussion

Beginning the day after treatment, the stations with heavy and moderate macrophyte growth displayed consistently negative oxygen budgets; i.e., community oxygen production. Approximate equilibrium between days with positive and days with negative oxygen budgets was reached 6 to 7 weeks after treatment. This balance was still in effect a year later. The dashed regression lines (oxygen budgets against days after treatment) of the heavy and moderate growth stations have negative intercepts and slopes significantly different from zero at $P<0.005$ (t-test of the regression), substantiating periods of consistently negative oxygen budgets and trends toward recovery. Net community oxygen consumption, represented by negative oxygen budgets after treatment, was supported by diffusion from the atmosphere maintaining DO at levels sufficient to prevent fish mortality. The light growth station showed no posttreatment change in the pattern of its daily oxygen budgets. The light growth regression line has a positive intercept and the slope does not significantly deviate from zero. This indicates a slight, steady predominance of positive oxygen budgets.

Consistently negative oxygen budgets at the heavy and moderate growth stations after treatment are probably due to the cessation of macrophyte photosynthesis and the beginning of bacterial degradation. The subsequent recovery, however, is not due to macrophyte regrowth because the macrophytes disappeared from the water column in 6 weeks and did not reappear until the following spring. Return of total aerobic community metabolism to equilibrium was probably due in part to gradual loss of dead plant material from the water column and in part to increases in numbers and productivity of phytoplankton. At the heavy and moderate growth stations, phytoplankton numbers increased after treatment and returned to pretreatment levels the following summer. The 24-hr oxygen budgets of dry weight) of egeria per m^2 was lost from the water column during the 6 weeks following treatment decreasing the pretreatment biomass by 97%. Assuming ash-free dry weight to be $(CH_2O)_n$, there was a calculated loss of 6.2 moles per m^2 of reduced carbon compounds. Complete oxidation of this reduced carbon would require approximately the same number of moles of O_2 ($CH_2O + O_2 \rightarrow CO_2 + H_2O$). The possible range in number of moles of O_2 consumed per m^2 in the heavy growth station during the 6 weeks after treatment was calculated from the extremes in possible oxygen budgets to be from 1.5 to 4.7 moles O_2 per m^2. Depending on actual diffusion between 24 and 76% of the macrophyte biomass that disappeared from the water column may have been broken down aerobically. The remainder contributed to the bottom sediments of were decomposed anaerobically.

The reduction of a large crop of macrophytes following a chemical weed control program in Chickahominy Reservoir altered aerobic community metabolism in areas of moderate and heavy infestation. The return of aerobic community metabolism in the affected areas to equilibrium within 6 weeks, without a period of DO depletion, was an important factor in the overall impact of the project including the avoidance of fish kills, the stability of the macroinvertebrate community, and favorable public reaction.

HEALTH EFFECTS

Acute and Subacute Toxic Effects

The acute oral LD_{50} for diquat dibromide (Table 6) ranges between 100 and 231 mg/kg in rabbits, guinea pigs, dogs, mice, and rats. Although a residue of ethylene dilumide exists in the commercial product, no toxic effects at the level used for weed control have been observed. (12,13,16,21,22,24,25,26,38,42).

The acute oral LD_{50} for humans is reported to be 50 mg/kg. A case of human poisoning by inhalation of diquat aerosol has been reported. The symptoms began with myalgia, periorbital headache, and a cough productive of thick, red sputum. On admission to a hospital four days later, the man was confused, with neck stiffness, cough, and a fever of nearly 105°F. He had consolidation of part of the right lung. Three days later he had not responded to treatment (the cause was not yet known) and his temperature was higher, and the following day he had wet rales over his entire chest, his eyes were slightly yellow, and he had a rash on his arm. After discovery that the man had been spraying diquat, treatment was begun. Improvement was rapid with chest X-rays normal after five days of this treatment.

Symptoms of human ingestion of a lethal dose of diquat included gastrointestinal symptoms, ulcerations of mucous membranes, acute renal failure, toxic liver damage, cerebral symptoms due to bleeding into the brain stem, and pulmonary complications including exudate and hyaline membranes. (11,30,41,44).

Although one drop of 20% diquat in the eye of a rabbit is reported to cause only minor redness which clears in two days (16), several cases of severe injury to human eyes have been reported (14,15) after splashing a mixture of diquat and paraquat, a closely related compound, plus a surface-active agent. In each case, initial irritation was mild, but after a delay of several days, a serious superficial ocular burn developed. In two cases, this injury left corneal scarring.

Inflammation and bleeding of the nasal mucosa have been observed in people handling diquat powder or walking through spray drift. A 20% solution of diquat in contact with the base of the nail for a few minutes disturbs nail growth by preventing normal maturation of cells (16).

Oral administration of a lethal dose of diquat to rats causes accumulation of water in the lumen of the gastrointestinal tract with dehydration of other tissues including blood (17,18). 50% of the rats died in three days and the rest within nine days. Histological changes after diquat poisoning are not severe enough to account for death, and these authors propose that death is due to severe dehydration.

Diquat ingested orally is poorly absorbed. About 95% is excreted in the feces in two days, with 70% of this being in the form of metabolic products produced by the bacteria of the gastrointestinal tract (19). The other 5% appeared in the urine within two days.

Diquat given intravenously is not metabolized. Diquat administered subcutaneously is nearly all excreted in the urine, and no metabolities are found (19). This suggest that a small part of the metabolities produced by bacteria can be absorbed.

Diquat is absorbed very slowly through the lungs of rats, probably because of its lipid insolubility. It is also very poorly absorbed through the skin as only 0.3% of the dose applied to the human forearm is excreted in the urine within five days. (35).

Feeding Studies

After a single oral dose of ^{14}C diquat dibromide to cows about 0.001 to 0.015% of the dose is excreted in the milk. (41).

When rats were fed 250 pmm diquat ion for eight weeks, analysis of tissues intervals indicated the absence of any accumulation. After seven days back on normal diet, diquat could not be detected in any tissue (30). Slices of rat lung and brain in vitro did not accumulate diquat significantly (34).

Administration of diquat to starved rats prevents the normal depletion of liver glycogen. There is an increase in blood glucose which returns to normal values after about seven hours. Plasma corticosteroids increase to very high concentrations and remain high for at least 24 hours, but plasma ACTH is only increased for four hours (33). These increases are delayed about one hour after oral administration, and can be prevented by pretreatment of the rats with dexamethasone (18).

Effect on Reproduction and Fertility

One three-generation study in rats has been done (22) and showed no effect on fertility or reproduction at 125 ppm, although there was some growth retardation. The higher dose used, 500 ppm, was inappropriately high for type of study and caused growth retardation in all litters. It also caused cataracts in the eyes of more than half of the adults. No physical anomalies or behavioral changes were observed.

Two reproduction studies have been cited as evidence for the non-teratogenicity of diquat (22) but the methodology is inappropriate because the mother rats had time to alter their processing of the chemical for excretion before the sensitive period, organogenesis.

The same test was applied to CD-1 mice using oral route of administration, and no antifertility effect was noted (1). This study used more animals and more stringent assay for fertility prior to treatment, but the dose was much lower. The methods and discussion section say the maximum dose used was 10 mg/kg day, but all seven tables give the maximum as 1 mg/kg. 10 mg/kg is 1/23 of the oral LD_{50}, far below the LD_5. This dose was given five consecutive days, totaling 1/5 LD_{50}, but even counting the apparent cumulative toxicity of diquat, this dose was still low.

Mutagenic Effects

Diquat was consistently negative in many different microbial mutagenicity screening systems (1,2,23,36,37).

Diquat was negative for mutagenic activity in the Drosophila sex-linked recessive lethality test (3). The rate was 0.11% after treatment, compared to a spontaneous rate of 0.14%. The spontaneous rate usually found in this test, averages 0.10%.

Carcinogenic Effects and Chronic Toxicity

In long-term studies designed to characterize the induction of cataracts by diquat, cataract formation required chronic feeding of 2.5 mg/kg/day in rats or 5 mg/kg/day in dogs. These did not progress when diquat was removed from the diet (16).

Diquat cataracts differ from others in the rat. They develop through a posterior opacity, which may be rich in ribonucleoprotein, to a dense nuclear cataract, with cortical opacity developing only at a late stage as the lens shrinks. In this respect, it resembles cataract due to irradiation, but is unlike it as no damage to cell nuclei of the lens epithelium occurs. Fresh extracts of bovine lens form free radicals of diquat in the dark by reduction with glutathione reductase and NADPH. Sunlight catalyzes the formation of free diquat radical and the oxidation of ascorbic acid by diquat (22,29). However, the amount of light does not affect the rate of cataract formation, and the defect is not inhibited by giving supplementary ascorbic acid even through ascorbic acid content is often lower than normal in the aqueous humor of an eye showing cataract (16).

Chronic feeding of diquat produces cataracts in the eyes of rats and dogs at doses of 2.5 mg/kg/day and 5 mg/kg/day respectively. It is not known whether the injury leading to cataract formation is repaired when exposure ceases or is merely dormant until further exposure. Cataracts have not been reported in people having regular occupational exposure to diquat.

Mode of Action

Diquat can be reduced to an autooxidizable free radical by reduced nicotinamide adenine dinucleotide (NADPH*) and glutathione reductase, and photochemically in the presence of ethylene-ditetro amine (EDTA) or other electron donors. Hydrogen peroxide is formed in the aerobic autooxidation of diquat free radical, and superoxide radicals are produced by the air oxidation of diquat free radicals (39). Diquat stimulates NADPH oxidase activities in rat liver microsomes and postmicrosomal soluble fraction. It has little effect on oxygen uptake by rat liver mitochondria, and so probably does not penetrate the mitrochondrial membrane (26). Diquat increases the activity of the pentose phosphate pathway in order to generate more NADPH (35).

Microsomal mixed-function oxidases are extremely important in the biotransformation of lipophilic chemicals, and this ubiquitous enzyme system requires NADPH and molecular oxygen for maximum catalytic activity. The microsomal electron transport system shuttles reducing equivalents from NADPH to the terminal oxidase, cytochrome P-450, which is a carbon monoxide binding hemoprotein (41).

Interactions between microsomal enzymes and bipyridyls have received little attention, (26) reported that diquat (0.1 mM) and paraquat (1.0 mM) stimulate a carbon monoxide insensitive, microsomal NADPH oxidase, and further be demonstrated formation of diquat and paraquat free radicals under anaerobic conditons.

The redox properties of the microsomal electron transport system are not well defined, but acceptors such as cytochrome c (+0.22 v) and methylene blue (+0.01 v) are well-known inhibitors of microsomal oxidations. To define better the mechanism of diquat inhibition the inhibitory potency of a series of compounds with redox potentials ranging between -0.18 and -0.55 v was measured. The most effective inhibitor had a redox potential of -0.18 v and the least potent had a redox potential of -0.55 v.

To determine whether a simple electro-chemical interaction was responsible for inhibition, diquat was preincubated with each of the components of the incubation medium, but such a procedure did not change the degree of inhibition. Epoxidation, miline hydroxylation, dihydroisodrin hydroxylation, and p-chloro-N-methylaniline demethylation can be inhibited by low concentrations $10^{-6} - 10^{-5}$M) of diquat (39) and it is likely that such inhibition is associated with disruption of the microsomal electron transport system which includes cytochrome P-450. Biphasic reduction of diquat and paraquat has been demonstrated under anaerobic conditions, and these rate profiles contrast with the monophasic curves (26). The hypothesis that bipyridyls inhibit due to interference with microsomal electron transport is being further tested in efforts to describe the mode of action of these potent inhibitors of microsomal mixed-function oxidases.

Chemical weed management with diquat is often undertaken to increase or protect the recreational potential of a reservoir. The success of the program depends not only on the control of the nuisance plant(s), but also avoidance of detrimental side effects to the fishery. Direct harm may occur from toxicity of herbicides to fish or food chain organisms. The effects of professional diquat herbicide application, however, are rarely a problem due to speedy disappearance of the chemicals from the water, and rapid reproduction of sensitive food chain organisms. Indirect harm may occur from detrimental alterations in habitat or food supply following weed removal.

If weed management, not eradication, is employed, the net result of weed control on fish food supply is not negative and there is evidence that fish production may increase due to better efficiency in energy flow. A successful weed management program can be both well received by fishermen and economically sound, producing a high benefit to cost ratio. In short, chemical weed control can be a useful technique in reservoir fishery management if applied judiciously with an understanding of effects on all components of the ecosystem.

REFERENCES

1. Anderson, Kenneth J., E.G. Leighty, and M.T. Takahashi. 1972. Evaluation of herbicides for possible mutagenic properties. J. Agr. Food Chem. 20, 649-656

2. Anderson, Diana, D.B. McGregor, and I.F.H. Purchase. 1976. Dominant lethal studies with paraquat and diquat in male CD-1 Mice. Mutation Research 40, 349-358.
3. Benes, V. and Sram, R. 1969. Mutagenic activity of some pesticides in **Drosophila melanogaster**. Industr. Med Surg. 38, 442-444.
4. Berry, C.R., C.B. Schreck, and R.V. Corning. 1975. Control of egeria in a Virginia water supply reservoir. Hyacinth Contr. J. 13:24-26.
5. Berry, C.R., and C.B. Schreck. 1975. Aquatic macroinvertebrates response to field application of the combined herbicides diquat and endothall. Bull. Environ. Contam. Toxical. 14:374-379.
6. Berry, C.R., and C.B. Schreck, S. Van Horn, and R. Strange. 1975. Angler oriented objectives of an aquatic weed control program. Proc. 29th Ann. Conf. Southeast. Assoc. Game Fish. Comm.
7. Blackburn, R.D. 1963. Evaluating herbicides against aquatic weeds. Weeds 11:21-24.
8. Blackburn, R.D., L.E. Bitting, and L.W. Weldon. 1966. Control of elodea in a residential situation. Hyacinth Contr. J. 8:4-9.
9. Blackburn, R.D., L.W. Weldon, R.R. Yeo, and T.M. Taylor. 1969. Identification and distribution of certain similar appearing submersed aquatic weeds in Florida. Hyacinth Contr. J. 8:17-21.
10. Blackburn, R.D. 1976. Effective Control of an aquatic weed nuisance. Public works. (May 1976.)
11. Burton, Jerry A., T.H. Gardiner, and L.S. Schanker. 1974. Absorption of herbicides from the rat lung. Arch. Environ. Health 29, 31-33.
12. Bus, J.S., M.M. Preache, S.Z. Cagen, H.S. Posner, B.C. Eliason, C.W. Sharp, J.E. Gibson. 1975. Fetal toxicity and distribution of paraquat and diquat in mice and rats. Toxicology and Applied Pharmacology 33, 450-460.
13. Calderbank, A., "The Bipyridylium Herbicides," 1968. Advances in Pest Control Research, 8:127-235.
14. Cant, J. Stanley and Lewis, D.R.H. 1968a. Ocular damage due to paraquat and diquat. British Medical Journal 2:224.
15. Cant, J. Stanley and Lewis, D.R.H. 1968b. Ocular damage due to paraquat and diquat. British Medical Journal 3:59.
16. Clark, D.G. and Hurst, E.W. 1970. The toxicity of diquat. British Journal of Industrial Medicine 27, 51-55.
17. Crabtree, Helen C., Lock, Edward A., and Rose, Michael S. 1977. Effect of diquat on the gastrointestinal tract of rats. Toxicology and Applied Pharmacology 41, 585-595.
18. Crabtree, Helen C. and Rose, Michael S. 1976. Early effects of diquat on plasma corticosteroid concentrations in rats. Biochemical Parmacology 25, 2465-2468.

19. Daniel, H.W. and Gage, J.C. 1966. Absorption and excretion of diquat and paraquat in rats. Brit. J. Industr. Med. 23, 133.
20. Davies, P.J. and Seaman, D.E., 1969. "The tetrazolium reaction as a measure of the action of diquat in elodea," Weed Science, Vol 16, pp 329-331.
21. Folmar, L.C. 1977 Bibliograph of diquat toxicity to aquatic organisms. Technical paper No. 88. Fish and wildlife service. USDI. Washington, D.C.
22. FAO/WHO 1973. Evaluations of Some Pesticide Residues in Food. FOA/AGP/1972/M/9/1.
23. Fahrig, R. 1974. Comparative mutagenicity studies with pesticides. IARC Sci. Publ. 10, 161-176.
24. Faust, S.D. and A. Zarins. Interaction of diquat and paraquat with clay minerals and carbon in aqueous solutions. 1964. Residue Review, 29:151-170.
25. Funderburk, H.H., Jr., 1969. Diquat and paraquat, **in Degradation of Herbicides**, K.C. Kearney and D.E. Kaufman, ed., Marcel Dekker, N.Y.
26. Gage, J.C. 1968. The action of paraquat and diquat on the respiration of liver cell fractions. Biochem J. 109:757-761.
27. Gangstad, E.O. 1978. Chemical control of hydrilla. J. Aquatic Plant Manage. 16:38-40.
28. Hesser, E.F., R.W. Lowry and E.O. Gangstad. 1972. Aquatic plant problems in the Walla Walla District. Hyacinth Control J. 11:9-13.
29. Larsson, B., A. Oskarsson and J. Tjalve. 1977. Binding of parquat and diquat on melanin. Exp. Eye Res. 25, 353-359.
30. Litchfield, M.H., J.W. Daniel and S. Longshaw. 1973. The tissue distribution of the bipyridylium herbicides diquat and paraquat in rats and mice. Toxicology 1:155-165.
31. MacKenzie, J.W. and L. Hall. 1967. Elodea control in southeast Florida with diquat. Hyacinth Contr. J. 6:37-44.
32. Manning, J.H. and R.E. Johnson. Water level manipulation and herbicide application an integrated control method for Hydrilla in a Louisiana Reservoir. Hyacinth Contr. J. 13:11-17.
33. Rose, Michael S., H.C. Crabtree, K. Fletcher and I. Wyatt. 1974. Biochemical effects of diquat and paraquat. Biochem J. 138, 437-443.
34. Rose, Michael S., E.A. Lock, L.L. Smith and I. Wyatt. 1976a. Paraquat accumulation; tissue and species specificity. Biochemical Pharmacology 25, 419-423.
35. Rose, Michael S., L.L. Smith and I. Wyatt. 1976. The relevance of pentose phosphate pathway stimulation in rat lung to the mechanism of paraquat toxicity. Biochemical Pharmacology 25, 1763-1767.

36. Shirasu, Y., M. Moriya, Y. Kato, A. Furuhashi and T. Kada. 1976. Mutagenicity screening of pesticides in the microbial system. Mutation Research 40, 19-30.
37. Siebert, D. and E. Lemperle. 1974. Genetic effects of herbicides: Induction of mitotic gene conversion of Saccharomyces cerevisiae. Mutation Research 22, 111-120.
38. Simsiman, G.V., T.C. Daniel and G. Chester. 1976. Diquat and endothall: their fates in the environment. Residue Reviews 62, 131-174.
39. Stancliffe, T.C. and A. Antoinette. 1971. The production of superoxide radicals in reactions of the herbicide diquat. Febs Letters 17, 297-299.
40. Stanford Research Institute. 1970. *Investigations of Herbicides in Water and Crops Irrigated with Water Containing Herbicides*, Stanford University, Stanford, Calif.
41. Stevens, M.A. and J.K. Walley. 1966. Tissue and milk residues arising from the ingestion of single doses of diquat and paraquat by cattle. J. Sci. Fd. Agri. 17, 472-475.
42. U.S. Environmental Protection Agency. 1981. Tolerances for pesticides in food administered by the Environmental Protection Agency-Diquat Federal Register 46:58 343.
43. Weiss, Susan V. and W.H. Beckert. 1975. Herbicide effects on cultured animal cells. J. Cell Biol. 67, 451a.
44. Wood, Tom E., E. Edgar and J. Salcedo. 1976. Recovery from inhalation of diquat aerosol. Chest 70, 774-775.
45. Yeo, R.R. 1972. Annual Report. U.S. Department of Agriculture, Agricultural Research Service, University of California, Davis, California.

Table 1.   Herbicide Activity and Fish Toxicity of Selected Herbicides on Hydrilla in Growth Pool Studies.[1]

Herbicide	Rate (ppmw)	Weeks After Treatment			Fish Toxicity[2]
		2	4	8	
Diquat	0.5	53	60	80	0
	1.0	65	85	93	0
Diquat + CSP	0.5 + 0.5	72	100	100	0
	1.0 + 1.0	90	100	100	0
Copper sulfate	1.0	57	48	37	0
Copper sulfate encapsulated[3]	1.0	10	28	35	0

[1]Each value is the average of three replications expressed as percent control.
[2]Percent mortality of bluegills 8 weeks after treatment.
[3]Encapsulated slow release experimental herbicide.
From: Gangstad. 1978. Chemical control of hydrilla. J. Aquatic Plant Manage. 16:38-40. With permission.

Table 2.   Comparison of Diquat Plus Copper Complex and Diquat Plus Copper Sulfate for Percent Control of Hydrilla in Inglis Reservoir.[1]

Treatment Means	Days After Treatment						
	3	7	14	28	48	82	128
Diquat + Copper[2] 1.0 + 0.46	3	43	60	48	70	76	44
Diquat + Copper[3] 1.0 + 0.86	12	43	60	78	90	93	74

[1] Hydrilla control expressed as average of visual observation at 8 sampling stations.
[2] Copper in form if triethanolamine copper complex (Cutrine).
[3] Copper in form of inorganic copper sulfate pentahydrate.
From: Gangstad. 1978. Chemical control of hydrilla. J. Aquatic Plant Manage. 16:38-40 with permission.

Table 3. Copper and Diquat in Solution (ppmw) After Treatment for Control of Hydrilla in Inglis Reservoir.[1]

Water Sample	Days after treatment			
	1	3	7	14
	Copper content			
Diquat + Cutrine copper				
1.0 + 0.46				
Top	0.040	0.015	0.009	0.006
Bottom	0.032	0.015	0.011	0.006
Diquat + CSP				
1.0 + 0.86				
Top	0.168*	0.064	0.011	0.009
Bottom	0.092	0.040	0.026	0.023
	Diquat content			
Diquat + copper				
1.0 + 0.46				
Top	0.90	0.26	ND	ND
Bottom	0.45	0.29	ND	ND
Diquat + CSP				
1.0 + 0.86				
Top	1.69*	0.92*	0.02	ND
Bottom	0.66	0.11	0.02	ND

[1] Top and bottom water samples were collected at 8 stations, below the surface and 0.3 m above the hydrosoil, respectively. Asterisk denotes significance at 95% of the significance level.
From: Gangstad, 1978. Chemical Control of hydrilla, J. Aquatic Plant. Manage. 16:38-40. With permission.

Table 4. Water Quality Data of Diquat Plus Copper Sulfate and diquat Plus Copper Complex Treated Plots in Inglis Reservoir for Control of Hydrilla, for Pretreatment (8-1) and Post Treatment Sampling, 30 Days (9-17) and 60 Days (10-14) After Treatment.

Date and treatment	Dissolved oxygen (ppm)	Calcium Carbonate Alkalinity (ppm)	NH$_3$	Nitrogen NO$_3$-N (ppm)
	Diquat plus copper sulfate			
8-1	6.8	94	0.47	0.06
9-17	6.8	119*	0.26*	0.10*
10-14	5.7	116*	0.15*	0.06*
	Diquat plus copper complex			
8-1	8.0	85	0.40	0.06
9-17	7.3	110*	0.26*	0.10*
10-14	5.7	117*	0.18*	0.06*
	Dates after treatment means			
8-1	7.4	90	0.44	0.06
9-17	7.1	115	0.26*	0.10*
10-14	5.7	117	0.17*	0.06*
	Copper treatment means			
Sulfate	6.4	108	0.29	0.73
Complex	7.0	104	0.28	0.73

*Significant effect associated with diquat treatment.
From: Gangstad, 1978. Chemical control in hydrilla. J. Aquatic Plant Manage. 16:38-40. With permission.

Table 5. Diquat Residues in Irrigated Crops

		Herbicide Application Data			
Crop	Irrigation	Rate ppm	Stage of Maturity of Crop	Days Before Harvest	Diquat Residue, ppm
Potatoes	Sprinkler	0.67	Late	10	< 0.05
	Soil	0.67	Late	10	< 0.05
Sorghum	Sprinkler	0.45	Early	32	< 0.1
	Sprinkler	0.45	Late	10	< 0.1
	Soil	0.45	Early	32	< 0.1
	Soil	0.45	Late	10	< 0.1
Soybeans	Soil	0.45	Early	63	< 0.1
	Soil	0.45	Late	26	< 0.1
	Soil	0.09	Late	26	< 0.1
	Sprinkler	0.45	Early	63	< 0.1
	Sprinkler	0.45	Late	26	< 0.1
Carrots	Sprinkler	0.09	Early	47	< 0.05
	Sprinkler	0.45	Late	14	< 0.05
	Sprinkler	2.25	Late	14	< 0.05
	Soil	2.25	Late	14	< 0.05
Lettuce	Soil	0.09	Late	5	< 0.05
	Sprinkler	0.09	Late	5	< 0.05
	Soil	0.45	Late	5	< 0.05
	Sprinkler	0.45	Late	5	< 0.05
Onions	Soil	2.25	Late	10	< 0.05
	Sprinkler	2.25	Late	10	< 0.05
	Soil	0.45	Late	10	< 0.05
	Sprinkler	0.45	Late	10	< 0.05

From: Yeo. 1972. Annual report. USDA, ARS, Davis, California.

Table 6. Diquat toxicity to aquatic organisms.

Organism	Type of test	Experimental conditions	Toxicity	Reference
Tendipedidae	L,ST,A	a	>100 T(96 H)	Wilson and Bond(1969)
Unnamed chironomids	FP	-	0.5 K (incomplete)	Tatum and Blackburn(1965)
Callibaetis spp.	L,ST,A	a	16.4 T (96 h)	Wilson and Bond(1969)
Lemenphilus spp.	L,ST,A	a	33.0 T (96 h)	Wilson and Bond(1969)
Daphnia pulex	L,ST,A	a,b,c,d,e	1.0 T (8 d) 3.0 K (8 d)	Gilderhaus(1967)
D. magna	L,ST,A	a,b,c,d,e,f	7.1 IC_{50}(26 h)	Crosby and Tucker(1966)
Hyalela azeteca	L,ST,A	a	0.048 T (96 h)	Wilson and Bond(1969)
Unnamed oligochaetes	FP	-	0.5 K (incomplete)	Tatum and Blackburn(1965)
Cardium edule	L,ST,A	-	>10.0 T (24 h)	Portmann and Wilson(1971)
Crassostrea virginica	L,CFT,A	-	1.0 NTE (96 h)	Butler(1965)
Enallagma spp.	L,ST,A	a	>100 T (96 h)	Wilson and Bond(1969)
Libellula spp.	L,ST,A	a	>100 T (96 h)	Wilson and Bond(1969)
Penaeus setiferus	L,CFT,A	-	1.0 NTE (48 h)	Butler(1965)
Crangon crangon	L,ST,A	-	>10.0 T (24 h)	Portmann and Wilson(1971)
Aquatic insects, amphipods, copepods, ostracods	FP	-	1.0 NTE (7 d)	Hilsenhoff(1966)
Pimephales promelas	L,ST,A	a	10.0 NTE (96 h)	Lawrence et al.(1965)
P. promelas	L,ST,A	a,b,c,d,e	Soft water 14.0 T (96 h)	Surber and Pickering(1962)

Table 6. Diquat toxicity to aquatic organisms. (cont.)

Organism	Type of test	Experimental conditions	Toxicity	Reference
P. promelas	FP	-	Hard water 14.0 T (96 h)	Lawrence(1962)
Fundulus similis	L,CFT,A	-	0.5 + 0.5 Paraquat NTE	Butler(1965)
Carassius auratus	FP	a,b,c,d,e	1.0 NTE (48 h)	Gilderhaus(1967)
Rasbora heteromorpha	L,ST,A	a,b,c,d,e	35.0 T (96 h)	Alabaster(1969)
Ictalurus punctatus (fry)	L,ST,A	a,b,c,d,e	70.0 T(48 h)	Jones(1965)
I. punctatus	L,ST,A	a	10.0 NTE (72 h)	Lawrence et al.(1965)
Lepomis cyanellus	FP	a,b,c,d,e	10.0 NTE (96 h)	Yeo(1967)
L. gibbosus	FP	-	1,000 NTE 0.5 + 0.5 Paraquat NTE	Lawrence(1962)
L. macrochirus (fry)	L,ST,A	-	10.0 NTE (12 d)	Hiltibran(1967)
L. macrochirus (fingerlings)	L,ST,A	a,b,c,d,e	525 T (24 h) 150 T (48 h)	Hughes and Davis(1962)
L. macrochirus	FP	a,b,c,d,e	25.0 T (96 h)	Gilderhaus(1967)
L. macrochirus (fry)	L,ST,A	a,b,c,d,e	4.0 NTE (72 h)	Jones(1965)
L. macrochirus	L,ST,A	a	10.0 NTE (96 h)	Lawrence et al.(1965)
L. macrochirus	L,ST,A	a,b,c,d,e	Soft water 140 T (96 h)	Surber and Pickering(1962)

Table 6. Diquat toxicity to aquatic organisms. (cont.)

Organism	Type of test	Experimental conditions	Toxicity	Reference
Micropterus salmoides (fry)	L,ST,A	a,b,c,d,e	Hard water 140 T (96 h)	Jones(1965)
M. salmoides	L,ST,A	a,b,c,d,e	1.0 NTE (72 h) Soft water 7.8 T (96 h)	Surber and Pickering(1962)
M. salmoides	FP	a,b,c,d,e	1,000 NTE	Yeo(1967)
M. salmoides	L,ST,A	-	11.0 T (48 h)	Muirhead-Thompson(1971)
M. salmoides	L,ST,A	a	10.0 NTE (96 h)	Lawrence et al.(1965)
M. salmoides	FP	a	0.5 + 0.5 Paraquat NTE	Lawrence(1962)
Morone saxatilis (larvae)	L,ST,A	a,b,c,e	1.0 T (24, 48, 72, 96 h)	Hughes(1973)
M. saxatilis (fingerlings)	L,ST,A	a,b,c,e	35.0 T (24 h) 25.0 T (24 h) 15.0 T (72 h) 10.0 T (96 h)	Hughes(1973) Hughes(1973
M. saxatilis (fry)	L,ST,A	a,b,c,d,e	35.0 T (34 h) 25.0 T (48 h) 15.0 T (72 h) 10.0 T (96 h)	Hughes(1969)
M. saxatilis (fingerlings)	L,ST,A	a	315 T (24 h)	Wellborn(1969)

Table 6. Diquat toxicity to aquatic organisms. (cont.)

Organism	Type of test	Experimental conditions	Toxicity	Reference
Stizostedion vitreum	FP	a,b,c,d,e	155 T (48 h)	Gilderhaus(1967)
			80.0 T (96 h)	
Esox lucius	FP	a,b,c,d,e	2.1 T (96 h)	Gilderhaus(1967)
Trout	-	-	16.0 T (96 h)	Holden(1964)
			20.0 T (24 h)	Muirhead-Thompson(1971)
Onchorynchus tshawytscha	L,ST,A	-	29.0 T (48 h)	Lawrence et al.(1965)
Salmo gairdneri	L,ST,A	a	5.0 NTE (96 h)	Gilderhaus(1967)
S. gairdneri	FP	a,b,c,d,e	11.2 T (96 h)	Folmar(1976)
S. gairdneri	L,CFT,A	a,b,c,d,e	10.0 NTE; no avoidance	

From: Folmar, L.C. Technical paper NO 88, Fish and Wildlife Science, U.S. Department of the Interior, Washington, D.C. 1977.

Table 6.   Diquat toxicity to aquatic organisms. (cont.)

1. Type of test, letters represent:
   T = Toxicity test, used in conjunction with
   - ST = static
   - CFT = continuous flow
   - A = acute
   - C = chronic
   L = Laboratory toxicity test
   F = Field study, used in conjunction with
   - R = river, stream, or creek
   - M = marine
   - E = estuarine, and
   - O = other
2. Experimental conditions. Factors reported in cited articles:
   - a = water temperature
   - b = pH
   - c = alkalinity
   - d = dissolved oxygen
   - e = dissolved solids
   - f = photoperiod
3. Toxicity, active ingredient. All values in mg/l (ppm) unless otherwise noted. Letters included with numerical values represent:
   - T = LC_{50} (also accompanied by a time factor, e.g., 96 h)
   - K = Kill
   - SB = Sublethal effects
   - NTE = No toxic effect

PART II

EVALUATION OF SELECTED AQUATIC HERBICIDES

Chapter 11

HERBICIDAL, ENVIRONMENTAL AND HEALTH EFFECTS OF ENDOTHALL[1]

INTRODUCTION

Endothall (7-oxabicyclo(2.2.1)heptane-2,3-dicarboxylic acid) is related to cantharidic acid, a chemical found in nature, and unlike almost all other herbicides contains only carbon, hydrogen, and oxygen. It was discovered as having herbicidal properties in 1950 as a dessicant for terrestrial plants. The aquatic herbicidal properties were discovered in 1953, and it was first registered for this purpose in 1960. Endothall, (Aquathol K[R]) is a moderately selective contact herbicide.

The determination of the distribution, persistence, and activity of herbicides in aquatic environments represents an important basic effort leading to an understanding of the true impact of a herbicide on that ecosystem. We need to understand the ecological changes caused by herbicides as well as the acute and chronic toxicity of the chemicals to fish and fish food organisms. Although considerable acute toxicity may result from contact with a herbicide, consequences of long-term exposure of aquatic organisms to the herbicide, is undoubtedly just as significant. A knowledge of the nature of these consequences is essential to permit an evaluation of the total hazard associated with the use of specific herbicides in the aquatic environment.

HERBICIDAL EFFECTS

Endothall is widely used for the control of submersed aquatic weeds in the United States. The USDA conpiliation of registered aquatic uses is given in Table 1. The herbicide is not applied as the free acid, but is applied as the inorganic or amine salts. The most active salts of endothall are: disodium, dipotassium, mono and di-(N,N-dimethyl alkylamine), and dihydroxy aluminum (1,2,29,31).

Endothall is a typical contact type, membrane-active, herbicide. Translocation in aquatic species is apparently limited to the symplast (27). Related research has shown that elodea (**Elodea canadensis**

---

[1]The findings in this report are not to be construed as an official Department of the Army position unless so designated by other authorized documents.

Michx.) metabolizes endothall considerably faster than does pond-weed (**Potamogeton nodosus** Poir.), which may explain the relative resistance of one species and relative susceptibility of another (9,16,20,26).

Extensive field testing of the dihydroxy aluminum salt of endothall showed an increase in herbicidal activity on submersed aquatic weeds (3). The release of the anion of endothall by ion exchange with endogenous anions of the water in the vicinity of the target species appears to be the advantage of this formulation of endothall.

Gatun Lake, Panama Study.

In April 1979, a cooperative field study with the Panama Canal Commission (PCC), and the U.S. Army Engineer Waterways Experiment Station was initiated in the Frijoles Bay area of Gatun Lake, Panama (30). The objectives were to: (a) evaluate the efficacy of two endothall formulations, *i.e.*, Aquathol K[R] and Hydout[R], for hydrilla control; (b) determine the effects of each formulation on water quality and the nontarget planktonic community; (c) evaluate the extent of herbicide dispersion in the test area; and (d) determine persistence of herbicide residues in water, hydrilla, and sediment within the test plots for supporting Federal registration of Hydout and expansion of the current Federal label for Aquathol K.

Three equivalent treatment rates of each formulation were selected for comparison based on a preliminary site survey. The endothall acid equivalent (a.e.) treatment rates were 27, 34, and 50 kg a.e./ha. The treatment rate and formulation combination were randomly assigned to six of eight plots. The remaining two plots were considered as reference areas.

Aquathol K[R] and Hydout[R] were effective at controlling hydrilla within the treatment plots. Aquathol K[R] provided control within 24 to 72 hr posttreatment at each application rate; however, Hydout was much slower, requiring 14 to 21 days before hydrilla knockdown was evident at the two higher application rates. The 27 kg a.e./ha Hydout treatment showed only slight evidence of hydrilla defoliation and biomass reduction prior to plant regrowth to the water surface.

No adverse impacts on selected water quality parameters, e.g. dissolved oxygen, pH, water temperature, total Kjeldahl nitrogen, ammonia nitrogen, and total phosphorus, were observed. Only transitory shifts in the plankton community composition and vertical distribution were observed over the 49-day study period.

Herbicide dispersion from the treated area was apparent during the first 3 days following treatment. Endothall was detected in the water from the buffer zones of those plots treated with Aquathol K[R]. Negligible endothall residues were found in the buffer zones surrounding the plots treated with Hydout throughout the 90-day posttreatment study period. Persistence of endothall in the water from those plots treated with Aquathol K^R and Hydout^R was less than 7 days. However, endothall persistence from those plots treated with Aquathol K^R was less than 3 days in sediment and less than 7 days in plant tissue. Endothall levels in sediment and plant tissue from Hydout-treated plots persisted for more than 21 days following treatment.

Pat Mayse Lake, Texas Study

The problem species within Pat Mayse, a 6000-surface-acre lake is Eurasian watermilfoil which expanded from 50 acres in 1978 to 1000 acres in 1981 and 1982. High lake levels and turbid conditions caused by floodwaters in June, July, and August 1982 reduced the watermilfoil infestation level to approximately 500 acres by August 1982; however, the reduction was only temporary and by October 1983, the watermilfoil had expanded to approximately 600 acres. As a result of the previous infestation levels, conditions in 1983 again resulted in over 90 percent of the recreational shoreline being inaccessible and the seven swimming beaches and three of the projects' eight boat ramps became unusable.

To minimize treatment impacts and maximize public benefits, the control program was limited in its scope by directing efforts toward opening the recreational shoreline, swimming beaches, and boat ramps. As a result, the total treatment acreage was reduced to 93 acres. To further minimize application impacts, within the 93 acres a granular formulation of dipotassium salt of endothall (Aquathol) was selected. Based upon the watermilfoil biomass, shoot density, and 6-to 10-ft water depths, the granular endothall was applied at a rate of 250 lb/acre to achieve the desired concentration level of 2.5 ppm.

Endothall was not detected in the vicinity of the City of Paris is water intake and the drinking water standard for endothall was not exceeded. No endothall was detected in the water, sediments, or fish samples that were collected 30 days after herbicide treatment. None of the water quality parameters were significantly altered due to herbicide use. No impacts of nontarget aquatic organisms were detected. Endothall rapidly dissipated within 72 hr from the treatment areas. Both dispersion (dilution) and biodegradation probably contributed significantly to rapid transfer and degradation.

The rapid removal of endothall from Pat Mayse Lake water was expected. The lack of sorption and persistence of endothall in sediments was also predictable as were the undetectable concentrations in fish tissue.

The treatment program was very successful and approximately 100-percent control of milfoil was obtained in the treatment areas with no adverse effects observed. The aquatic weed problem was alleviated and the lake was returned to normal usage capacity. There was an apparent increase in visitation to Pat Mayse Lake and usage of the treated sites. However, rapid regrowth and dispersal capabilities of milfoil may mean that regular monitoring and continued application of management techniques will be required. Initial reestablishment of milfoil in treated areas was observed approximately 2 months after treatment (19).

ENVIRONMENTAL EFFECTS

Endothall is absorbed by roots and translocated to the tops of plants via the transpiration stream, but it is not translocated from the tops to the roots via the phloem (14,21). Freed *et al.* (9) observed that beet plants rapidly metabolized ^{14}C-endothall and that the $^{14}CO_2$ resulting from this metabolism was incorporated into the constituents. Thomas (26) and Thomas and Seaman (27) investigated the uptake and metabolism of ^{14}C-endothall by excised leaves of **Potamogeton nodosus and Elodea canadensis**. Internal concentrations of ^{14}C label equivalent to 12 and 8 times the concentration of the external solution (0.1 ppm) were obtained in **Potamogeton** and **Elodea**, respectively, after 48 hours of absorption. Endothall moved via phloem in intact **Potamogeton** plants and in unrooted branched plants of **Elodea**. No movement of the herbicide occurred following root treatment in **Potamogeton**. Endothall was metabolized by excised leaf tissue of both **Potamogeton** and **Elodea**; however, the identity of the metabolites resulting from herbicide degradation was not determined in these studies.

Freed (9) investigated the fate of endothall in soil and observed that under conditions favoring high microbiological activity, nearly all of the chemical was degraded in a period of 7-10 days. The results indicated that dissipation of endothall was greater in moist soil than in air-dry soil. Also, the rate of inactivation of the herbicide was more rapid at 20-30°C than at lower temperatures. Horowitz (13) also reported that endothall persisted considerably longer in dry soil than in moist soil. The above findings suggest that the breakdown of endothall in soil is mainly microorganisms enhanced the inactivation of the compound.

In their studies dealing with persistence of various herbicides in pond water and hydrosoil, Frank and Comes (8) found that the amine salt of endothall was relatively less persistent in water than dichlobenil or fenac and was no longer found 24 days following treatment. Hiltibran (12) studied the persistence of endothall in water, both in aquaria and under field conditions. In the field, endothall applied at 0.3 to

10 ppm was not detectable after an average of 2.5 days and a maximum of 4 days. In aquaria, endothall at these rates was detectable for a much longer period. The rate of disappearance of endothall varied directly with the amount of organic material and organisms present in the water.

RESPONSE OF CROPS TO ENDOTHALL IN IRRIGATION WATER

Post Planting Treatments.

Monoamine salt of endothall. Within 3 or 4 days after treatment, the monoamine salt of endothall at 25 ppmw severely wilted soybean plants. Treatments at 1.0 ppmw caused some drooping of the leaves and petioles. After 7 days, 42 percent of the plants on plots treated at 25 ppmw were severely wilted, stunted, and necrotic, and about half of those were almost completely desiccated. Growth on plots treated at 1.0 ppmw was somewhat retarded. One month after treatment at 25 ppmw, 9 percent of the plants were dead. Root systems had been injured extensively. Plants that were not injured fatally had recovered or were recovering rapidly. At the time of observation, injury symptoms were no longer apparent on plots treated at 1.0 ppmw. Despite the early-season injury, seed yields, especially on plots treated at 25 ppmw, were not significantly reduced.

Within 1 week after treatment with the monoamine salt of endothall at 25 ppmw, some of the corn plants, particularly the smaller ones, were slightly stunted, retarded, shrivelled, or partly desiccated. Symptoms characteristic of moisture stress (bluish discoloration to partial chlorosis) were also present. However, recovery was rapid, and yields were not reduced. No injury symptoms were apparent on plots treated at 1.0 ppmw.

The monoamine salt of endothall at 1 or 25 ppmw did not visibly injure the foliage nor reduce the stand or yield of sugarbeets.

Preplanting Treatments

Monoamine salt of endothall. The monoamine salt of endothall at 1.0 or 25 ppmw had not reduced the stand and fresh weight of soybean plants at 6 weeks after emergence of the seedlings. In comparison, the disodium salt of endothall at 1.0 ppmw, which was applied to field beans in 1961 at the 4- to 6-trifoliate leaf stage, caused severe injury and reduced yields (14). The monoamine salt of endothall at 1.0 or 25 ppmw did not decrease the stand or fresh weight of 6-week-old corn plants. No symptoms of injury were noted in the foliage of the sugarbeet seedlings. However, the treatments at 25 ppmw decreased the stand and the fresh weights of the 6-week-old plants significantly at the 5- and 10-percent levels of probability, respectively.

HEALTH EFFECTS

Animal Toxicity

The oral LD_{50}j rates for disodium endothall formulation (Aquathol[R]) (15.5% endothall) is 198 mg/kg and for technical endothall is 51 mg/kg. The oral LD_{50} of di-(N,N-dimethylalkylamine) salt of endothall (Hydrothol 47[R]) (containing 28% endothall) is 206 mg/kg for rats. Subacute toxicity studies with sodium endothall for four months in the diet of dogs revealed no harmful effect at 1,000 ppm. Hydrothol 47[R] was not harmful at 108 ppm, the highest concentration tested.

Radioactive endothall administered orally to rats at 50 ppm in the feed was eliminated completely from all tissues and organs within 72 hours. Endothall was not found in milk nor fat, nor was it transferred through the milk pathway to the feeding pups.

It has been demonstrated in the long term feeding studies in rats and dogs and three generation studies in rats that the apparent "no harmful effect" dosage level for disodium endothall in the most sensitive animal tested (the rat) is in excess of 300 ppm in the diet. This dosage level would be equivalent to a total daily intake of 750 mg per day for a 50 kg human. Based on a one kilogram per day diet, this represents the equivalent to eating one-half of the daily food intake having a residue of 1,500 parts per million of disodium endothall.

This level after being extrapolated to residues in water where a person consumes 2 kg of water on day of application, all of which contains endothall residues, would mean that 3.75 ppm would not constitute a hazard when normally acceptable safety factor of 100 to 1 is used. An additional important safety factor is that endothall residues in water have rapid biological breakdown with smaller amounts being consumed each day for only a few days per year (18).

Dogs given undiluted disodium endothall in capsules at dosages of 20 to 50 mg/kg/day died within three to eleven days. Dogs receiving lower doses showed no definite signs of toxic ill effects except for vomiting and diarrhea before they were sacrificed after six weeks. All dogs showed pathological changes in the gastrointestinal tract after 1 mg/kg/day or more, but no significant changes were found in other organs (18).

When a lethal dose of endothall was given to dogs, rabbits, or cats, they showed a gradual decline in blood pressure until they died from respiratory failure. Electrocardiograms revealed no striking changes until after respiration ceased (18).

Application of 1% endothall to the skin of rabbits produced no lesions, but 10 to 20% produced necrotic lesions with death from absorption occurring in the cases showing the most severe skin lesions. Intravenous administration of 5 mg/kg was sometimes lethal in the dog and rabbit, with the heart as the primary organ of failure. Preliminary findings demonstrated a depressing effect of endothall in dilutions up to 1:200,000 on the isolated frog ventricle and the isolated rabbit auricle (10).

Dermal application of the di-(N,N-dimethyltridecylamine) salt of endothall equivalent to feeding levels of 20 mg/kg/day and 50 mg/kg/day for three weeks to rabbits resulted in deaths of 6 to 20 animals at the higher dose rate. Otherwise, there were no differences between test and control animals in appearance, behavior, or weight changes. The herbicide produced desquamation of the skin, and specific histopathological changes of the liver and kidneys were found in 3 of 20 rabbits at the high dose.

Endothall can cause eye irritation. 0.1 ml of Aquathol[k] in the eyes of rabbits caused conjunctival inflammation and corneal clouding which was not healed seven days later. This might be expected because of its corrosive nature.

Inhalation of endothall at 20 mg/liter caused lung congestion, hemorrhage, and production of mucus in the trachea, and four of ten animals died within one hour at this dose. The cause of death is not given, but the other symptoms are those of severe local irritation (18).

Toxicity to Fish and Water Organisms

The inorganic salts (sodium and potassium) of endothall are safe to fish in concentrations of 100 to 800 ppm. Endothall, because of its low toxicity to fish, low toxicity to the eggs or fry, and the rates of aquatic use, appears to be one of the safest herbicides to use during spawning season. In addition, the toxicity of endothall in water is of relatively short duration.

On the other hand, long chain amine salts are toxic to fish under laboratory conditions at concentrations of 0.5 to 3 ppmw. It is interesting that these amine salts are two to three times more active on aquatic weeds than inorganic salts and 200 to 400 times more toxic to fish. However, these amine salts have been employed in practice with little, if any, fish kill because: *1.* A portion of the chemical is quickly absorbed and decomposed by plants and soil; *2.* For control of algae rates below those toxic to fish are employed; *3.* Label recommendations are to treat lakes or ponds in sections at a time rather than overall bodies of water; *4.* Fish detect presence of these amine salts and move from treated areas; *5.* In irrigation canals concentrations decrease rapidly due to movement of water.

On oysters and clams the inorganic salts (the only ones tested) are safe at 5 to 10 ppm. Endothall is the safest aquatic herbicide on Daphnia, besides 2,4-D. Other fish food organisms are not affected at all by normal rates of either type of endothall salt formulation (6,7,8,22,23).

A summary of toxicity studies on aquatic organisms is given in Table 2 for the type of test, experimental conditions, toxicity in mg/l of the toxicant and the particular formulation.

Chemistry

Endothall has commonly been called 3,6-endoxohexahyhydrophthalic but the proper nomenclature is 7-oxabicyclo[2.2.1]-heptane-2,3-dicarboxylic acid. It is related to cantharidic acid, a chemical found in nature, and unlike almost all other pesticide chemicals it contains only carbon, hydrogen, and oxygen.

Highest herbicidal activity occurs in the amine salts having 12 to 16 carbons. Short chain amine salts are less active. It was established early in the development of endothall that defoliant activity on terrestrial plant foliage was accelerated by the addition of ammonium sulfate, but this is not true for soil or aquatic applications.

The endothall salts are supplied as water concentrates for aquatic use. It is not necessary to use organic solvents or emulsifiers. The tradename for the sodium and potassium salts is Aquathol[R] and for the fatty amine salts Hydrothol[R]. Both control a variety of aquatic weeds. Hydrothol[R], in addition, controls several types of algae. The average recommended use rate for Aquathol[R] is 2 to 3 ppmw for large or total area treatment with a maximum of 5 ppmw for marginal or spot treatment. Recommended use of Hydrothol[R] covers a range of 0.05 to 4 ppmw (15).

Impurities and Breakdown Products

Endothall is synthesized from two four-carbon molecules, furan and maleic anhydride, which contain only carbon, oxygen, and hydrogen atoms. By-products of the reaction are trace amounts of succinic, fumaric, maleic, and malic acids, all four-carbon molecules normal to human metabolism. These impurities are not hazardous (5,15,22,23).

Metabolism in Animals

When ^{14}C-labeled endothall was administered orally to rates, over 90% of the radioactivity was recovered in the feces. The remainder of the radioactivity was recovered from the urine and as expired CP_2. Virtually complete recovery of the administered dose was obtained within 48 hours. The radioactivity in urine and feces was due to unchanged endothall. Small quantities were absorbed and distributed to various tissues; however, none was detected in the fat nor excreted in the milk. This is consistent with the hydrophyllic nature of endothall (24,25).

Three and four week feeding studies in rats were done for the Pennwalt Corporation. 10,000 ppm was lethal to all of the rats, but 1000 ppm (equal to LD_{50}/day) caused no deaths. Slight liver degeneration and focal hemorrhagic areas in the kidneys of a few animals were seen during histopathological examination. 2400 ppm disodium endothall did not affect weight gain and food consumption, but the same level of dipotassium endothall lowered these parameters (18).

Metabolism in Fish

When bluegills were exposed in aquaria to water containing 2 ppm of [^{14}C]endothall, less than 1% of the herbicide was absorbed by the fish. The maximum concentrations of endothall in the fish (0.1-0.2 ppm) was observed 12 hr after treatment; thereafter it did not change significantly up to 96 hr. Radioactivity was detected in viscera, flesh, scales, skin, and head. At all sampling times, the concentration of ^{14}C residues was highest in the viscera and lowest in the flesh. A small but detectable amount of ^{14}C was found in the blood 30 min after treatment.

There was no measurable difference in the herbicide uptake by the fish when they were placed in water bubbled with air alone or a mixture of ozone and air. The results show that the concentration of ^{14}C in the whole fish reached a maximum of 0.1-0.2 ppm 12 hr after treatment. Longer exposure up to 96 hr did not result in a significant change in the total ^{14}C concentration. These findings suggest that bioaccumulation of endothall by fish from water treated with the herbicide is unlikely. This is expected as endothall, due to its polar, hydrophilic nature, is not likely to partition from water into fish (21).

At all sampling times, the concentration of ^{14}C was highest in the viscera and lowest in the flesh. The concentration of radioactivity in the viscera increased up to 24 hr after exposure and declined thereafter, which suggests that it was distributed to other tissues. The relative distribution of total radioactivity in the various tissues was in the following order: viscera > scales > flesh > head + fins > skin. The results of the Pennwalt Corporation (personal communication) have shown that, under field conditions, the residues of endothall in the flesh of fish sampled 24 hr or longer after treating the water with 0.5-5 ppm of the herbicide were below detectable limits (0.02 ppm) as determined by gas-liquid chromatography. In the fish removed within 24 hr of treatment, endothall concentration in the flesh ranged from 0.02 to 0.1 ppm.

After 30-min exposure to water containing 2 ppm of [^{14}C]-endothall, ^{14}C-labeled residues (expressed as endothall) ranging from 0.02 to 0.04 ppm were detected in the blood. After 60 min, the concentration of ^{14}C in the blood increased up to 0.08 ppm. Longer exposure up to 4 hr did not significantly increase the level of radioactivity in the blood.

The concentration of ^{14}C in the various tissues, 48 hr after the fish were fed [^{14}C]endothall through the digestive tract, show that the herbicide is absorbed by the intestinal tract, though the fish were observed to eliminate 73% of the administered herbicide during this period. In the fish fed ^{14}C-labeled herbicide through the digestive tract, like the bath-exposed fish, the concentration of radioactivity was highest in the viscera and lowest in the flesh. The pattern of distribution of radioactivity in the various tissues in the feed-exposed fish was similar to that observed for the bath-exposed fish, with the exception that the scales had a relatively lower proportion of the total radioactivity.

These findings have demonstrated that bluegills absorb endothall directly from water as well as through the intestinal tract. Absorption of endothall on the scales also contributes to the herbicide residues in the fish. This is supported by the observation that the proportion of ^{14}C in the scales decreased when the fish were fed endothall through the digestive tract.

Thin-layer chromatographic analysis of the methanol extract from the fish treated with the herbicide for 48 hr showed that all the ^{14}C in the alcohol extractable fraction was present in the form of unchanged endothall (R$_f$ j0.48 and 0.75 on silica gel and cellulose plates, respectively). The ^{14}C in the extract cochromatographed with authentic [^{14}C]-endothall. In contrast to aquatic microorganisms which were found to readily degrade endothall, bluegills do not appear to be capable of metabolizing the herbicide (22,23).

Metabolism by Aquatic Microorganisms.

When ^{14}C-endothall [7-oxabicyclo(2.2.1)heptane-2,3-dicarboxylic acid] labeled at positions 1 and 2 of the ring was added to a sample of pond water and hydrosoil at a concentration of 5 ppm, more than 25% of the initial radioactivity was evolved as $^{14}CO_2$ within ten days, indicating that aquatic microorganisms readily degrade endothall, possibly through a pathway involving splitting of the oxabicyclo ring. A species belonging to the genus **Arthrobacter** isolated from hydrodoil by an enrichment culture technique was able to utilize endothall as the sole source of carbon for its growth. The growth of the organism increased with an increase in the concentration of endothall up to 2000 ppm in the medium. After short-term (30-60 sec.) incubation of the cells with

^{14}C-endothall, ^{14}C was incorporated into glutamic, aspartic, and citric acids and unknown compound. ^{14}C-glutamic acid accounted for a large proportion of the total ^{14}C assimilated by the cell. It appears that endothall is incorporated into glutamic acid via the TCA cycle as well as through an alternate pathway (22,23).

Tests for Developmental Toxicity.

An adequately designed standard test for teratogenesis in rats was performed for the Pennwalt Corporation, and the result was negative. This study indicates that endothall is not a prenatal teratogen (18).

Test for Effects on Reproduction and Fertility.

An adequately designed, three-generation reproduction study done by Pennwalt was negative, indicating that chronic exposure to low levels of endothall does not interfere with fertility or reproduction in rats (4,10).

Tests for Mutagenic Effects.

Endothall was tested for its ability to induce point mutations in three different miscrobial systems: reversion of 8 different histidine mutants of **Salmonella typhimurium,** forwarded mutation of phage T$_4$, and reversion of rII mutants of T$_4$. It was negative in all of these assays. A test for ability to induce sex-linked recessive lethal mutations in **Drosophila melanogaster** (fruit flies) revealed a mutation rate of 8.5 times the spontaneous rate but an assay for dominant lethal mutations in the rat was negative, and the relationship of these tests to human mutations has not been determined.

Disodium endothall was fed to male rats at 0, 150, 300, or 600 ppm for five days. Two days later, each of the two rats in each group were mated to two females per week for seven weeks. Uteri were examined and did not indicate either pre- or post- implantation dominant lethality. Rat bone marrow cytogenetic analysis was negative for chromosome aberrations (19).

When mixed in the diet, very little endothall is absorbed, but when a concentrated dose is given orally, damage to the lining of the gastrointestinal tract allows greater absorption. Absorption through the skin also seems to be proportional to the degree of desquamtion and necrosis. Limpid solubility appears to be the main factor determining the relative absorption rates of herbicides from the rat lung. Thus, it appears that animal absorption of endothall by any normal route of environmental exposure would be minimal. Administration by the intravenous or intraperitoneal routes is not considered relevant to the environmental risk assessment (17,25).

Endothall is produced by the Diels-Alder reaction of furan and maleic anhydride, followed by reduction of the remaining carbon-carbon double bond, and hydrolysis of the anhydride to a dicarboxylic acid. Endothall is not an epoxide, although cursory viewing of its structure would give that impression. IT is, however, a strained-ring structure, as can be seen from an attempt to build the molecule with space-filling molecular models (CPK models). Because of this property, it is conceivable that it could act as an alkylating agent and might be imagined to have biological effects resembling those of the epoxides or 2-propiolpactone, and a report finding that endothall is a transforming agent in BALB/3T3 cells, in contrast to its apparent lack of activity in other short-term tests for genotocicity and in long-term tests for carcinogenic activity (19). Of particular relevance to transformation data is the finding that endothall was inactive (with or without activation) in producing forward mutations to obtain resistance in BALB/3T3 cells.

It is clear that endothall is not a potent carcinogen in experimental animals. Short-term mutagenesis assays in bacteria and mammalian cells have failed to detect mutagenicity, and a transformation assay in a permanent line of mouse cells shows activity that is not dose-related. In view of the short biological persistence of endothall and its projected infrequent usage, endothall appears to be an appropriate agent for occasional use as an aquatic herbicide (29).

SUMMARY AND CONCLUSIONS

Endothall is the common name for an organic acid (7-oxabicyclo(2.2.1)-heptane-2,3-dicarboxylic acid). Since the defoliant and herbicidal properties of endothall were discovered in 1950, it has been used as a defoliant for a wide range of crops and as a herbicide for a variety of terrestrial and aquatic plants. Commercial formulations available for aquatic use include the granular Aquathol and liquid Aquathol[K], manufactured by the Pennwalt Corporation. Endothall is approved for use on lakes and ponds as a herbicide and algaecide, and as a dessicant and herbicide for terrestrial seed crops. The results of a number of studies show that aquatic microorganisms readily metabolize endothall so the herbicide is not persistent in the aquatic environment. Similar results are obtained in the terrestrial environment. Label requirements for Aquathol[R] include a "danger" that the substance may be fatal if absorbed through the skin, is harmful or fatal if swallowed, and causes skin and eye irritation or damage but the herbicide, used as directed, is not found to be a health hazard.

REFERENCES

1. Armstrong, James G. 1974. A Review of the Literature on the Use of Endothall in Fisheries. Bureau of Sport Fisheries and Wildlife, Washington, D.C.
2. Bartley, T.R. and E.O. Gangstad. 1975. Environmental aspects of aquatic plant control. Journal of the Irrigation and Drainage Division, ASCE. 100:231-244.
3. Blackburn, Robert D. 1966. Weed control in fish ponds in United States. Proc. of World Symp. on Warm-Water Pond Fish. FAO Fisheries Report No. 44. 5:1-17.
4. Blackburn, Robert D. and L.W. Weldon. 1969. A new concept in aquatic weed control. Proc. SWC. 22:315.
5. Comes, R.D., D.W. Bohmont and H.P. Alley. 1961. Movement and persistence of endothall (3,6-endoxohexahydrophthalic acid) as influenced by soil texture, temperature and moisture levels. J. Am. Soc. Sugar Beet Technol. 11:287-293.
6. Crosby, D.G. and R.K. Tucker. 1966. Toxicity of aquatic herbicides to **Daphnia magna.** Sci. 154:289-291.
7. Frank, P.A., N.E. Otto, and T.R. Bartley. 1961. Techniques for evaluating aquatic weed herbicides. Weeds. 9:515-521.
8. Frank, P.A. and R.D. Comes. 1967. Herbicide residues in pond water and hydrosoil. Weeds. 15:210-213.
9. Gangstad, E.O. 1978. Weed control methods for river basin management, CRC Press Inc., Boca Raton, Flordia. 248 pp.
10. Goldstein, Franz. 1952. Cutaneous and intravenous toxicity of endothall, disodium-3,6-endoxohenxahydrophtalic acid. Fed. Proc. *11*, 349.
11. Hadder, John C. 1970. Endothall induced mutations in **Drosophila Melanogaster.** Trans. of Illinois State Academy of Sciences, *63*, 157-159.
12. Hiltibran, Robert C. 1962. Duration of toxicity of endothall in water. Weeds. 10:17-19.
13. Horowitz, M. 1966. Breakdown of endothall in soil. Weed Res. 6:168-171.
14. Kakunaga, T. 1973. A quantitative system for assay of malignant transformation by chemical carcinogens using a clone derived from BALB/3T3, Int. J. Cancer. 12:463-473.
15. Keckemet, Obren. 1969. Chemical, toxicological, and biological properties of endothall. Hyacinth Cont. J. 8:50-51.
16. Maestri, M. 1967. Structural and functional effects of endothall on plants. Thesis. University of California. 122 p.
17. Pienta, R.J. 1979. A hamster embryo cell model system for indentifying carcinogens *in* Griffin, A.C., and Shaw, C.R., Eds., Carcino-

gens: Identification and Mechanisms of Action, Raven, New York. pp. 121-141.
18. Pennsalt Chemicals Corporation. 1956-1966. Results of various biological studies. Unpubl.
19. Rodgers, J.H., K.H. Reinert and M.L. Hinman. 1984. Pat Mayse Lake, Texas, Aquatic Plant Management Program: Water Quality Monitorin. Misc. paper 84-4. U.S. Army Engineer Waterways Experiment Station, Vicksburg, Miss.
20. Seaman, D.E. and T.M. Thomas. 1966. Translocation of herbicides in American pondweed. Weed Sci. Soc. Abstr. 65.
21. Sikka, H.C., Dennis Ford and Robert S. Lunch. 1975. Uptake, distribution and metabolism of endothall in fish. Agr. Food Chem. 23:849-851.
22. Sikka, H.C. and C. Rice. 1973. Persistence of endothall in the aquatic environment as determined by gas-liquid chromotography Agric. and Food Chem. 21:842-846.
23. Sikka, H.C. and J. Saxena. 1973. Metabolism of endothall by aquatic microorganisms Agric. and Food Chem. 21:402-406.
24. Simsiman, G.V., T.C. Daniel, and G. Chester. 1976. Diquat and endothall: their fates in the environment. Residue Reviews *62*, 131-174.
25. Soo, Alexander, Ian Tinsley, and S.C. Fang. 1967. Metabolism of ^{14}C-endothall in Rats. J. Agr. Food Chem. *15*, 1018-1021.
26. Thomas, T.M. 1966. Uptake and fate of endothall in submersed aquatic plants. Thesis. Univ. of California. 105 p.
27. Thomas, T.M. and D.E. Seaman. 1968. Translocation studies with endothall-^{14}C in **Potamogeton nodosus** Poir. Weed Res. 8:321-326.
28. Tischler, N. 1950. A new group of defoliant herbicidal chemicals. Proc NEWCC. 4:51-84.
29. Walker, C.R. 1963. Endothall derivatives as aquatic herbicides in fishery habitats. Weeds. 11:226-232.
30. Westerdahl, H.E. 1983. Effects of Hydout and Aquathol[K] in Gatun Lake, Panama. J. Aquat. Plant Manage. 21:17-21.
31. Yeo, R.R. 1970. Dissipation of endothall and effects on aquatic weeds and fish. Weed Sci. 18:282-284.

Table 1.   USDA compilation of registered Aquatic uses of endothall

Chemical name: 7-oxabicyclo [2,2,1]heptane-2,3-dicarboxylic acid;
                  or 3,6-endoxohexahydrophthalic acid

Other names: Endothall[R] (technical acid)
                The technical acid is formulated as:

(I)   Di (N,N-dimethylalkanolamine salt: (A) as 66.7% LC (1.5 lb
        a.i./gal); (B) as 17.5% G

(II)   Di(N,N-dimethyltridecylamine salt at 68.0% LC (1.6 lb a.i./gal)

(III)   Dipostassium salt: (A) as 40.3% SC(3.0 lb a.i./gal); (B) as
        10.1% (7.2% a.i.) G

(IV)   Mono (N,N-dimethylalkylamine salts: (A) as 53.0% LC (2.0 lb
        a.i./gal); (B) as 11.2% (5% a.i.) G

(V)   Mono (N,N-dimethyltridecylamine salt at 54.68% LC (2.0 lb
        a.i./gal)

(VI)   Mono (N,N-dimethyltridecylamine salt at 9.1% plus 5.1%
        pyrazon, see under Pyrazon

(VII)   Disodium salt at 11.25% (9.08% a.i.) to 19.2% (15.0% a.i. or
        1.46 lb a.i./gal)

Weeds Controlled

The various salts of endothall will control many broadleaf weeds and
grasses including:

I. Aquatic weeds:
    A. Preemergent and free floating:

algae	Chara, Cladophora, Pithosporium and Spirogyra spp.
arrowhead	Sagittaria spp.
burreed	Sparganium spp.
spikerush	Eleocharia spp.
waterhyacinth	Eichornia crassipes
waterlily	Nymphaea spp.
waterprimrose	Jussiaea spp.

B. Submerged:

bladderwort	Uticularia spp.
cabomba (fanwort)	Cabomba spp.
coontail	Ceratophyllum spp.
lotus	Nelumbo spp.
naiad	Najas spp.

pondweed:

American	Potamogeton nodosus
curleyleaf	Potamogeton crispus
fineleaf	P. filiformis
flatstem	P. zosteriformiis
floating	P. natans

Table 1. USDA compilation of registered Aquatic uses of endothall (cont.)

horned	Zannichellia pulustris
largeleaf	Potamogeton amplifolius
sago	P. pectinatus
small	P. pusillus
waterhead	P. diversifolius
watercress	Nasturtium spp.
watermilfoil	Myrophyllum spp.

Aquatic Uses

CANALS (drainage and irrigation)—To control floating and submerge weeds: Formulations (I-B) and (IV-A) at 1:0 to 5.0 ppm a.i.; Formulation (IV-B) at 0.5 ppm a.i.

NOTES AND LIMITATIONS: Apply liquids undiluted (or in as little water as possible with equipment used) as a surface spray, or inject under surface or water. Apply granules evenly by aerial or ground equipment. Use 1.0 to 2.0 ppm a.i. for light to moderate weed growth, and 3.0 to 5.09 ppm for heavy growths. Do not use treated water for irrigation of crops. Do not use where fish are important resources. Do not use fish from treated water for food of feed within 3 days after treatment. Do not use treated water for watering livestock or domestic purposes within the following periods: Up to 0.3 ppm - 7 days after application; 3.0 ppm - 14 days; 5.0 ppm - 25 days. Approval and limits from State authorities must be obtained before applying to public waters or to water which flows into public water.
TOLERANCE: 0.2 ppm in potable water.

LAKES, PONDS—To control algae use: Formulation (I-A), (I-B) or (IV-A) at 0.05 to 0.8 ppm a.i.; Formulation (I-B) or (IV-B) at 0.05 to 1.5 ppm a.i. To control submerged weeds use: Formulation (I-B) or (IV-B) at 0.5 to 2.5 ppm a.i.; Formulation (IV-B) at 0.5 to 5.0 ppm a.i.; Formulation (III-A) of (VII) at 0.5 to 5.0 ppm endothall salt. To control algae and other floating weeds use: Formulation (VII) at 0.5 to 5.0 ppm endothall salt.

NOTES AND LIMITATIONS: Use dosages over 1.0 ppm only on very narrow margins or in areas where some fish kill is not objectionable. Do not treat more than 1/10 of lake or pond at one time with dosages above 1.0 ppm. Do not apply granular products more frequently than once/year. Treated areas may be used for swimming 24 hr. after application.
TOLERANCE: 0.2 ppm in potable water.

Table 2. Endothall: toxicity to aquatic organisms.

Organism	Type of test	Experimental conditions	Toxicity	Reference
Semotilus atromaculatus	L,ST,A	a,b,c,e	1,600 NTE (24 h)	Gilette et al. (1952)
Lepomis macrochirus	L,ST,A	a,b,c,e	428 T (24 h)[a]; 268 T (48 h)	Davis and Hughes (1963)
Salmo gairdneri	L,CFT,A	a,b,c,d,e	10 NTE; no avoidance[a]	Folmar(1976
Garmarus fasciatus	L,CFT,A	a,b,c,d,e	3.1 T (24 h)[b]; 2.1 T (48 h); 0.48 T (96 h)	Sanders(1970
Salmo gairdneri	L,ST,A	—	1.5 T)48 h[b]	Cope(1965)
Lepomis macrochirus (fingerlings)	L,ST,A	a,b,c,d,e	0.8 T (24 h)[b]; 0.8 T (48 h)	Hughes and Davis(1962)
L. macrochirus	RP	Pathological examination	S.B. 0.3. 0.03 (28 d)[b]	Eller(1969
L. macrochirus (fry)	L,ST,A	a,b,c,d,e	0.75 NTE (72 h)[c]	Jones(1965)
L. macrochirus (fingerlings)	L,ST,A	a,b,c,d,e	0.3 t (24 h)[c]	Hughes and Davis(1962)
L. macrochirus	L,A	—	376(3-4 weeks) i.p. injection[c]	Walker(1964b)
Micropterus salmoides (fry)	L,ST,A	a,b,c,d,e	0.075 NTE (72 h)[c]	Jones(1965)
Ictalurus punctatus	L,ST,A	a,b,c,d,e	0.2 NTE (72 h)[c]	Jones(1965)
Daphnia magna	L,ST,A	a,b,c,d,e,f	$46.0IC_{50}$ (26 h)[d]	Crosby and Tucker(1966)

Table 2. Endothall: toxicity to aquatic organisms. (cont.)

Organism	Type of test	Experimental conditions	Toxicity	Reference
Gammarus lacustris	L,CFT,A	a,b,c,d,e	100 T (6 h)[d]	Sanders(1969)
G. lacustris	L,ST,A	a	>320 T (96 H)[d]	Nebecker and Gaufin(1964)
Mercenaria mercenaria (eggs)	L,ST,A	a	50.0T(48 6)[d]	Davis and Hidu(1969)
M. mercenaria (larvae)	L,ST,A	a	>10.0 (10 d)[d]	Davis and Hidu(1969)
Crassostrea virginica	L,ST,A	a	>25.0(12 d)[d]	Davis and Hidu(1969)
N. lutrensis	L,ST,A	a,b,c,e	95.0 T (96 h)[d]	Walker(1963, 1964a)
N. umbratilis	L,ST,A	a,b,c,e	105 T (96 h)[d]	Walker(1963, 1964a)
Pimephales notatus	L,ST,A	a,b,c,e	110-120 T (96 h)[d]	Walker(1963, 1964a)
P. promelas	L,ST,A	a,b,c,d,e	Soft water 320 T (96 h)[d] Hard Water 6.0 T (96 h)	Surber and Pickering(1962)
Erimyzon sucetta (fingerlings)	L,ST,A	-	25.0 NTE (12 d)[e]	Hiltibran(1967)
Carassius auratus and Cyprinus carpio	L,ST,A	a,b,c,e	145-210 T (96 h)[e]	Walker(1963, 1964a)
Ictalurus punctatus (fry)	L,ST,A	a,b,c,d,e	100 NTE (72 h)[3]	Jones(1965)
I. nebulosus	L,ST,A	a,b,c,e	170-175 T (96 h)[d]	Walker(1963, 1964a)
I. melas	L,ST,A	a,b,c,e	180-185 T (96 h)[d]	Walker(1963-1964a)
Lepomis cyanellus	FP	a,b,c,d,e	3.0 NTE[d]	Yeo(1970)
L. macrochirus (fry)	L,ST,A	a,b,c,d,e	50.0 NTE (72 h)[e]	Jones(1965)

Table 2. Endothall: toxicity to aquatic organisms. (cont.)

Organism	Type of test	Experimental conditions	Toxicity	Reference
L. macrochirus	L,ST,A	-	100 NTE (12 d)[e]	Hiltibran(1967)
L. macrochirus (fingerlings)	L,ST,A	a,b,c,d,e	Soft water 180 T (96 h)[e] Hard water 160 T (6 h)	Surber and Pickering(1962)
L. macrochirus (fingerlings)	L,ST,A	-	25.0 NTE (12 d)[e]	Hiltibran(1967)
L. macrochirus	L,ST,A	a,b,c,e	125-150 T (96 h)[d]	Walker(1963, 1964a)
L. macrochirus	L,ST,A	a,b,c,d,e	450 T (48 h)[e] 280T (96 h)	Hughes and Davis(1965)
L. microlophus (fingerlings)	L,ST,A	a,b,c,e	125 T (96 h)[d]	Walker(1963, 1964a)
M. dolomieui (fingerlings)	L,ST	-	10.0 NTE (12 d)[d]	Hiltibran(1967)
M. dolomieui	FP	a,b,c,d,e	3.0 NTE[d]	Yeo(1970)
M. salmoides (fry)	L,ST,A	a,b,c,d,e	10.0 NTE (72 h)[d]	Jones(1965)
M. salmoides (fingerlings)	L,ST,A	a,b,c,d,e	Soft water[d] 2.0 T (96 h)	Surber and Pickering(1962)
M. salmoides	L,ST,A	a,b,c,e	100-125 T (96 h)[d]	Walker(1963, 1964a)
Morone saxatilis (fingerlings)	L,ST,A	a,b,c,d,e	??? T (24 h) ??? T (48 h) ??? T (96 h)	Wellborn(1971)
Notropis umbratilis	L,ST,A	-	??? NTE (21 d)[f]	Lindaberry(1961)

Table 2. Endothall: toxicity to aquatic organisms. (cont.)

Organism	Type of test	Experimental conditions	Toxicity	Reference
N. lutrensis	L,ST,A	-	??? NTE (21 d)f	Lindaberry(1961)
Pumephales notatus	L,ST,A	-	??? NTE (21 d)f	Lindaberry(1961)
Erimyzon sucetta (fingerlings)	L,ST,A	-	10.0 NTE (12 d)f	Hiltibran(1967)
Ictalurus punctatus	L,ST,A	a,b,c,d,e	50.0 NTE (72 h)f	Jones (1965)
Lepomis macrochirus	L,ST,A	-	100 NTE (21 d)f	Lindaberry(1961)
L. macrochirus (fry)	L,ST,A	a,b,c,d,e	2.0 NTE (72 h)f	Jones(1965)
L. macrochirus (fry)	L,ST,A	-	50.0 NTE(12 d)f	Hiltibran(1967)
L. macrochirus (fingerlings)	L,ST,A	-	10.0 NTE (12 d)f	Hiltibran(1967)
L. macrochirus	L,ST,A	a,b,c,d,e	650 T (48 h) / 280 T (96 h)	Hughes and Davis(1965)
L. cyanellus (fingerlings)	L,ST,A	-	10.0 NTE (12 d)f	Hiltibran(1967
Micropterus salmoides	L,ST,A	-	10.0 NTE (21 d)f	Lindaberry(1961)
M. salmoides (fry)	L,ST,A	a,b,c,d,e	2.0 NTE (72 h)f	Jones(1965)
Salmon	L,ST	-	-NTE (21 d)f	Lindaberry(1961)
Salmo gairdneri	L,ST,A	-	10.0 NTE (21 d)f	Lindaberry(1961)

From: Folmar, L.C. Technical report NO 88, U.S. Fish and Wildlife Service, Washington, D.C. 1977.

Table 2.   Endothall: toxicity to aquatic organisms. (cont.)

1. Type of test, letters represent:
   - T = Toxicity test, used in conjunction with
       - ST = static
       - CFT = continuous flow
       - A = acute
       - C = chronic
   - L = Laboratory toxicity test
   - F = Field study, used in conjunction with
       - R = river, stream, or creek
       - M = marine
       - E = estuarine, and
       - O = other
2. Experimental conditions. Factors reported in cited articles:
   - a = water temperature
   - b = pH
   - c = alkalinity
   - d = dissolved oxygen
   - e = dissolved solids
   - f = photoperiod
3. Toxicity, active ingredient. All values in mg/l (ppm) unless otherwise noted. Letters included with numerical values represent:
   - T = LC_{50} (also accompanied by a time factor, e.g., 96 h)
   - K = Kill
   - SB = Sublethal effects
   - NTE = No toxic effect
4. Formulation
   - [a] di K salt formulation
   - [b] TD-191 (mono-N,N dimethylococoamine salt) formulations.
   - [c] TD-47 (di-N,N dimethylocoamine salt) formulation.
   - [d] di Na salt formulation.
   - [e] di Na salt formulation—liquid.
   - [f] di Na salt formulation—granular.

PART II

EVALUATION OF SELECTED AQUATIC HERBICIDES

Chapter 12

HERBICIDAL, ENVIRONMENTAL AND HEALTH EFFECTS OF GLYPHOSATE

INTRODUCTION

Glyphosate herbicide is a water-soluble formulation of the isopropy-lamine salt. It is the common orgeneric name assigned to N-phospho-nomethyl glycine, the parent acid. The formulated product contains three pounds of acid equivalent per US gallon of N-phosphonomethyl glycine or four pounds per US gallon of the isopropylamine salt of glyphosate. The aquatic (Rodeo[R]) herbicide controls a broad spectrum of annual, biennial and perennial grasses, sedges and broadleaved weed and woody species. It is applied as a post-emergence foliar-absorbed material and is slowly translocated throughout the plant system giving outstanding destruction of underground roots and rhizomes, thereby controlling many deep-rooted perennial species. At the same time, shallow-rooted annual species are completely destroyed. Soil persistence of the herbicide is negligible.

For many persistent weed species, commonly controlled by silvex prior to cancellation of silvex registrations, glyphosate is a suitable substitute. The isopropylamine salt of glyphosate (Rodeo[R]) is labeled for use in all bodies of fresh water and in all types of aquatic sites. This includes lakes, rivers, streams, ponds, ditches, canals, and reservoirs. It should not be applied in tidewater areas or within 0.5 miles upstream of potable water intakes.

HERBICIDAL EFFECTS

Mode of Action

It has been postulated that glyphosate interferes with the biosynthesis of phenylalnine and, more specifically, with the metabolism of chorismic acid in the aromatic amino acid biosynthetic pathway (9). It is suggested that glyphosate may inhibit or repress chorismatic mutase and/or prephenate dehydratase. Glyphosate is actively translocated from leaf and stem tissue to underground roots or rhizomes of perennial weeds. Field and greenhouse studies with *Sorghum*

---

[1]The findings in this report are not to be construed as an official Department of the Army position unless so designated by other authorized documents.

halepense, and *Agrapyron repens* showed that glyphosate translocated basipetally to the rhizomes (14,15). This translocation was quite rapid and a major part of the absorbed chemical was moved into the rhizomes within the 24 hours after foliar application to the vegetative portions of the plant (8,10,13). Numerous other field and greenhouse studies indicate that, providing that enough leaf tissue has emerged from the soil at treatment time, most of the chemical is sufficiently translocated to underground root systems within a 24-hour period under normal growing conditions. Behrens and Mohamed (1) at Minnesota, Brockman et al. (2) at Cornell University, and others, relating treatment-tillage intervals prior to planting of a crop, report that tillage can take place from one to four days after the application of glyphosate to *A. repens* and excellent control is still obtained with very little, if any, regeneration from old rhizomes.

Stage of maturity

The stage of maturity of weed species to be treated is a primary consideration for obtaining the best results. The most effective destruction of certain deep rooted perennials such as *C. arvense, Convolvulus aryensis, S. halepense* and many others, appears to be when treatments are made at early bud or bloom stage for broadleaved species, or at the late boot or early head stage for grasses and sedges. Very early treatment of perennial vegetation is usually less effective, as many plants will not have emerged sufficiently to receive the spray. Perennial weeds must have adequate lead area, e.g. six to eight leaves, to permit absorption and translocation of the compound into the plant tissue and root system. Although applications at plant senescence may reduce effectiveness, good results have been obtained with applications made to full maturity. Annual species of both broad and narrow leaf weeds are most effectively controlled at very early growth stages and are considered rate sensitive. As the annual species becomes larger and more mature, higher rates are required for control. It appears that most annual species of grasses and broadleaf weeds are controlled at rates ranging from 0.5 to 1.0 kg/ha ae (16).

Under temperate conditions where there are seasonal variations, quackgrass (*A. repens*) appears to be more completely controlled with less rhizome regeneration if the application is made in the early autumn rather than in the spring. However, the stage of growth will dictate when spring treatments can best be made. At the same time, johnsongrass (*S. halepense*) was more completely controlled when treated at the early head stage in late summer or early autumn (16). Under tropical conditions, where species are growing continuously, varied stages of maturity may be represented within an area. Under such conditions, spray programs should be directed toward reducing total ground cover at all times.

The herbicide (Rodeo [R]) mixes readily with water and (Ortho [R]) X-77 surfactant, 1/4 to 1/2 percent by volume, to be applied as a postemergence spray for the management of emerged aquatic vegetation.

(Rodeo [R]) may be applied with a boom or handgun from a boat or from the ditchbank with terrestrial positioned spray equipment. When using hand-held or high-volume equipment, application should be made on a spray-to-wet basis insuring uniform and complete coverage. With broadcast sprays from ground or boat equipment and aerial equipment, apply the recommended rate of this product in 3-20 gallons of water per acre.

Surfactant relationships

Aquatic levels of surfactant are contained in the commercial formulations of (Round up [R]). The aquatic herbicide (Rodeo [R]) is formulated without a surfactant. Add 1-2 quarts of X-77 surfactant per 100 gallons of spray solution. (16).

Climatic conditions

Rainfall occurring up to six hours after application may reduce the effectiveness of the treatment depending on the intensity and duration of the rain. As is true with more slowly absorbed herbicides applied to foliage, rain falling soon after application may wash off some of the material. On the other hand, there are reports where glyphosate has been applied during a light drizzle without any visible adverse effect on performance. Thus to be certain, spraying should be avoided when rain is imminent. If sudden rain does occur, a repeat treatment may be necessary. Calculations have yet to be made that will predict the percent reduction in weed control in relation to the amount of rain and the time after treatment when the rain falls. If treatments are made under shade or extremely cloudy conditions it may take longer for visible effects on certain weeds species to appear but the ultimate results are normally comparable to treatment made in sunlight (3).

Rate response

Rate of use response varies widely depending on the species and stage of development. In herbicide screening trails and field plots, post-emergence application has provided consistent and excellent control of many annual, biennial and perennial weeds of both grassy and broadleaved species at rates ranging from 0.375 to 5.0 kg/ha acid equivalent (a.e.). Most annual species are easily controlled at the lower rates up to 1.0 kg/ha. Some perennial species may require the higher rates which exceed 2.5 kg/ha. The majority of perennial weeds, however, are controlled quite well in the 1.5 or 2.0 kg/ha a.e. rate. Data accumulated show that certain perennial grasses such as *A. repens, S. halepense, Paspalum* supp., *Panicum* spp., and *Brachiaria* spp., are easily controlled at rates of 1.0 to 2.0 kg/ha a.e.

Complete control of certain persistent or deep routed perennial weeds such as *Convolvulus arvensis, Cynodon dactylon* and *Cirsium arvense* may require further applications at somewhat lower rates than initially applied, at various intervals (generally 30-60 days after treatment) depending on the degree of regeneration. As the compound is a non-residual herbicide, additional and timely treatments at low rates will be required to control germinating annual species, which may reinfest the treated area after the original perennial or first flush of annuals has been destroyed. Weed species controlled by glyphosate (Rodeo [R]) are given in Table 1. (17).

Phragmites (*Phragmites communis* Trin.) is a plant of wide distribution, occurring in flood plains, tidal marshes, ditches, and other low-lying, poorly drained areas over much of the world. Although various civilizations have used this plant for thatching and other useful purposes, it is often detrimental to mankind's interest. It crowds out desirable wildlife food plants, its roots penetrate and clog various types of underground pipelines, and it poses a serious fire threat during the winter when the above-ground portions of the plant die and dry out. It is, therefore, desirable that safe, efficient, and economically feasible control methods be developed for phragmites Riemer (11) observed that N-(phosphonomethyl) glycine (glyphosate) applied to phragmites and was effectively controlled for four growing seasons. Additional surfactant is effective only when the herbicide is applied at low rates. Within the range of 20 gpa to 80 gpa, the effects of spray volume are minimal, except with very low rates of herbicide. The application of glyphosate to phragmites for two successive years is a very effective means of control.

Waterlilies belonging to the general Nuphar and Numphaea are serious aquatic weed problems in many areas of the United States. They occur in shallow lakes and reservoirs, abandoned mill ponds, ditches, slow moving streams, and other shallow-water habitats. They interfere with recreational use of water and can choke ditches, seriously impeding water flow. Reimer and Welker (12) found that fragrant waterlily (*Nymphaea odorata* Ait.) and spatterdock (*Nuphar* sp.)[1] treated with N-(phosphonomethyl) glycine (glyphosate) were controlled for above-ground portions within 2 months of treatment. No regrowth occurred the following spring.

Submersed aquatic weeds are not well controlled by glyphosate. About 80 percent of the north Cayuga Lake is infested with submersed aquatic weeds. Watermilfoil (*Myriophyllum* sp.) accounts for 54 percent of all plants, eel grass (*Vallisneria americana*) makes up 32 percent, and *Najas* sp. about 8 percent. Applications of glyphosate did not eliminate these plants, except at excessively high rates. (7).

ENVIRONMENTAL EFFECTS

Residual activity

Soil inactivation is rapid and complete when sprayed onto soil or onto vegetation that ultimately comes into contact with soil. The exact mechanism of soil inactivation is not known but microbiological degradation is involved. This lack of residual activity allows the compound to be considered as a potential candidate for: zero or minimum tillage, stale seedbeds, chemical fallow, stubble applications, weed control in shelterbelts, weed control around desirable trees and shrubs, pre-tillage treatments prior to seeding of crops, levee or ditchbank weed control in rice and other crops, vegetation control in irrigation or drainage ditches, turf or forage crop renovation and reseeding, and many other uses where residual herbicides are undesirable or are not required.

If residual activity is required, then residual herbicides such as triazines, substituted ureas or other products of similar nature, show promise as tank mixtures or separate applications to supplement or complement the glyphosate salt. Mixtures with simazine, atrazine, prometone, diuron, bromacil and possibly other residual herbicides may be used for industrial vegetation control where long-term weed control is required and where bare soil is not objectionable. Mixtures with residuals have potential uses in citrus, deciduous fruits, vineyards and other tree crops. In addition, mixtures with pre-emergence herbicides such as alachlor, metribuzin, linuron, atrazine, simazine and others may fit well into cropping systems involving no-till and reduced tillage practices for maize and soybean production, where seasonal weed control is required.

In some situations where tank mixtures with residuals are utilized, the degree of foliage activity of the glyphosate salt is temporarily suppressed. In most situations where this suppression was observed, in about 30 days or less after treatment, the weed control was comparable to that of the glyphosate salt used alone, and continued to be outstanding throughout the season. (16,17).

When used as directed, glyphosate herbicide effectively controls many weeds that other herbicides cannot control, without any adverse effect on cropping systems or the environment. Glyphosate utilizes the plant's nutrient transport system to translocate or move from the plant foliage, where it is applied, to the underground root system. For maximum control, good application conditions are important. Glyphosate is most effective when applied to the emerged weed foliage at or near the bud to flower stage of growth. Application is not recommended when winds exceed 5 mph to prevent physical drift of spray solution, or when rain is expected within six hours to prevent washing the herbicide from the foliage. Tillage should not be done prior to or immediately after application, since sufficient time (3-7 days) must be alloted for the complete translocation of glyphosate. The glyphosate formulation is not volatile and will not damage any plant not contacted during application. (16,17).

Hazard assessment

Extensive testing is required to assess the potential impact of the compound on man and the environment. The safety/hazard assessment is based upon an evaluation of the test compound's ability to produce adverse effects and the probability of these adverse effects actually occurring under normal use conditions of the compound.

A compound's ability to produce adverse effects is established in recognized, standard toxicological tests conducted at dosage levels at or far in excess of normal expected exposures. These tests determine the toxicity of the compound. From the toxicity information, an evaluation is made of the probability that the toxic effect could occur under normal use conditions. This involves a determination of the environmental fate and an extrapolation of the data to estimate the probable safety/hazard posed to man. (16,17).

Edwards, Triplett and Kramer (5) studied the persistence of glyphosate in the soil and its presence in runoff water from field-sized watersheds where it had been used as an herbicide in the production of no-tillage corn and in the establishment of fescue pastures without tillage were evaluated. Each significant runoff event during the growing season was sampled. During the three year study the greatest transport of glyphosate in runoff from any watershed was 165 g/ha, or 1.85% of the amount applied. Most of that loss resulted from a single storm occurring 1 day after an abnormally high glyphosate treatment of 8.96 kg/ha had been applied. At all other sample testing times, the runoff was less than 1% of the glyphosate applied. Both the application rate and the time interval between application and cause for runoff influenced the amount of glyphosate in the runoff. Runoff occurring as a result of a long duration, low intensity storm taking place when the ground was already wet had a lower glyphosate concentration than would be otherwise expected. It was concluded that runoff from fields treated with glyphosate herbicide at recommended concentrations would not constitute an environmental hazard.

Sullivan, Sullivan and Bisalputra (18) studied the effect of glyphosate on diatom populations. The glyphosate was applied post emergence to small streams running through a coastal Douglas fir plantation in British Columbia to determine the effects of the compound on aquatic diatom populations. The herbicide was applied aerially at a rate of 2.2 kg a.i./ha, and slide and sediment samples were taken to identify and count diatom populations. In a second experiment, glyphosate was applied manually to a stream at a field dose of 2.2 kg/ha and at ten times this dose further downstream. Slide samples from the manually sprayed stream were collected and examined as in the first experiment. Sediment samples from the aerially sprayed area generally contained a greater density of diatoms than those from the control area.

Neither glyphosate [N-(phosphonomethyl)glycine] nor the soil metabolite aminomethylphosphonic acid were detected in the first flow of water through two canals following application of glyphosate at 5.6 kg/ha to ditchbanks when the canals were dry. Soil samples collected the day before canals were filled (about 23 weeks after treatment) contained about 0.35 ppm glyphosate and 0.78 ppm aminomethylphosphonic acid in the 0 to 10-cm layer. When glyphosate was metered into the water at a rate calculated to provide 150 ppb in the canal water at a single site on two flowing canals, about 70% of the glyphosate was accounted for 1.6 km downstream from the application site. Thereafter, the rate of disappearance diminished, and about 58% of the applied glyphosate was present at the end of the canals 8 or 14.4 km downstream from the introduction sites. (3).

HEALTH EFFECTS

The apparent low mammalian toxicity of the compound and excellent handling characteristics of the formulation should appeal to those workers who make applications with hand sprayers. Further indications of low toxicity to bees and wildlife should encourage acceptability in the area of environmental safety and surroundings. Glyphosate, the parent compound, is classified as only slightly toxic by oral ingestion with an acute LD_{50} of 4900 mg/kg to rats. Both the parent material and the salts are classified as practically non-toxic by skin contact since rabbits survived single dermal dosages greater than 7940 mg/kg. Glyphosate produces no apparent skin irritation, but formulations of glyphosate are regarded as mild skin and severe eye irritants to rabbits. Consequently, eye protection such as goggles should be worn to prevent introduction into the eyes. In the event of contact, the eyes should be flushed with plenty of water for 15 minutes. If irritation persists, consult a physician. (16,17,19).

Toxicological investigations conducted with bobwhite quail, mallard ducks, honeybees, rainbow trout, bluegills, and other species of fish show that these species have an extremely high tolerance to glyphosate. Technical material was fed to rats and dogs at dietary levels of 200, 600, and 2000 ppm for 90 days. No significant differences from control animals were observed in mean body weight, food consumption, behavioral reactions, mortality, hematology, blood chemistry or urinalysis. Two year feeding studies at dietary levels of 30, 100 and 300 ppm produced no adverse effects.

Metabolism test results show that glyphosate does not accumulate in animals, birds, and aquatic species, and thus will not be passed up the food chain. The lack of accumulation is also supported by the high water solubility of Roundup herbicide and rapid depletion of glyphosate from the body. In fact, when milk from lactating cows and eggs from chickens fed diets with glyphosate were analyzed, residues were not detectable (<0.025 ppm parent and metabolite).

Toxicity tests have been conducted on a wide variety of aquatic and avian species. The aquatic test organisms included fresh and salt water species, as well as vertebrates and invertebrates. Ducks, quail, trout, carp, bluegill, water fleas (Daphnia magna), oysters, and shrimp are a few examples. The acute (short-term) tests conducted with the avian species, honeybees, and fish show that glyphosate is essentially nontoxic. While the formulation of Roundup herbicide is slightly more toxic to fish than glyphosate, it is still considered to be only moderately toxic and would not pose a hazard under normal use conditions. (6,9).

SUMMARY AND CONCLUSIONS

Safety/hazard evaluation studies have been performed on the formulation of the herbicide glyphosate, and aminomethylphosphonic acid. These include short- and long-term tests on various weeds, crops, and soils to determine the efficacy, residues, and persistence. Also included were toxicology tests with rats, rabbits, mice, dogs, quail, and fish to determine toxicity and the potential to cause cancer, tumors, fetal abnormalities, and genetic damage. The test results have been very impressive.

Glyphosate herbicide has a rare combination of favorable properties unequaled by most herbicides available today. It will control hard-to-kill weeds effectively without adversely affecting man or the environment when it is used according to the label directions. It is not a very satisfactory herbicide for control of submerged aquatic weeds. Application should be limited to emersed and marginal aquatic weeds.

REFERENCES

1. Behrens, R., and Mohamed Elakkad. 1972. Herbicides for quack-grass control. Twenty-ninth A. Res. Rep. North Carolina Weed Conf. p. 40-41.
2. Brockman, F.E., W.B. Duke and J.F. Hunt. 1973. Agronomic factors affecting use of glyphosate for quackgrass control. Abstr. 1973 Meeting Weed Sci. Soc. Am. 6-8 February 1973.
3. Cornes, R.D., V.F. Burns and A.D. Kelley. 1976. Residues and persistence of glyphosate in irrigation water. Weed Science 24:47-50.
4. Davis, D.E. 1980. Effects of Herbicides on Submerged Seed Plants Dept. of Botany and Microbiology. Report Auburn Univ., Al.
5. Edwards, W.M., G.B. Triplett, Jr. and R.M. Kramer. 1980. A Watershed Study of Glyphosate Transport in Runoff. Journal of Environmental Quality, 9:661-665.
6. Folmar, L.C., H.O. Saunders and A.M. Julin. 1979. Toxicity of the herbicide glyphosate and several of its formulations to fish and aquatic invertebrates. USDI Columbia Natl. Fishery Research Lab. Mo. Archives Env. Contam. & Tox. 8:269-278.
14. Sprankle, P., W.F. Meggitt and D. Penner. 1972. Quackgrass weed control with MON-0468. Abstr. 1972 Meeting Weed Sci. Soc. Am. 8-10 February 1972. p. 80.
15. Sprankle, P., et al. 1973. The movement of glyphosate and bentazon in corn, soybeans and several weeds species. Abstr. 1973 Meeting Weed Sci. Soc. Am. 6-8 February 1973. p. 75.
16. Spurrier, E.C. 1973. Control of johnsongrass with glyphosate as affected by rate of application and stage of maturity. Abstr. 1973 Meeting Weed Sci. Soc. Am. 6-8 February 1973.
17. Spurrier, E.C. 1973. Glyphosate, a new broad-spectrum herbicide. PANS 19: 607-613.
18. Sullivan, D.S., T.P. Sullivan and T. Bisalputra. 1981. Northwest Ecological Animal Research Ltd., Vancouver (British Columbia). Bulletin of Environmental Contamination and Toxicology, 26: 91-96.
19. Weed Science Society of America. 1979. Herbicide Handbook. Champaign, Ill.

Table 1.　Technical Data Sheet

GLYPHOSATE
N-(phosphonomethyl) glycine

A. Nomenclature, Chemical and Physical Properties of the Pure Chemical
1. Common name: glyphosate (gli-fo-sate) (ANSI, WSSA)
2. Trade name and manufacturer:
   Rodeo[R] for herbicide formulation of isopropylamine salt of glyphosate—Monsanto Company
3. Structural formula:

$$\text{HO-C-CH}_2\text{-N-CH}_2\text{-P-OH}$$

with O above each carbonyl/phosphorus, H below the N and OH below the P

4. Molecular formula: $C_3H_8NO_5P$
5. Wiswesser line notation: QV1M1PQQO
6. Molecular weight: 169.1
7. Physical state, color, and odor: Solid, white, odorless.
8. Density: 0.5 gm/cc for pure chemical.
9. Melting point: 200 C
10. Boiling point: Note determined
13. Vapor pressure: Negligible
14. Solubility:

Solvent	Temperature	Solubility
Water	25 C	1.2%
Other solvents		None

15. Other chemical formulations available: MON-0139 or aqueous solution of isopropylamine salt of glyphosate for experimental purposes only.

B. Herbicidal Use
1. General: Glyphosate is a very broad spectrum herbicide, is relatively nonselective, and is very effective on deep-rooted perennial species and on annual and biennial species of grasses, sedges and broadleaved weeds. Selectivity may be achieved by directional application.
2. Application method: Apply as postemergence spray to foliage of vegetation to be controlled. Use diluent volumes of 20 to 30 gpa for normal use. Higher volumes may be necessary for heavy, tall, and dense foliage to assure adequate spray coverage of understory vegetation. Uese low pressures of 30 to 40 psi and suitable nozzles to avoid small droplets which could lead to spray drift and to injury of nearby susceptible plants.
3. Rates: Rates of use vary with species to be controlled. Normally from 0.3 to 1.0 1b/A a.e. will control annual species. Perennials

will require rates form 1.0 to 4.0 lbs/A a.e. with the majority of perennials requiring 1.5 to 2.0 lb/A a.e.
4. Usual carrier: Water at 10 to 30 gpa or higher volumes if extremely dense foliage. Does not need agitation during application.
C. Use Precautions
   1. Flammability: Formulation is a water based salt.
   2. Possible incompatibilities: Tank mixtures with residual type herbicides, such as substituted ureas, triazines, or others may reduce activity of Roundup. Other combinations with foliage absorbed herbicides such as paraquat, dalapon, MSMA, phenoxy, or other hormone type herbicides may modify or lower action of glyphosate.
   3. Corrosiveness: Most metals are resistant. Thorough flushing of equipment with water alleviates any problem.
   4. Cleaning glassware and spray equipment: Glassware can be cleaned with thorough washing and rinsing. Thoroughly flush tank, pump, hoses and boom with several changes of water.
   5. Storage ability: Formulations of Roundup are quite stable under temperatures up to 140 F, however will freeze at −20 F, but will go back into solution upon thawing. Does not require heated facilities.
D. Physiological and Biochemical Behavior
   1. Foliar absorption characteristics: Absorbed through foliage and other photosynthetically active portions of plant. Visual effect on foliage may not occur for 2 to 4 days for annual species and 10 days or more for perennial species. May be washed off plant foliage by rain, if rain occurs within 6 hours of application.
   2. Translocation characteristics: Facile translocation throughout aerial and underground portions of the contacted plant following absorption through foliage. The underground plant parts of perennial species are affected, resulting in failure of regrowth from these propagation sites and subsequent destruction of plant tissue. Root uptake from soil is one or two orders of magnitude lower than for other types of herbicides.
   3. Mechanism of action: Not known at this time, but the herbicide appears to inhibit the aromatic amino acid biosynthetic pathway and may inhibit or repress chlorismate mutase and/or prephenate dehydratase.
   4. Metabolism and persistence in plants: Studies with ^{14}C labeled glyphosate show that plants can metabolize glyphosate to give CO_2 and natural organic products.

From: Herbicide Handbook. Weed Science Society of America. 1979.

Table 2. Application rates for Rodeo[R] **herbicide.**

ed	Boom + Rate/Acre	Handgun + %Solution	Timing and Comments
ANNUALS			
Grasses/ Broad Leaves	1 1/2-3 pints	3/4% (3 qts/100 gal)	Young and actively growing. Use the higher rate for more mature plants in taller growth stages.
PERENNIALS			
Alligatorweed	6 pints	1 1/4% (5 qts/100 gal)	Apply when most plants are in bloom. Repeat application will be required to maintain partial control.
Bemudagrass	7 1/2 pints	1 1/2%(6 qts/100 gal)	Apply when actively growing and when seed heads appear. Best results in late summer or fall.
Canada thistle	3-4 1/2 pints	1 1/2%(6 qts/100 gal)	Apply when most plants are at or beyond the bud stage of growth
Cattail	4 1/2-7 1/2 pints	3/4%(3 qts/100 gal)	Apply when most plants are in bloom. Best results during summer or fall months.
Field bindweed	4 1/2-7 1/2 pints	1 1/2%(6 qts/100 gal)	Apply when actively growing and at or beyond full bloom. Best results in late summer or fall. Use 6 to 7 1/2 pints/acre in semi-arid areas (west of Mississippi River).

Table 2. Application rates for Rodeo[R] herbicide. (cont.)

ed	Boom + Rate/Acre	Handgun + %Solution	Timing and Comments
Giant cutgrass	6 pints	1%(4 qts/ 100 gal)	Apply when actively growing and most plants have reached the 7-10 leaf stage of growth. Repeat application will be required to maintain partial control.
Guineagrass	4 1/2 pints	3/4%(3 qts/100 gal)	Apply to actively growing plants when most have reached the 7 leaf stage of growth.
Johnson-grass/Reed canarygrass	3-4 1/2 pints	3/5%(3 qts/100 gal)	Apply to actively growing plants when most have reached the boot to head stage of growth.
Maidencane/ Paragrass	6 pints	3/4%(3 qts/100 gal)	Apply when most plants are at least in the 7 to 10 leaf stage of growth. Repeat application may be necessary, especially to vegetation partially submerged in water. Allow regrowth to recommended stage prior to treatment.
Nutsedge	4 1/2 pints	3/4%(3 qts/100 gal)	Apply when plants are in flower or when new nutlets can be found at rhizome tips. Repeat treatments will be required for long-term control.

Table 2.   Application rates for Rodeo^R herbicide (cont.)

ed	Boom + Rate/Acre	Handgun + %Solution	Timing and Comments
Phragmites	6-7 1/2 pints	3/4%-1 1/2%(3-6 qts/100 gal)	Apply when most plants are in full bloom, or during the fall months. Repeat treatments will be required to maintain partial control. Use the higher rates in Southeastern states.
Quackgrass/ Kikuyugrass	3-4 1/2 pints	3/4%(3 qts/100 gal)	Apply to actively growing plants when most have reached 8 inches in height or 3-4 leaf stage of growth.
Spatterdock	6 pints	3/4%(3 qts/100 gal)	Apply when most plants are in full bloom. Best results in summer or fall months.
Swamp Smartweed	4 1/2-7 1/2 pints	3/4%(3 qts/100 gal)	Apply when most plants are in full bloom. Use the higher rates under partially submerged conditions.
Torpedograss	6-7 1/2 pints	3/4%(3 qts/100 gal)	Apply to actively growing plants when most are at or beyond the seedhead stage of growth. Use the lower rates under terrestrial conditions, and the higher rates under partially submerged or a floating mat condition. Repeat treatments will be required to maintain partial control.

Table 2.   Application rates for Rodeo^R herbicide. (cont.)

ed	Boom + Rate/Acre	Handgun + %Solution	Timing and Comments
WOODY BRUSH AND TREES			
Berries	4 1/2-6 pints	3/4-1%(3-4 qts/100 gal)	Apply when canes are actively growing and most are at or beyond the full bloom stage of growth. Use the higher rates for plants that have reached the woody stage of growth. Best results in late summer or fall after berries are formed.
Maples/Oaks	—	3/4-1%(3-4 qts/100 gal)	Apply when at least 50% of the new leaves are fully developed. Use the higher rates for large, mature trees.
Poison Ivy/ Poison Oak	6-7 1/2 pints	1 1/2%(6 qts/100 gal)	Apply to actively growing plants when most are at or beyond the early to full bloom stage of growth. Repeat applications may be required to maintain control.
Willow	—	3/4%(3 qts/100 gal)	Apply when trees are actively growing and when foliage is full and well developed. Fall treatments must be made before any fall color occurs.

From: Monsanto, ROD 82 LO1

PART II

EVALUATION OF SELECTED AQUATIC HERBICIDES

Chapter 13

HERBICIDAL, ENVIRONMENTAL, AND HEALTH EFFECTS OF SIMAZINE[1]

INTRODUCTION

Simazine (2-chloro-4,6-bis(ethylamino)-s-triazine) is practically insoluble in water. It is formulated as an 80 percent water-dispersible powder, as a 4 percent granular product, as a 4 pound per gallon flowable and as a 90% water dispersible granule. All formulations are used for the nonselective control of vegetation on areas where any plant growth is undesirable.

Simazine is adsorbed by soil colloids. High cation-exchange capacity, high organic-matter content and, to a less extent, high clay content of soils reduces its toxicity to plants and it is deactivated by soil micro-organisms. Simazine has little or no contact action on foliage, so there is no drift hazard. It cannot penetrate an unbroken leaf cuticle and is absorbed only through the roots. Simazine is ineffective on terrestrial plants until water carries it to the root zone, and its action is slow. It is easily removed from equipment by washing. It forms a suspension in water that requires agitation to keep the herbicide from separating out.

Simazine formulated as Aquazine, CIBA-GEIGY Corporation's trade name for simazine for aquatic use, is registered for control of algae and most submersed and floating problem aquatic weeds as appropriate in swimming pools, large aquaria, ornamental fish ponds, fountains, and farm and recreational ponds. Aquazine is formulated as an 80% active ingredient powder.

HERBICIDAL EFFECTS

Extensive tests conducted with simazine in the United States and other countries indicate that the compound has considerable herbicidal activity against many broadleaf and grassy weeds. In experimental field trials, pre-emergence applications of simazine gave excellent control of annual broadleaf and grassy weeds in corn for the entire

---

[1]The findings in this report are not to be construed as an official Department of the Army position unless so designated by other authorized documents.

season with no injury to the crop; and commercial applications have verified earlier investigations (8).

The nomenclature, chemical and physical properties of simazine are given in table 1 and examples of weeds controlled are given in table 2.

Many unicellular algae and benthic filamentous algae in ponds are controlled with 1.7-3.4 lbs. of simazine per acre foot of water (0.5-1 ppm active ingredient). *Chara* sp. (stonewort), *Hydrodictyon* sp. (waternet), and most other algae, including *Cladophora* sp., which form on pond bottoms or which form plumes that break loose and float at the surface, require approximately 4.25 lbs. per acre foot (1.25 ppm) (6).

Blue-green algae are generally the most sensitive of all the classes of algae to simazine. Some sensitive algae within this group are certain species of *Anabaena, Anacystis,* and *Aphanizomenon.* These algae sometime give odor and foul taste to water.

Norton and Ellis (13) reported that green algae as a group are less sensitive to simazine than blue-green algae. They further reported that most diatoms and flagellates are tolerant of simazine at suggested use rates.

Submersed weeds controlled by simazine include coontail (*Ceratophyllum* spp.), naiad (*Najas* spp.), pond weeds (*Potamogeton* spp.), watermilfoil (*Myriophyllum*) spp.) and fanwort (*Cabomba* spp.). With the exception of fanwort, these weeds may be controlled at rates of 3.4 to 6.8 lbs. of simazine 80W per acre foot (1-2 ppm active ingredient). Control of fanwort requires 8.5 lbs. (2.5 ppm) of simazine per acre foot of water.

Floating weeds controlled by simazine include duckweed (*Lemna* spp.) and watermeal (*Wolffia* spp.). Rates of simazine labeled for control of these species range from 3.4-6.8 lbs. per acre foot (1-2 ppm). Where watermeal occurs, a split application of simazine should be made with an interval of 3-4 weeks between applications. One-half the total rate of simazine should be used at each application.

The judicious use of simazine can be beneficial to fish farming and related aquatic operations. This assumes that there is desirable to keep nuisance algae and certain vascular weeds from uncontrolled growth.

Simazine does not commonly have a detrimental effect on fish productivity where commercial fish foods are routinely used. When inorganic fertilizers are used to stimulate algal bloom for the aquatic food chain, for shading, or for other purposes, adjusting applications of simazine relative to applications of fertilizer provides effective control of nuisance plant life.

Simazine also has the ability to control algae in recirculating water cooling towers. Here the object is to prevent the buildup of algae, which reduce the operating efficiency of cooling towers.

ENVIRONMENTAL EFFECTS

Several studies have been conducted on absorption and translocation of simazine by aquatic plants. Lawrence *et al.* (8) found that there was absorption and upward movement of simazine into stems and leaves of waterstargrass (*Heteranthera dubia*) following application to roots. They further reported varying degrees of downward (basipetal) movement following leaf absorption. Sutton *et al.* (18) observed that simazine was absorbed by roots of parrotfeather (*Myriophyllum brasiliense*) and translocated to the plant shoots, where it tended to accumulate in the upper parts. On the other hand, they observed little or no absorption of simazine by elodea (*Elodea canadensis*) or common duckweed (*Lemna minor*).

Runke (16) reported no detectable simazine uptake by freshwater algae, although Hawxby and Mehta (6) reported greater simazine uptake in light than in dark. *Anacystis nidulans* took up more simazine at 25 and 35°C, than at 8°C, while *Lyngbya* sp. gave opposite results.

In the submersed aquatic plant, curlyleaf pondweed (*Potamogeton crispus* L), Sutton & Bingham (19) found slight basipetal movement of radioactive C^{14} simazine after foliar applications of 1 ppm. Funderburk & Lawrence (13) reported considerable accumulation of labeled material in the tips of the leaves following root treatment of radioactive C^{14} simazine to emersed alligatorweed (*Alternanthera* sp.) Seaman & Baldia (17) reported considerable apoplastic movement of basally applied simazine in emersed parrotfeather (*Myriophyllum* sp.).

The primary mechanism of action of simazine is considered to be inhibition of the Hill Reaction of photosynthesis. This affects the normal transfer of energy necessary for vital cellular processes.

In photosynthetic plants, other than blue-green algae, the photosynthetic centers are located in structural units or plastids. In blue-green algal cells, the photosynthetic centers do not exist as distinct cellular structures, but rather are scattered throughout the cell.

The metabolism of simazine by aquatic plants is considered to be similar to that of terrestrial plants. Those algae and vascular aquatic weed species capable of altering simazine to less phytotoxic or nonphytotoxic entities are more tolerant of simazine than those species which lack such ability.

In tolerant terrestrial plants, simazine is readily metabolized to hydroxy-simazine, amino acid conjugates and other unidentified polar conjugates. The hydroxy-simazine can be further degraded by dealkylation of the side chains, hydrolysis of the resulting amino group on the ring and some CO_2 production from side chain oxidation to form dihydroxy metabolites. These alterations of simazine are considered to be a major protective mechanism in most tolerant plant species.

There have been instances of the use of simazine treated water to irrigate various plant species. These have involved use from bodies of water to which simazine had been applied to control algae and/or vascular weeds.

Lembi *et al*. (9) concluded that irrigation water from a pond treated with a concentration of 0.65 ppm could be applied to turf, and ornamentals without injury. The simazine treated water was applied at a rate of 1 inch per week over an 8 week period to bentgrass and bluegrass turf varieties, to Grandiflora and Floribunda rose, aborvitae, Global yew, forsythia, lilac and azalea without injury.

Flanagan *et al*. (2), employing simulated conditions at Vero Beach, Florida, observed phototoxicity of simazine to cantaloupe, carrots, cucumber, peppers, red beets, squash, sugarbeets, and wheat. Concentrations of simazine ranging from 0.01-0.0.5 pm were applied in irrigation water every 2 weeks at a rate of 2 inches of water per irrigation. Injury became apparent after a few irrigations.

Hiltibran and Turgeon (7) reported results of irrigation of turf with simazine treated water both from a simulated and pond use condition. Severe injury resulted to bentgrass, but bluegrass was unaffected when one inch of water was applied weekly for 8 weeks using concentrations of simazine determined from a dissipation curve of 0.5 ppm simazine initially in natural water. There was less damage to bentgrass when irrigated with comparable volumes of water from a pond that contained 0.5 ppm simazine initially.

In order to determine the influence of the aquatic environment on simazine-soil interactions, studies were conducted by CIBA-GEIGY researchers (4) in three natural bodies of water wherein simazine was applied at a concentration of 0.5 ppm as a surface treatment. When the water and hydrosol from a given body of water were sampled at the same time interval, low concentrations of simazine were detected in both.

When simazine was applied to dry bottoms of drained ponds and the ponds subsequently refilled, higher concentrations of simazine were detected in the hydrosol than in water when samples were taken periodically. With increasing intervals between application and sampling, decreasing concentrations of simazine in the hydrosol were associated with increasing concentrations in water.

Mauck *et al*. (11) conducted a relatively thorough investigation of simazine residue dynamics in five physically and biologically similar ponds for more than two years after the herbicide had been applied at four rates in early spring. They found the amount of simazine in the pond mud to be directly related to application rate. Simazine concentrations in the mud reached a plateau after about 30 to 45 days, then declined in all ponds.

In laboratory studies, it has been demonstrated that microorganisms are able to degrade chlorotriazines mainly via dealkylation. In aquatic situations, the rate of decomposition of simazine by nonphotosynthetic microorganisms appears to be quite slow. This is suggested by the relatively slow rate of loss when no or little biomass is present and once the photosynthetic plant mass in a treated body of water has been markedly reduced.

There is some degradation of simazine adsorbed to the hydrosol. A portion of this degradation is undoubtedly the result of microbial activity. However, it appears that the rate of degradation in hydrosol is not appreciable as compared to some other means. The rate of hydrolysis is dependent primarily upon the pH of the water as related to the dissociation constant value of simazine. Hydrolysis is not a significant mechanism of degradation in the aquatic environment.

Photodecomposition is another method by which simazine may be degraded. However, available data suggest that under normal field or aquatic conditions, photolysis is of little importance in simazine dissipation. It has been observed that when chlorotriazines are irradiated in water the major metabolites are hydroxy triazines, Pape and Zabik (14). Hydroxy triazines are basically inactive biologically.

The environmental effects of simazine herbicide stress on microcosm algal communities during a successional sequence is of special interest. Such parameters as metabolism, chlorophyll a concentration, pigment ratios, diversity and species dominance were monitored over time. Of interest was whether the communities would recover from various concentrations of the herbicide, simazine, and, if so, by what mechanisms. The effect of this herbicide on algal species is also of interest since it is considered to have the potential for controlling aquatic weeds and algae in static water conditions.

Biological communities are known to respond to stress in a variety of ways. Dominant among the responses appear to be changes in community structure and productivity relationships. In recent years, particular emphasis has been placed upon examining the effects of various kinds of pollutants as stressing agents. A common pattern in aquatic communities appears to involve a change in community structure as reflected by lowering of species diversity or a change in species dominance.

For a compilation on simazine toxicity to non-target aquatic organisms refer to Mauck (11). He reported no effect on survival or growth of either bluegills or invertebrates following two annual applications up to 3 ppm. Harman (5) observed that simazine applications of 0.5 ppm in a lake had severely debilitating effects on sublittoral populations of the viviparus snail, *Viviparus georgianus* (Lea), killing immature individuals.

Ponds used for intensive culture of channel catfish (*Ictalurus punctatus* L.) often develop dense phytoplankton blooms as a result of additions of nutrients from supplemental feeding (15). These blooms, especially if blue-green algae predominate, have been implicated in a number of water quality related problems the most severe of which is the risk of oxygen depletion. One potential way to reduce phytoplankton density and prevent related water quality problems is the use of herbicides. Two powerful algicides, copper sulfate and simazine, are currently registered with the U.S. Environmental Protection Agency for use with food fish (12). However, treatment of channel catfish (*Ictalurus punctatus*) production ponds with biweekly applications of 0.84 kg/hectare copper sulfate was ineffective in reducing phytoplankton density. Three periodic applications of simazine totaling 1.3 mg/liter drastically reduced phytoplankton density. But extended periods of low dissolved oxygen concentrations following simazine applications resulted in decreased fish yields and poor conversion ratios as compared to control ponds.

HEALTH EFFECTS

Mauck et al. (12) studied the extent of uptake and accumulation of simazine in aquatic invertebrates, mainly dragonfly nymphs, midge larvae and mayflies. The simazine residues in these benthic invertebrates were directly proportional to the rates applied, but usually far exceeded those in water for about the first 100 to 200 days after treatment, depending on the year. Simazine residues then decreased sharply with no evidence of bioaccumulation. Simazine treatments or residues appeared to have no adverse effects on survival or growth of either fish or invertebrates.

Lawrence *et al.* (8), using radioactive carbon, found that simazine accumulated in the viscera and in the fleshy portion of the body of bluegill. He further observed that if fish from water treated with simazine containing radioactive carbon were placed in simazine free water the carbon was practically eliminated in 4 weeks.

Rodgers (15) observed that bluegill exposed to simazine in the laboratory absorbed it in amounts proportional to its concentration in the ambient water. Most of the simazine was found in the viscera, and it disappeared after the fish had been in fresh water for 3 days.

Thomas (20) followed residues of simazine over a 30-day period in a simazine treated pond. He found that residues in both the viscera and meat followed the same dissipation pattern in bullhead, bluegill, greensunfish, pumpkinseed sunfish and goldfish. The residues were highest on the first day of exposure and continued to decline. Residues in the skin of fish reached the highest level at 8 days after exposure and continued to decrease thereafter.

Mayer and Sanders (12) reported that simazine was accumulated by fish up to 55 times that in their exposure water. They further reported that no simazine residues were found after the fish had been in uncontaminated water for three days.

The Environmental Protection Agency has established tolerances for residues of simazine in fish of 12 ppm. Correspondingly, a tolerance of 0.01 ppm was established in potable water.

Researchers at CIBA-GEIGY Corporation (4) have studied the metabolism of ring labeled simazine in bluegills and catfish. When water was treated at 2.5 ppm bluegill accumulated five times the water concentration and catfish twice the water concentration as total ^{14}C residues in muscle tissue after a 28-day exposure. Bluegills were found to metabolize simazine much faster and more intensively than catfish. Both fish degrade simazine in a similar manner primarily be dealkylation of side chains with some hydrolysis of the chlorine atom to hydroxy analogs. Further metabolism to complex water soluble products and insolubles occurs with longer exposure. Placement of fish into untreated water for seven days results in a rapid depletion of all extractable non-polar radioactivity, including simazine and its dealkylated metabolite. Uptake of simazine by fish in a treated pond would be expected to be much less than was found in a laboratory study because of the presence of soil in these aquatic environments.

As a result of failure to observe mortality to mollusks in laboratory studies at simazine concentrations several times greater than that at which mortality occurred in the lake study, he theorized that synergistic reactions with substrate or dying algal cells were responsible for the mortality of benthos observed.

Mayer and Sanders (12) evaluated the effects of continuous simazine exposures on daphnid reproduction, midge emergence and growth, reproduction and survival of fathead minnows using flow-through diluter systems and on fathead minnows using simulated use-pattern exposure. No adverse effects on daphnid reproduction were observed at simazine concentrations of 3 mg/l. Midge emergence was temporarily delayed at 0.66 and 2.2 mg/l simazine exposures. Egg hatch and fry growth of fathead minnow were reduced in continuous simazine exposures of 1.7 mg/l. No adverse effect was found with simazine in the use-pattern exposure.

SUMMARY AND CONCLUSIONS

No direct effect of simazine on fish has been confirmed when use-pattern exposure was employed for control of aquatic plants. There have been indirect effects due primarily to depletion of dissolved oxygen associated with death and decay of aquatic plant life. Species of fish with high oxygen demands (e.g. trout and bass) are more susceptible to this condition than those with low oxygen demands (e.g. catfish).

To reduce the incidence of oxygen depletion to critical levels in ponds when using simazine, applications are suggested prior to the buildup of heavy populations of algae, before submersed weeds reach the surface of the ponds, and before water temperatures exceed 75°F.

In the event dissolved oxygen in water approaches critical levels as evidenced by the behavior of fish, there are corrective actions that may be taken. These include introducing compressed air, adding adequately aerated water from another source, recycling water from the affected area and aerating it during the process, and churning the affected water to induce aeration.

REFERENCES

1. Blackburn, R.D. and J.B. Taylor. 1976. Aquazine™ A promising algacide for use in southeastern waters. Proc. Soc. Weed Sci. Soc. 29:365-373.
2. Flanagan, J.H., J. Hensley, and N.T. Helseth. 1977. Unpublished data. CIBA-GEIGY Research Station, Vero Beach, Florida.
3. Funderburk, H.H., Jr. and J. M. Lawrence. 1963. Absorption and translocation of radioactive herbicides in submersed and emersed aquatic weeds. Weed Res. 3:304-311.
4. Gunther, F.A. (Editor). 1970. The Triazine Herbicides. Residue Reviews 32.
5. Harman, W.M. 1977. The effects of simazine treatments on the benthic fauna of Moriane Lake, Madison County, New York. Proceedings — NEWSS. 31:122-137.
6. Hawxby, K. and R. Mehta. 1978. Sorption of four herbicides by various algae. Proc. SWSS 31:235.
7. Hiltibran, R.C. and A.J. Turgeon. 1975. Turfgrass response to some herbicides and metals in irrigation water. Proc. North Central Weed Control Conference. Vol. 30, pp. 174.
8. Lawrence, J.M., P.G. Beasley, and R.B. Jones. 1963. Chemical control of weeds in ponds, herbicides on submersed aquatic weeds, and determination of their residues. Annual Report, Auburn University, Alabama.
9. Lembi, Carole A., M.R. Mueller and T. Hippensteel. 1975. Plant responses to irrigation water from a simazine-treated pond. Proc. North Central Weed Control Conference. Vol. 30, pp. 174.

10. Mauck, W.L. 1974. A review of the literature on the use of simazine in fisheries. NTIS No. PB-235 455. National Technical Information Service—U.S. Dept. of Commerce. 46 pp.
11. Mauck, W.L., F.L. Mayer, Jr., and D.D. Holz. 1976. Simazine residue dynamics in small ponds. Bull. Env. Cont. & Tox. 16(1):1-8.
12. Mayer F.L. and H.D. Sanders. 1977. Simazine effects on nontarget aquatic organisms. A preliminary report, 30th Annual Meeting Southern Weed Science Society.
13. Norton, J. and J. Ellis. 1976. Management of aquatic vegetation with simazine. Proc. Southern Weed Science Soc. 29:359-364.
14. Pape, B.E. and M.J. Zabik. 1970. Photochemistry of selected 2-chloro- and 2-methylthio-4,6-di(alkylamino)-s-triazine herbicides. J. Agr. Food Chem. 18(2):202-207.
15. Rodgers, C.A. 1970. Uptake and elimination of simazine by greensunfish (*Lepomis cyanellus* Raf.) Weed Sci. 18:134.
16. Runke, H.M. 1975. Algicidal and algastatic effects of the herbicide simazine on freshwater phytoplankton. M.S. Thesis. Utah State Univ., Logan, Utah.
17. Seaman, D.E. and J.D. Baldia. 1968. Translocation of solutes in three species of *Myriophyllum*. WSSA Abstracts p. 59.
18. Sutton, D.L., D.A. Durham, S.W. Bingham, and C.L. Foy. 1969. Influence of simazine on apparent photosynthesis of aquatic plants and herbicide residue removal from water. Weed Science 17:56.
19. Sutton, D.L. and S.W. Bingham. 1968. Translocation patterns of simazine in *Potamogeton crispus* L. Proc. NEWCC 22:357-361.
20. Thomas, R.E. 1967. Simazine treatment of Ravenna Lake for control of aquatic vegetaion. Nebraska Game, Forestation, and Fish Commission, July 1, 1967. 9 p.

Table 1. Nomenclature, Chemical and Physical Properties[1]

1. *Common Name:* simazine (ANSI approved), G-27692
2. *Trade Name:* Princep 80W, princep TM 4L, Princep 4 G, Aquazine[R] and Princep Caliber [R]90.
3. *Chemical Name:* 2-chloro-r,6-bis(ethylamino)-*s*-triazine
4. *Structural Formula:*

$$\begin{array}{ccc} & \text{Cl} & \\ & \text{N} \quad \text{N} & \\ H_5C_2\text{-NH} & \text{N} & \text{NH-C}_2H_5 \end{array}$$

5. *Molecular Formula:* $C_7H_{12}ClN_5$
6. *Molecular Weight:* 201.7
7. *Color and Physical State:* White, crystalline powder.
8. *Melting Point:* 225-227°.
9. *Vapor Pressure:*

Temperature° C	mmHg
10	9.2×10^{-10}
20	6.1×10^{-9}
30	3.6×10^{-8}
50	9.0×10^{-7}

10. *Solubility:*

Solvent	Temperature° C	ppmw
Chloroform	20	900.0
Methanol	20	400.0
n-pentane	25	3.0
Petroleum ether	20	2.0
Water	0	2.0
Water	20	3.5
Water	85	84.0

From: Herbicide Handbook, Weed Science Society of America, Urbana, Illinois, 19.

Table 2.   Compilation of Weeds Controlled by Simazine.

Simazine
Chemical name: 2-Chloro-4,6-bis(ethylamino)-s-triazine

Trade names: Aquazine[R], Princep[R]

Available alone as 0.1 to 0.6% liquids (L); 0.167 to 2.0% granules in fertilizer and as 4.0% to 90.0% granules (G); 1.0 and 41.9% liquid concentrates (LC); 5.0% impregnated tapes, and 80.0% wettable powder (WP).

Weeds Controlled

Simazine will control most annual broadleaf weeds and grasses and many perennials, including:

alyssum	Allssum spp.
amaranthus	Amaranthus spp.
bassia, fivehook	Bassia hyssopifolia
barnyardgrass	Echinochloa crus-galli
bluegrass (annual)	Poa annua
brachiaria	Brachiaria spp.
bromegrass, downy	Bromus secalinus
bromegrass, smooth	Bromus inermis
burclover	Medicago spp.
burdock	Actium spp.
carpetweed	Mollugo verticillata
chickweed, common	Stellaria media
chickweed, mouseear	Cerastium vulgatum
cockle, white (seedlings)	Lychnis alba
crabgrass	Digitaria spp.
dandelion (seedlings)	Taraxicum spp.
dogfennel	Eupatorium cepillifolium
fescue, rattail	Festuca myuros
fiddleneck	Amsinchia spp.
filaree	Erodium spp.
fireweed	Epilobium angustifolium
foxtail	Setaria spp.
goosegrass	Eleusine indica
groundsel	Senecio spp.
knawel	Scleranthus annuus
kochia	Kochia scoparia
lambsquarters, common	Chenopodium album
lettuce, prickly	Lactuca serriola
morningglory, annual	Ipomoea spp.

Table 2.   Compilation of Weeds Controlled by Simazine. (cont.)

mustard	Brassica spp.
nightshade	Solanum spp.
nimblewill (wiregrass)	Muhlenbergia schreberi
oats, wild	Avena fatua
orchardgrass	Dactylis glomerata
pennycress, field (fanweed)	Thalaspi arvense
pepperweed (peppergrass)	Lepidium spp.
pigweed	Amaranthus spp.
pineappleweed	Matricaria matricicariodes
plantain	Plantago spp.
puncturevine	Tribulus terrestris
purpletop (Tall Red-top)	Tridens flava
purslane	Portulaca oleracea
pusley, Florida	Richardia scabra
quackgrass	Agropyron repens
ragweed	Ambrosia spp.
redtop	Agrostis alba
rocket, yellow	Barbarea vulgaris
rockpurslane, redmaids menziesii	Calandrina caulescens var.
ryegrass (Italian)	Lolium multiflorum
shepherdspurse (seedlings)	Capsella bursa-pastoris
silver hairgrass	Aira caryophyllea
smartweed	Polygonum spp.
sowthistle	Sonchus spp.
spanishneedles	Bidens bipinnata
speedwell	Veronica spp.
strangler vine	Morrenia oderata
tansymustard	Descurainia pinnata
tassleflower, red	Emilia sonchifolia
thistle, bull	Cirsium vulgare
thistle, Canada	Cirsium arvense
thistle, Russian	Salsola kali var. tenuifolia
witchgrass	Panicum capillare

[1] USDA Compilation of Registered uses of Herbicides, June 17, 1980.

PART II

EVALUATION OF SELECTED AQUATIC HERBICIDES

Chapter 14

HERBICIDAL, ENVIRONMENTAL AND HEALTH EFFECTS OF FLURIDONE[1]

INTRODUCTION

Fluridone, 1-methyl-3-phenyl-5-[3-(trifluoromethyl)phenyl]-4(1H)-pyridinone, has been shown to be an effective terrestrial and aquatic herbicide (6,8,10,11,14). For terrestrial plant control, the mode of action of fluridone was suggested by Berard, Rainey, and Lin (4) to be through disruption of the development and/or stability of newly formed cell pigments. Anderson (1) suggested that the synthesis of specific light-induced RNA's is blocked, indicating that fluridone remains active in the plant for a short time before it is inactivated. Under field conditions he found that fluridone at 1.0 mg/l will control American pondweed (**Potamogeton nodosus**) and Sago pondweed (**Potamogeton pectinatus**) during sprouting, only when sufficient light and a 1- to 6-day contact time is available. Results of other fluridone efficacy and field dissipation studies in lakes and ponds, treated to provide 0.02, 0.03, and 0.3 mg/l fluridone concentrations relative to the total water column, showed that the half-life of fluridone in water is about 5 days (15). Sanders and Theriot (11) showed that fluridone in small quanities (6-14 ug/l was detected in untreated areas of Gatun Lake, Panama, within 24 hr following treatment, indicating that the herbicide dispersed out of the treated area. Fluridone efficacy in the treated and untreated areas indicates that a much lower fluridone concentration in the water could be effective at controlling aquatic macrophytes. Marzuis, Comes and Yang (7) showed that submersed Sago pondweed and Richardson pondweed (**Potamogeton Richardsonii** Rydb.) developed typical fluridone injury systoms (retarded growth, albescent young leaves, and leaf necrosis) whether they were growing in treated water or emerging from treated sediment. Less than 1 percent of the ^{14}C fluridone applied at 100 ug/l was absorbed by the roots and shoots over a 14-day period. Less than 5 percent of the sediment-applied fluridone was translocated to the lower stem and shoots, plant injury was observed. These finding suggest that a very low fluridone concentration ($<$0.1 ug/l) may be sufficient to control these submersed aquatic plants. Results of these studies show that fluridone

---

[1]The findings in this report are not to be constructed as an official Department of the Army position unless so designated by other authorized documents.

dissipates very rapidly in water through absorption to plants and sediment and dispersion out of the treated area and that the fluridone concentration required to control a wide variety of submersed aquatic plants appears to be less than 0.1 ug/l.

HERBICIDAL EFFECTS

Fluridone was reported as an aquatic plant herbicide in 1979 (8,10,11) and has since been successfully used to control noxious aquatic weeds, including hydrilla (**Hydrilla verticillata**), elodea (**Elodea** spp.), watermilfoil (**Myriophylum** spp.) pondweeds (**Potamogeton** spp.) and cabomba (**Cabomba** spp.).

The Corps of Engineers' Aquatic Plant Control Research Program (APCRP) initiated a study to determine the lowest sustained, aqueous fluridone concentration required to control the growth of **Hydrilla verticillata** Royle (hydrilla) and **Myriophyllum spicatum** L. (Eurasian watermilfoil) on sand-peat and natural sediment substrates under laboratory conditions over a 12-week study period. Results of these tests will be used in considering fluridone for ongoing controlled-release research within the APCRP to develop a formulation that releases fluridone constantly over a defined 6- to 8-week posttreatment period, thereby providing a continuous and constant low-level herbicide exposure to plants within a defined treatment area. Plant injury was assessed after 12 weeks of continuous exposure to the various fluridone concentrations. Results of this study indicate that the threshold fluridone concentration required to control **Myriophyllum spicatum** growing on both substrates was between 10 and 20 ug/l. When root and shoot biomass data and percent injury ratings were considered for **Hydrilla verticillata**, the fluridone threshold concentration necessary to provide greater than 50-percent control was estimed to be 20 ug/l.

ENVIRONMENTAL EFFECTS

The nomenclature and related chemical, physiological, and toxicological properties of fluridone are summarized in Table 1 as abstracted from the WSSA handbook on herbicides (16). Applied as directed, there are few if any undesirable effects on the environment and there are few restrictions to application as an aquatic weed herbicide. It does not have toxic properties to fish of fish food organisms.

A large scale management study to utilize fluridone(6) to control hydrilla was made in Sampson Lake, Florida in 1984. Data from the study are given in talbes 2, 3 and 4. About 800 acres of hydrilla were controlled without seriously changing the natural vegetation, as indicated in table 2. The harvestable sportfish for each habitat are given in table 3 and 4. The comparisons do not indicate that hydrilla seriously limited sport fishing and that the cost of eradication would have to be borne by other components.

HEALTH EFFECTS

Use precautions of fluridone are typical of most aquatic herbicides. The chemical is not hazardous and has an acute toxicity to rats and mice of less than 10 grams per kilogram. There are no serious subacute or chronic toxicities and no adverse effects have been observed at the levels used for weed control.

SUMMARY AND CONCLUSIONS

There are few aquatic herbicides that serve a more real purpose in the control of hydrilla than fluridone. It promises to be one of the most useful herbicides for the vegetative management of noxious aquatic weeds, particularly hydrilla.

REFERENCES

1. Anderson, L.W.J. 1981. Effect of light on the phytotoxicity of fluridone in American pondweed (**Potamogeton nodosus**)and sago pondweed (**P. pectinatus**). Weed Science. 29: 723-728.
2. Back, A., and A.E. Richmond. 1971. Interrelations between giberellic acid, cytokinens and abscisic acid on retarding leaf senescence, **Journal of Plant Physiology**. 24: 76-79.
3. Bartels, P.G., and C.W. Watson. 1978. Inhibition of carotenoid synthesis by fluridone and norflurazon, Weed Science, 26: 198-203.
4. Berard, D.F., D.P. Rainey, and C.C. Lin. 1978. Absorption, translocation, and metabolism of fluridone in selected crop species, Weed Science. 26: 250-254.
5. Hall, J.F., H.E. Westerdahl and T.J. Stewart. 1983. Growth response of **Myriophyllum Spicatum** and **Hydrilla verticillata** when exposed to continuous low concentrations of fluridone. Tech. Report. A-83-, U.S. Army Experiment Station, Vicksburg, Miss.
6. Hinkle, J. 1985. The effects of a large scale fluridone treatment on the vegetation of Sampson Lake. Aquatics. 7: 8-11.

7. Marquis, L.Y., R.D. Comes, and C.P. Yang. 1981. Absorption and translocation of fluridone and glyphosate in submersed vascular plants, Weed Science. 29: 229-236.
8. McCowen, M.C. 1979. Fluridone, a new herbicide for aquatic plant management. J. Aquatic plant manage. 17: 27-30.
9. Muir, D.C.G. 1980. Persistence of fluridone in small ponds, J. of Enviro. Qual. 9: 151-156.
10. Rivera, C.M., S.D. West, and J. Perez. 1979. Fluridone: an experimental herbicide for aquatic plant management systems, Proceedings of the Western Weed Science Society. 32: 67-73.
11. Sanders, D.R., and R.F. Theriot. 1979. Evaluation of two fluridone formulations for the control of hydrilla in Gatun Lake, Panama Canal Zone, Technical Report A-79-3, U.S. Army Engineer Waterways Experiment Station, CE, Vicksburg, Miss.
12. Schmitz, D.C., L.E. Nall, and A.J. Leslie. 1984. Herbicide investigations in Lake Mann and Williams Pond following applications of Sonar (Fluridone). Abstracts. The Aquatic Plant Management Society Meetings. Richmond, Virginia. July 15-18, 1984.
13. Tarver, Dave and Lonnie Pell. 1984. Status Report on Sonar, 1984. Abstracts. The Aquatic Plant Management Society Meetings. Richmond, Virginia. July 15-18, 1984.
14. Waldrep, T.W., and H.M. Taylor. 1976 1-Methyl-3-phenyl-5-[3-(trifluoromethyl)phenyl]-4(1H)-pyridinone, A New Herbicide, J. of Agri. and Food Chem. 24: 1250-1251.
15. West, S.D., and S.J. Parka. 1981. Determination of the aquatic herbicide fluridone in water and hydrosoil: effect of application method of dissipation, J. of Agri. and Food Chem. 29: 223-226.
16. WSSA. 1979. Herbicide Handbook Fourth Edition, Weed Science Society of America, Champaign, IL.

Table 1.   Fluridone (1-methyl-3-phenyl-5-[3-(trifluoromethyl)phenyl]-4(1H)-pyridinone)

A. Nomenclature: Chemical and Physical Properties of the Pure Chemical.
1. Common name: fluridone (ANSI, BSI, WSSA)
2. Product name and manufacturer: --- Elanco
3. Structural formula:
4. Molecular formula: $C_{19}H_{14}F_3NO$
5. Wiswesser line notation: T6N DVJ A CR CXFFF& ER
6. Molecular weight: 329.3
7. Physical state, color, and odor: White crystalline solid.
9. Melting point (C): 154 to 155.
12. Relative resistance to decomposition by ultraviolet irradiation: Half line in deionized water (hr)

fluridone	23
trifluralin	2

13. Vapor pressure, mm Hg: less than 1×10^{-7} at 25 C
14. Solubility:

Solvent	Solubility (g/100 ml)
Methanol	>1
Diethyl ether	>0.1
Ethyl acetate	>0.5
Chloroform	>1
Hexane	<0.05
Water	0.0012

15. Other chemical formulations available: Fluridone is available as a 50% WP and as a 4 lb/gal aqueous suspension.

B. Use Precautions
1. Flammability: Neither formulation is flammable.
2. Possible incompatibilities: Incompatibility with water of any hardness has not been experienced. Fluridone has been successfully tank-mixed with many other herbicides.
3. Corrosiveness: Neither formulation has demonstrated corrosiveness.
4. Cleaning glassware and spray equipment: Clean glassware with soap and water or a solvent followed by water. Rinse spray equipment thoroughly with water.
5. Storage stability: The 50 WP has demonstrated good stability for 18 months at room temperature and for 9 months at 50 C. Studies on the 4AS indicate that chemical stability will equal that of the wettable powder. No adverse effects on the properties of the 4AS have been noted after freezing.
6. Safety precautions for handling and application: As with all chemicals, keep out of reach of children. Avoid breathing dust

Table 1.   Fluridone (1-methyl-3-phenyl-5-[3-(trifluoromethyl)phenyl]-4(1H)-pyridinone) (cont.)

or spray mist. The formulations may cause irritation after contact with eyes or skin. Wash affected areas with soap and water. In cash of eye contact, flush eyes with large quantities of water. Avoid contamination of feed or foodstuff.

C. Physiological and Biochemical Behavior
 1. Foliar absorption characteristics: Fluridone does have some postemergence activity against certain plants at excessive application rates. At use application rates, little contact activity is observed.
 2. Translocation characteristics: In cotton, a resistant species, fluridone is taken up by the roots; however, little or no translocation of root absorbed fluridone into the shoot portion of the plant occurs. In susceptible species root absorbed fluridone is readily translocated into the shoot.
 3. Mechanism of action: Inhibition of carotenoid synthesis which ultimately results in the formation of albescent tissue is susceptible plants.
 4. Metabolism and persistence in plants: Radioactive studies indicate no significant metabolism of fluridone in plants.

D. Behavior In or On Soils
 1. Adsorption and leaching characteristics in basic soil types: Fluridone is strongly adsorbed to organic matter in soil. Regression analysis suggests that organic matter can be used to predict the rate of fluridone required for herbicidal activity. There is also good correlation between adsorption/desorption coefficients and the organic matter content of the soil. Column leaching studies indicate that fluridone leaches slowly in the soil.
 2. Microbial breakdown: Microorganisms do not appear to be a major factor in the dissipation of fluridone in soil.
 4. Resultant average persistence at recommended rates: The persistence of fluridone is complex and not well defined. In most cotton producing areas, residues may carry over to the next cropping season and cause slight injury to crops such as corn, sorghum, soybeans, sugar beets, and tomatoes that follow in rotation. There appears to be little relationship between the rainfall pattern, soil texture and land tillage to soil persistence of fluridone.

E. Toxicological Properties
 1. General toxicity to wildlife and fish: One-week-old mallard and bobwhite were fed diets containing various concentrations of the compound for 5 days. LC_{50} values were: bobwhite quail approximately 10,000 ppm, mallard duck >20,000 ppm. Bluegills

Table 1.   Fluridone (1-methyl-3-phenyl-5-[3-(trifluoromethyl)phenyl]-4(1H)-pyridinone) (cont.)

and rainbow trout fingerlings were used in static toxicity tests. LC_{50} values were: bluegills (5-day exposure) >10 ppm, rainbow trout (7-day exposure) $\pm$ 0.6 ppm. Daphnia magna, less than 24 hr old, were placed in tanks containing various concentrations of fluridone. The LC_{50} for 48 hr exposure was approximately 8 ppm.

2. Acute toxicity:

Rat LD_0*	$>$ 10 g/kg
Mouse LD_{50}	$>$ 10 g/kg
Dog LD_0	$>$500 mg/kg
Cat LD_0	$>$250 mg/kg

   *No deaths occurred at this dosage.

3. Subacute toxicity: Rats and mice were fed diets containing 2000 ppm of fluridone for 90 days. Slight histological changes in the livers and kidneys were noted in treated animals. No other signs of toxicity were detected. Dogs were given oral doses of 50, 100, or 200 mg/kg of fluridone for 90 days. No adverse effects were noted.

4. Chronic toxicity: Two-year feeding studies in rats have shown no adverse effects.

5. Toxicity to skin and possible danger through inhalation: Fluridone was nonirritating when applied to the skin of white rabbits and was nontoxic in inhalation studies in rats.

6. Symptoms of poisoning: No cases of poisoning have been reported or observed.

7. First aid and antidotes: Keep out of reach of children. May be harmful if swallowed. Avoid prolonged or repeated contact with skin or eyes. Wash thoroughly after handling. If fluridone gets in eyes, gently rinse with water.

From: WSSA. 1979. Herbicide Handbook.

Table 2. Sampson Lake Vegetation

Species	Acreage 1983	1984
Hydrilla verticullate	800.0	0.1
Typha spp.	125.0	120.0
Nelumbo lutea	50.0	40.0
Nymphaea odorata	35.0	35.0
Fuirena sciropoidea	25.0	25.0
Panicum hemitomon	20.0	20.0
Vallisneria americana	15.0	16.0
Bacopa caroliniana	5.0	5.0
Filamentous algae	5.0	10.0
Paspalidium geminatum	5.0	5.0
Utricularia purpurea	5.0	3.0
Najas guadalupenis	4.0	4.0
Pontederia lanceolata	3.0	3.0
Cephalanthus occidentalis	2.0	2.0
Hydrochloa carolinensis	2.0	2.0
Brachiaria purpurascens	1.0	1.0
Cyperus spp.	1.0	1.0
Eichhornia crassipes	1.0	0.5
Eleocharis spp.	1.0	1.0
Hydrocotyle spp.	1.0	1.0
Juncus spp.	1.0	1.0
Nuphar luteum	1.0	1.0
Alternanthera philozeroides	0.5	0.5
Lachanthes caroliniana	0.5	0.3
Ludwigia arcuata	0.5	0.5
Nitella spp.	0.5	60.0
Salvinia rotundifolia	0.5	0.1
Total	1110.5	358.0
Percent Plant Coverage	54.5%	17.5%
Percent Hydrilla Coverage	39.2%	0.0%
Percent Hydrilla Composition of Plant Community	72.0%	0.0%

From Hinkle, 1984, with permission.

HERBICIDAL, ENVIRONMENTAL AND HEALTH EFFECTS OF FLURIDONE   351

Table 3. Harvestable Sportfish for Each Habitat

Habitat	(lbs./acre)	Samples
(1) Limnetic	7.8	2
(2) Littoral vegetation	27.7	2
(3) Littoral vegetation interface with limnetic habitat (no hydrilla)	55.9	3
(4) Interface of deep water sparse hydrilla and limnetic habitat	54.3	1
(5) Topped out hydrilla	11.3	1

From Hinkle, 1984, with permission.

Table 4. Comparison of Harvestable Sportfish in Sampson Lake

Habitat Type	Prehydrilla		During Hydrilla Domination		After Fluridone Treatment	
	Acres of Habitat	Harvestable Sportfish Total Lbs.	Acres of Habitat	Harvestable Sportfish Total Lbs.	Acres of Habitat	Harvestable Sportfish Total Lbs.
Limnetic (open water)	1,642	12,808	932	7,270	1,684	13,135
Littoral vegetation	340	9,418	310	8,587	298	8,255
Littoral vegetation interface with lemnetic habitat (no hydrilla)	60	3,354	—	—	60	3,354
Interface of deep water sparse hydrilla with limnetic habitat	—	—	50	2,715	—	—
Topped-out hydrilla	—	—	750	8,475	—	—
Total lbs. harvestable sportfish		25,580		27,047		24,744

From Hinkle, 1984, with permission.

PART III

EVALUATION OF VEGATATIVE MANAGEMENT PROGRAMS

Chapter 15

STRATEGIES FOR FRESHWATER FISHERIES MANAGEMENT[1]

INTRODUCTION

Obnoxious aquatic plant nuisances affecting recreational and potable waters may curtail or eliminate bathing, boating, water skiing, and sometimes fishing, perpetrate psychosomatic illness in man by emitting vile stenches, impart tastes and odors, shorten filter runs or otherwise hamper industrial and municipal water treatment; interfere with the manufacture of a product in industry, on occasion become toxic to certain warm-blooded animals that ingest the water; and cause skin rashes and hayfever-like symptoms in man. These plant nuisances may be grouped into the algae and various higher aquatic plants. Algae appear as floating scums; suspended matter giving rise to murky, turbid water or water having a "pea soup" appearance attached filaments; and bottom dwelling types that may be confused with the rooted higher aquatic plants. The higher plants grow as submersed, floating, or emergent plants and/or marginal aquatic plants.

Algae

Most algal problems occur when growth conditions permit the formation of a "bloom." A bloom is an unusually large number of cells (usually one or a few species) per unit of surface water, which often can be discerned visually by the green blue-green, brown or even brilliant red discoloration of the water. Of the countless species of freshwater algae, only a few produce disturbances which attract our attention. Some of the American freshwater trouble-forming species (12) are listed as follows:

I. Cyanophyta (blue-green algae)
    Microcystis aeruginosa Kuetzing
    Coelosphaerium Kuetzingianum Naegeli

Oscillatoria rubescens De Candolle
O. lacustris (Klebahn)
Anabaena circinalis Kuetzing
A. flos-aquae (Linnaeus)
A. Lammermanni Richter
Anbaenopsis Elenkini Miller

---

[1]The findings in this report are not to be construed as an official Department of The Army position unless so designated by other authorized documents.

Dinobryon sertularia
Ehrenberg
D. social Ehrenberg
Synura unvella Ehrenberg
Fragilaria spp.
Tabellaria fenestrata Kuetzing
Asterionella gracillima
(Hantzch)

II. Chrysopyta (yellow-green
algae and diatoms)
III. Pyrrophyta (dinoflagellates)

Coscinodiscus spp.
Melosira granulata
(Ehrenberg)
Stephanodiscus niagarae
Ehrenberg

Ceratinum hirundinella
(Mueller)

Lakes which have been enriched by various kinds of pollution from human habitats, runoff from agricultural lands, wastes from farm animals, (2) are the ones in which algae blooms appear. Accordingly, blue-green algae follow man about as he colonizes and pioneers new areas creating situations favorable for agricultural and industrial development.

Toxic Algae

Cases of animal poisonings related to algal blooms, and from a growing appreciation of the strictly scientific and biological problems involving the physiology of algae, especially those that produce toxic, substances, antibiotics, and growth-stimulating excretions is well documented (5). Algae that have been responsible for mammalian, avarian, and fish deaths through some toxic action are all to be found in the blue-green algal group, the Cyanophyta. The Cyanophyta species that have been associated with animal deaths belong in the genera: *Microcystis, Aphanizomenon, Anabaena, Nodularia, Coelosphaerium,* and *Gloeotrichia.*

Toxic algae as a public health hazard are reviewed by Gorham (5). He concluded that the fish and livestock poisons produced by waterblooms are nuisances and economic hazards rather than public health hazards. It was estimated that the oral minimum lethal dose of decomposing toxic *Microcystis* bloom for a 150-pound man would be 1- to 2-quarts of thick, paint-like suspension. Gorham states that this amount would not be ingested voluntarily; however, in the case of an accident, such a quantity might be ingested involuntarily.

Aquatic Vascular Plants

In the long-term cycle of the change in the aquatic terrain there is a continuing tendency for the land to encroach upon shallow ponds and shallow areas of lakes, decrease their size, make them more shallow, and eventually return them to dry land. Rooted aquatic vegetation plays a prominent role in this gradual process by invading shallow water areas through entrapment of particulate silt that is carried into lakes and ponds. The rooted vegetation will continue to spread as water areas become more shallow and the bottom mud provides suitable anchorage for roots. Plants contribute also to the filling in of lakes through both the precipitation of calcium carbonate and the accumulation of their remains upon death and decay (4).

Infestations of Eurasian watermilfoil have become a serious threat to ponds, lakes, and tidewater areas by reducing their use for recreation, as well as hampering navigation, diminishing the size of open waterfowl feeding areas and reducing the value of waterfront real estate. Since 1961, watermilfoil has doubled its water surface coverage in the Maryland tidewater area and now inhabits an estimated 100,000 acres. Heavy concentrations of this weed also have been found in the waters of New Jersey, New York, North Carolina, Alabama, Indiana, Ohio, California, Washington and Texas. In the Tennessee Valley Authority watershed, (15) and the U.S. Army Corps of Engineers, Lake Seminole (4) reservoir infestations have demanded major programs of control. Problems associated with Eurasian watermilfoil infestation are curtailment of recreational uses, commercial fishing and human health through the increase of disease-causing organisms.

Although the term "bacterial flora" is glibly used to refer to microbiotic residents of the human gut, the public does not connote these key organisms as the plant life. The current problem in American water bodies is an example of the significance of bacterial pollution whether the bacteria are pathogenic or not. The natural biological cycle in aquatic environments is a fact. The key element in the normal cycle is oxygen; the key aquatic plant is the bacterium that convert soluble organic matter into other bacterial cells and inorganic elements. The inorganics are absorbed by algae and metabolized into other algal cells. Both cell types become food for protozoans, rotifers, and crustaceans. Some bacteria, algae, and animal life serve as basic food for minnows and young fish; small fish are devoured by large fish. Sewage wastes are discharged into the water body where bacteria metabolize the organics. However, if organic waste concentrations increase over normal, bacterial populations explode with increased oxygen demand (BOD). As this life-giving element decreases, the higher animal forms perish, the game fish first, then crustaceans, rotifers, and the higher protozoa. Bacteria remain dominant and in the absence of dissolved oxygen (DO) undergo anaerobic metabolism producing vile odors and black water.

Taste-Odor Problems

Public acceptance of drinking water supplies, whether purified or not, hinges to a great degree on absence of detrimental tastes and odors. If poor taste and odor are of chemical origin (saline or sulphurous) the public is resigned to its fate; but if these are of microbiotic origin, great clamor is raised and the sanitary engineer is expected to defy nature and quickly bring the supply back to levels to which the user is accustomed (3).

Sewage Discharge and Pollution

Environmental changes caused by industrial waste effluents can be detrimental to aquatic life in varying degrees. These include decreases in dissolved oxygen to harmful levels; increases in turbidity; formation of sludge deposits by settleable inert and decomposable solids; increases in chemicals to toxic levels; changes in pH toward extremes in acidity or alkalinity; increases in temperature; tainting of fish flesh; and production of nutrients resulting in undesirable aquatic growths.

Many thousands of waterfowl have been destroyed by the pollutional effects of oil. This wasteful loss has deprived nature lovers, waterfowl hunters, and bird watchers of immeasurable enjoyment. The destruction of ducks such as the canvasback, redhead, and scaup comes at a critical period for these species, which are fighting for survival against the forces of nature and man. Additional waterfowl will be destroyed if oil dumping is continued, especially in late winter. In this age of technical development, the discharge of oil into a river system indicates man's irresponsibility in the preservation of our natural resources.

Wastes with concentrations of nitrogen and phosphorus (fertilizers) increase certain organism populations to such magnitudes as to interfere with water uses and create nuisances. Organisms that respond to such nutrients are certain floating and attached algae and rooted aquatic plants. If streams, lakes, and manmade impoundments continue to be enriched with industrial, municipal, and agricultural wastes, existing biological nuisance problems will intensify in many areas, and develop in others that do not now have them.

Turbidity, which is an expression of the optical property of water that causes light rays to be scattered and absorbed rather than transmitted in straight lines, is caused by a variety of suspended particulate matter. Such matter may be living or dead phytoplankton or zooplankton cells, as algae, protozoans, bacteria, and small crustaceans, or silt or other finely divided inorganic and organic waste materials. Many industrial operations contribute turbidity and settleable solids to water; the resulting bottom deposits affect aquatic life in varying degrees.

Fine particulate inorganic and organic waste materials that remain in suspension limit the penetration of sunlight, thus restricting the growth of attached bottom plants, as well as suspended algae. Also, solids flocculate planktonic algae and animals out of water and carry them to the bottom to die. Thus, in limiting growths of aquatic plant meadows, food chains are interrupted, which results in a sparsity of animal life. As particulate matter settles to the bottom, desposits of settleable solids blanket the substrate and form undesirable physical environments for organisms. In addition, settleable solids may change heat radiation, retain organic materials and other substances which create unfavorable conditions on the bottom, interfere with fish feeding, smother fish eggs, and produce a grinding at crushing action deleterious to benthic forms (10,11,12).

Reservoir Discharge

Water flowing from a natural lake would be expected to be of a quality similar to that of the water in the uppermost stratum of the lake. However, when water in a free-flowing stream is impounded in a large storage reservoir, marked changes are produced in the physical, chemical, and mineral quality of the water.

Churchill (2) discusses the effect on downstream water quality of large storage reservoirs with discharge structures located deep within the reservoir. Because the reservoirs have been operated primarily for flood control and power production, the magnitude of high stream flows is reduced and the general level of low flows is increased. Discharge releases are often reduced over weekend and during other periods of off-peak power loads. The temperatures in the receiving stream may be substantially lowered, sometimes to 55°F; and may not exceed 68°F even in the summer. Because stratification beginning in March or April stops the vertical circulation that exists all winter, discharge through the low-level power structures removes cold water from this level. As the supply of cold water at this elevation is exhausted from the pool, warmer water from above sinks downs and is gradually discharged. By this process the discharged water may gradually warm to temperatures approaching 77° F during the summer and fall. Turbidity resulting from intense summer rains of short duration is reduced. Odors of hydrogen sulfide from decaying organic materials in the deeper portions of the reservoir may be a problem.

The dissolved oxygen concentration of the discharged water is often lower than that normally present in the inflow and may often approach zero at the point of discharge. "Low rates of released flow are reaerated in relatively short distances downstream from the dam, whereas higher discharges require many miles of open-channel flow before oxygen saturation is reached. As much as a 14 to 15° C decrease below "normal" summer stream temperatures was observed.

Love (11) lists important beneficial effects of impoundment on water quality as: reduction of turbidity, silica, color, coliform bacteria; depression of sharp variations in dissolved minerals, hardness, pH, and alkalinity; reduction in temperature, which sometimes benefit fish life; entrapment of sediment; and storage of water for release in dry periods. Detrimental effects were given as; increased growth of algae, which may give rise to tastes and odors; reduction in dissolved oxygen in the deeper parts of the reservoirs; increase in carbon dioxide and frequently iron, manganese, and alkalinity, especially near the bottom; increases in dissolved solids and hardness resulting from evaporation and dissolution of roch materials; and reductions in temperature, which, although sometimes beneficial, may also be detrimental to fish.

TOXIC SHELLFISH AND FISH

Seaweed and certain types of plankton (termed Protista) cause a serious form of human intoxication—shellfish poisoning—and produce disasters in marine biology. Shellfish poison is one of the most lethal known. Clinical effects are not completely understood, but the heart is definitely harmed. Death is usually attributed to respiratory paralysis. *Protista* are single-celled, animal-plant organisms in that their energy is derived by photosynthesis and their motion by flagaellation. Widely distributed in marine waters, they reach public attention as blooms called "red tide" and "red water." Massive fish destruction may accompany these blooms produced by a variety of environmental changes. The cause of mass mortality of marine life during and after the blooms is not clear, yet the best evidence points to physical rather than chemical factors (3,9).

Paralytic shellfish intoxication is caused by certain molluscs and a few echinoderms and arthropods that eat toxic *Protista* (dinoflagellates) and are then ingested by many (10). Some 21 dinoflagellates have been implicated; the best known is *Gonyaulax catenella* of the Pacific coast of North America. How the poison accumulates in molluscs is unknown. At least 28 species are involved including commonly known forms—clams, mussels, and oysters. Mostly the toxin is concentrated in the digestive glands of the mollusc. In Japan, nonparalytic form of poisoning may be contracted by ingestion of certain clams, oysters, and gastropods that consume toxic plankton.

The best method of control is simply to limit sewerage effluent discharge into fresh water bodies.

MOSQUITO DISEASES

Malaria

Water plants are favorable to anopheline mosquito development. In Puerto Rico, this includes coontail, fanwort, widgeon grass, water-weed, pondweed, stonewort, bladderwort, and filamentous green algae, especially *Spirogyra*. Also, the most important wetland or semiaquatic plants are Para grass, Carib grass, tropical carpet grass, sour paspalum, and small trumpet grass. Malaria mosquito larvae are inhibited by the duckweeds, waterfern, waterhyacinth, water lettuce, pond lilies, and water snowflake, certainly by total cover, and probably also by associated water quality changes. Iron bacteria, productive of rust colored flocculent masses and an oily surface in stagnant water, almost totally repels anophelines. Research by the Tennessee Valley Authority (TVA) provided leads on beneficial reduction of anopheline-supporting vegetation by seasonal manipulation of reservoir water levels (22).

Arboviruses

Sleeping sickness or virus encephalitis has been a problem in parts of Latin America and the U.S. for decades. From 1926 to 1950, 27,749 human cases were reported in the U.S.—the lowest number, 702, in 1932; the highest, 3516, in 1941. Only a few hundred cases have been reported annually during recent years. The decrease is most probably due to health education, better screening on houses, and promptness and efficiency of mosquito control incident to epidemics. Larvae of *Culex tarsalis*, the feared vector of St. Louis and Western encephalitis in midwestern and western U.S., thrive in vegetation-clogged irrigation and drainage ditches, seeps, and roadside impoundments. Two other species, *Culex pipiens* and *C. quinquifasciatus*, are not vegetation associated, but prosper in domestic containers, catch basins, cesspools, and filthy ditches. All mosquito larvae except *Mansonia* must breathe at the water surface. *Mansonia,* host of Eastern encephalitis, is unique in that both larvae and pupae derive their oxygen by puncture from air trapped in hollow plant stems (6).

Dengue fever, normally of low endemicity, exhibits occasional out-breaks—Panama in 1941, Yemen in 1954, and Puerto Rico in 1963. In the 1963 Puerto Rican epidemic, infections reached 33,000 in a population of 2.5 million. In a carefully monitored urban population, the prevalence was 35%. Dengue does not kill, but is a miserable illness. Yellow fever fortunately remains at a low ebb in the Old World and has been reported in man but a few times in recent decades in the Americas. It remains endemic as a sylvan animal form in limited parts of Latin America. *Aedes aegypti*, vector of both dengue fever and yellow fever against which there is a Western Hemisphere eradication program, lives well inside water plants, and aquatic plant control programs reduce the incidence of disease (3).

HELMINTHIC DISEASES

Aquatic plants are definitely associated with worm diseases affecting man. Snail vectors and larval stages of the parasitic life cycles are naturally abated by animal predators: (1) by duck, turtle, and fish consumption of snails; (2) by fish ingestion of crustaceans (crayfish, crabs, copepods); and (3) by fish predation of both miracidial larvae infective for small intermediate host and cercarial larvae infective for the final host, man. Numerous flukes of fish, amphibians, reptiles, and other insectivorous animals use aquatic arthropods as host such as dragonflies, caseworms, May flies. Considerable research data are available on the ability of guppies to control cercaria of the human blood fluke life cycle (3,14) which involves some 200 millions of cases internationally.

Some parasitoses representing flukes, tapeworms, and roundworms having stages vulnerable to predation are: filariasis which attacks some 250 million persons (Mosquito larvae); Chinese liver fluke, *Clonorchis* (Buliminid snails, miracidia, and cercaria); cattle and sheep liver flukes, *Fasciola hepatica* and *F. Gigantica* (Lymnaeid snails, miracidia, and floating cercaria); broad tapeworm *Diphyllobothrum* (crustacea); guinea worm, *Dracunculus* (copepods); giant intestinal fluke, *Fasciolopsis* (Planorbid snails, miracidia, and cercaria); Asiatic lung fluke, *Paragonimus* (Thiarid snails, crabs, crayfish, miracidia, and cercaria); blood flukes, *Schistosoma* (Planorbid snails, miracidia, and cercaria); and avian schistosomes responsible for swimmer's itch (several snail genera, miracidia, and cercaria).

Significantly, the giant intestinal fluke infection is obtained by the Asian custom of eating raw aquatic plants—water chestnuts, lotus parts, water bamboo, and water caltrop—on which cercariae are encysted. Normally, liver fluke infection occurs when encysted cercariae are ingested with grass. Thus, herbicide application might provide some control, but would not affect floating encysted cercariae normally drunk by cattle. *Fasicola* can be a human health problem as in Arequipa, Peru, where cercariae encysted on watercress are ingested with salads.

LARGE HYDROELECTRIC PROJECTS

The construction of hydroelectric dams produces social impacts through the displacement of local populations that present problems in public health (23). Tropical diseases arising from the operation of high dams impose a social cost upon the communities in close proximity to the project. These diseases arise due to unsuitable living conditions and lack of sanitation as well as from the alteration of the natural ecological cycle through the introduction of a body of water. Schistosomiasis is one of the diseases most commonly associated with the operation of large dams located in tropic regions. The Chinese use of certain species of fish to control the snail-host aspect of schistosomiasis is a proper path to follow to reduce the negative impacts of resource development. This campaign against schistosomiasis included making the snail's habitat uninhabitable for the mollusk, properly disposing of human wastes, maintaining proper water supplies, localizing infected individuals for treatment, and starting a mass education program. Other negative environmental effects are also noted. Problems of aquatic weed overgrowth already exist in several dams in Mexico. Erosion often takes place at the mouth of rivers whose waters have been harnessed for hydroelectric power production. As a possible solution, a new type of development (ecodevelopment) is recommended. This plan advocates the rational use of natural resources while meeting the needs of the population and balancing the interrelation between man and the environment.

INTRODUCTION OF PHYTOPHAGOUS FISHES

Gravity-flow type irrigation schemes used in the Sudan and in different areas of the world are subject to economic and biological problems associated with the buildup of aquatic weeds that present problems in public health (18). The largest and oldest of the irrigation schemes in the Sudan is the Gezira, which is also by far the largest single irrigated agricultural scheme of its type in the world. Water velocity varies between 0 and 1.0 m/s according to usage. Two species have been suggested as potential allies in the control of aquatic weeds in the Sudan. Attempts have been made to introduce the grass carp into the Sudan, and plans have been made to spend a considerable amount of money on this species, while the potential of the endemic *Tilapia zillii* is being ignored. The effect of phytophagous fishes on the abundance of water associated vectors of diseases is a very important consideration in tropical areas. Although theoretically beneficial effects of phytophagous fishes on the abundance of the vectors of malaria and schistomiasis would be expected, much research is needed in this area. Consideration should be given to the introduction of other species to control these vectors together with measures to control weeds biologically.

AQUATIC MACROPHYTE STANDING CROP

Although there is at present some research effort in almost all aspects of plant and ecosystem biology that can lead to the application of integrated control of aquatic plants, past research on the problem has been based largely upon the search for specific solutions to specific problems. In addition, much effort has been expended in trial-and-error searches for solutions to specific problems, with no scientific controls or technical reports of results. With this approach, some important achievements have been made in abatement of aquatic plant problems, particularly with respect to some species in some situations, but many problems still await solution. Further, despite the successes thus far, no control or management technique has yet been found that is suitable for any species in all situations where that species has become a problem.

The fragmented approach to research is inefficient in a number of ways. For example, it depends largely upon potential commercial value of the products of research (e.g. chemicals and equipment), and the research generally attacks the symptoms of the problem (well-developed pest populations) rather than the causes. Further, the cause-effect relations that lead to the problem are often not considered, so that a control strategy that proves effective in one geographic context cannot be readily translated to another geographic context; thus, a capability for predicting the need for special management to prevent pestiferous growths in any given aquatic system has not been developed.

A research study was initiated under contract NO. DACW 68-76-M-3433 with the University of Idaho, Moscow, Idaho and the U.S. Corps of Engineers District Walla Walla, Washington in 1975, to study the aquatic standing crop and oxygen levels.

Dissolved Oxygen Levels

Fall runoff conditions were indicated by the 13-19 C temperatures of the drains (Table 1). Most varied from 13 to 16 C through a daily cycle, but upper Indian Creek did range from 13-19 C. These temperatures are all above threshold temperatures for initiation of fall aquatic plant dieback in temperate waters. Conductivities ranged from 227 μmho/cm in South Middleton Drain to 77 μmho/cm in Conway Gulch. Diurnal variation was minimal in South Middleton to approximately 25% in Conway (Table 1). All valid oxygen data we obtained is presented in Table 2 as percent saturation.

Experience with aquatic macrophytes in Kansas, Pennsylvania, and north Idaho gives reason to conclude that summer standing crops persist until water temperatures drop below 12 C, after which top growth rapidly dies back to the sediments. Owens and Edwards (15) observed similar patterns in English chalk streams where September standing crops were annual highs. Therefore, in our estimates of August O_2 patterns, we are assuming similar standing crops as in September, merely higher rates of metabolic activity at the higher August water temperatures. For the same reason, we would expect diurnal O_2 curves to be similarly shaped but with higher peaks and slightly lower lows.

Table 3 details the diurnal oxygen data (mg/l) in Boise Valley September 29-October 3. Table 4 gives the estimated daily range of dissolved oxygen (%), using the percentage change in September from that stated time, to the peak or low to convert to August peaks or lows. Projected August peaks range from 91.2% O_2 to 114.9% O_2 at Indian Creek. Projected August lows range from 66.7% O_2 to 84.0%. As shown in Table 4, projected August O_2 ranges are similar to September, but slightly greater. Measured midmorning, August O_2 values generally fall between projected daily highs and lows. On the theoretical basis of greater metabolic activity in warmer water, slightly greater O_2 ranges are expected in August. February O_2 ranges are expected to be nil since submerged aquatic plant biomass is usually less than 5% of summer levels. Peltier and Welch (16) describe late winter plant standing crops as less than 1% of summer weights.

Plant Biomass

Average periphyton and macrophyte standing crop estimates for the Boise drains are given in Table 5. Data are given as oven-dry weight of standing crop (above ground biomass). Submerged plant standing crops were lowest in Conway (55.3 gm/m²) while highest in Upper Indian Creek (527.0 gm/m²). The tributary to Ten Mile Creek contained 620.7 gm/m².

These estimates are in agreement with literature values for turbid, mildly polluted streams. The River Yare in England, a mildly polluted fen river contained 281 O.D. gm/m² of *P. luciens* at maximum summer standing crop. The River Colne, a turbid sewage effluent channel held 120 O.D. gm/m² od *P. pectinatus* (8,13,15). The River Ivel contained 2.6-519.1 O.D. gms/m², the maximum in a polluted reach of stream. An unpolluted reach showed the following standing crop pattern:

March	19.8 O.D. gm/m²
June	107.2 O.D. gm/m²
August	107.3 O.D. gm/m²
December	3.8 O.D. gm/m²

Maximum standing crops were observed on September 9. Net productivity and efficiency were also highest at that time.

The important role of aquatic macrophytes in regulating O_2 levels of these drains is indicated by the strong relationship between standing crop and the morning minimum O_2 level. An r^2 of 0.79 was obtained. Submerged aquatic plant biomass was poorly related to channel discharge ($r^2 = 0.10$); inversely related to turbidity ($r^2 = 0.43$); and positively related to morning minimum O_2 level ($r^2 = 0.79$). It is important that some optimum level of plant biomass be maintained for good fishery management.

SUMMARY AND CONCLUSIONS

Problems of aquatic plant growth in fresh water fisheries have been known since the earliest of times. However, serious impacts on human health are largely related to fresh water fishery and supply impoundments, irrigation and drainage facilities, and specialized water recreation facilities. These uses demand some type of aquatic weed control for the benefit of fisheries and public use. Special strategies are required to control aquatic plant growths in particular situations, and it is necessary for the aquatic plant control specialist(s) to apply those particular strategies as needed for successful management of freshwater fisheries.

REFERENCES CITED

1. Bartsch, A.F. and M.O. Allum. 1957. Biological factors in treatment of raw sewage in artificial ponds, Limnology and Oceanography, 2 (2): 77-84.
2. Churchill, M.A. 1958. Effect of storage impoundments on water quality. Trans. Am. Soc. Civil Engs., 123: 419-464.
3. Ferguson, F.F. 1980. Aquatic weeds and man's well-being pp 3-15. E.O. Gangstad, *Ed. In* Weed Control Methods for Public Health Applications. CRC Press, Boca Raton, Florida. 299 pp.
4. Gholson, A.K., Sr. 1982. Aquatic weeds in Lake Seminole. pp 175-186. E.O. Gangstad, Ed. *In* Weed Control Methods for Recreation Facilities Management. CRC Press Inc. Boca Raton, Florida. 297 pp.
5. Gorham, P.R. 1964. Toxic algae as a public health hazard. Jour. American Water Works Assoc., 56 (11): 1481-1438.
6. Herms, W.B. 1950. Medical Entomology MacMillan, New York.
7. Hesser, E. and E.O. Gangstad. 1978. Nuisance aquatic macrophyte growth. J. Aquatic Plant Manage. 16:11-14.
8. Hynes, H.B.N. 1970. The Ecology of Running Waters. Univ. of Toronto Press, Toronto.

9. Ingram, W.M. and G.W. Prescott. 1954. Toxic fresh-water algae. The American Midland Naturalist, 52: 75-87.
10. Kittrell, F.W. 1959. Effects of impoundments on dissolved oxygen resources. Sewage and Industrial Wastes, 31 (9) : 1065-1078.
11. Love, S. 1961. Relationship of impoundment to water quality, Journ. American Water Works Assoc., 53 (5): 559-568.
12. Machenthun, K.M. and Ingram, W.M. 1967. Biological Associated Problems in Fresh Water Enviroments. U.S. Government Printing Office, Washington, D.C. 287. pp.
13. Odum, H.T. 1956. Primary production in flowing waters. Limnology and Oceanography, 1:102-117.
14. Oliver-Gonzalez, J. 1946. The possible role of the guppy, Lebistes retisulatus, on the control of Schistosonia. Science. 104 (2712) 605.
15. Owens, M. and R.W. Edwards. 1960. The effects of plants on river conditions. Summer crops and estimates of net productivity of macrophytes in a chalk stream. Journal of Ecology, 48:151-160.
16. Peltier, W.H. and E.B. Welch. 1969. Factors affecting growth of rooted aquatics in a river. Weed Science, 17:412-416.
17. Prescott, G.W. 1956. A Guide to the Literature on Ecology and Life History of the Algae. Botanical Review, 22 (3):167-240.
18. Redding-Coates, T.A. and Coates, D. 1981. Introduction of plytophagous fishes into gravity-flow irrigation systems in the Sudan. Fisheries Management. 12:89-99, Gezira Univ. Wad Meaani (Sudan).
19. Russell, F.S. 1965. Advances in Marine Biology Vol. 3. Academic Press, London.
20. Schwimmer M. and D. Schwimmer. 1968. Medical aspects of physcology in Algae, Man and the Enviroment. D.F. Jackson, Ed, Syracuse University Press. Syracuse, New York. 279 pp.
21. Schulthorpe, C.D. 1967. The Biology of Vascular Plants. Arnold Press, London. 610 pp.
22. Smith, G.E. 1982. Eurasian watermilfoil. pp 217-226. E.O. Gangstad, Ed. In Weed Control Methods for Recreation Facilities Management. CRC Press Inc. Boca Raton, Flordia. 297 pp.
23. Szehely, F. 1982. Environmental impact of large hydro-electric projects in tropical countries. Water Supply and Management 6:233-242. Texas University, Austin, Texas.

Table 1. Water temperature (°C) and conductivity (μ mhos/cm) during 24 hour periods, September 24-27, 1975.

Drain	Temp.	Time	Cond.	Temp.	Time	Cond.	Temp.	Time	Cond.	Temp.	Time	Cond.	Temp.	Time	Cond.
East Hartley	13.0	0625	345	14.0	1020	320	16.9	1430	345	—	—	—	16.0	2045	370
Mason Slough	13.2	0645	460	14.7	1040	500	15.6	1450	520	—	—	—	16.0	2105	480
Middleton North	13.1	0720	355	14.0	1100	352	16.2	1520	380	—	—	—	16.0	2135	348
Middleton South	13.8	0720	230	14.9	1100	227	16.9	1520	240	—	—	—	16.0	2135	230
Ten Mile	13.0	0740	305	14.2	1130	330	16.3	1545	365	—	—	—	16.3	2205	305
Field Trib. to Ten Mile Cr.	12.5	0700	455—	—	—	—	16.9	1500	415	—	—	—	—	—	—
Upper Indian Creek (018)	13.0	0815	660	—	—	—	19.0	1645	695	—	—	—	—	—	—
Dixie	13.4	0715	580	16.0	1105	630	17.0	1445	680	17.6	1900	630	16.1	2235	625
Conway	12.5	0650	620	15.1	1035	620	15.5	1515	745	15.1	1830	775	14.6	2300	675

From: Falter, C.M. and Jack Skille. 1975. University of Idaho, Contract DACW-68-76-M-3433, U.S. Army Corps of Engineers, Walla Walla District, Washington.

Table 2. Dissolved oxygen concentrations (mg/l) and percent saturation over 24 hour periods, September 24-27, 1975.

Drain	Replicate	Time	mg/l	% Sat.	Time	mg/l	% Sat.	Time	mg/l	% Sat.	Time	mg/l	% Sat.	Time	mg/l	% Sat.
East Hartley	A)	0625	8.06	75.5	1020	8.34	80.0	1430	8.18	83.0	—	—	—	2045	7.34	74.0
	B)		8.09	75.5		8.34	80.0		8.25	83.5		—	—		7.44	74.5
Mason Slough	A)	0645	8.19	77.0	1040	8.87	86.0	1450	9.48	94.0	—	—	—	2105	8.02	80.5
	B)		8.21	77.5		8.77	85.0		9.48	94.0		—	—		8.03	80.5
Middleton North	A)	0720	7.55	71.0	1100	8.57	82.0	1520	9.30	94.0	—	—	—	2135	7.30	72.5
	B)		7.48	70.5		8.68	83.0		9.35	94.5		—	—		7.33	73.0
Middleton South	A)	0720	7.42	70.5	1100	8.78	85.5	1520	9.39	95.5	—	—	—	2135	7.09	71.0
	B)		7.40	70.5		8.78	85.5		9.38	95.0		—	—		7.32	73.5
Ten Mile	A)	0740	7.85	73.0	1130	9.06	87.5	1545	9.47	95.5	—	—	—	2205	7.70	77.5
	B)		7.93	74.0		9.14	88.0		9.55	97.0		—	—		7.93	79.5
Field Trib. to Ten Mile Cr.	A)	0700	7.30	67.5	—	—	—	1500	8.76	88.5	—	—	—	—	—	—
	B)		7.46	69.0		—	—		8.68	88.0		—	—		—	—

Table 2. Dissolved oxygen concentrations (mg/l) and percent saturation over 24 hour periods, September 24-27, 1975. (cont.)

Drain	Repli-cate	Time	mg/l	% Sat.	Time	mg/l	% Sat.	Time	mg/l	% Sat.	Time	mg/l	% Sat.	Time	mg/l	% Sat.
Upper Indian Creek (018)	A)	0815	5.70	52.5	—	—	—	1645	7.63	81.0	—	—	—	—	—	—
	B)		5.66	52.5	—	—	—		7.67	81.5	—	—	—	—	—	—
Dixie	A)	0715	7.59	72.0	1105	8.76	87.5	1445	10.31	105.0	1900	9.07	94.5	2235	7.24	72.5
	B)		7.45	70.5		8.67	86.5		10.40	106.5		9.08	95.0		7.46	75.0
Conway	A)	0650	8.82	82.0	1035	8.87	87.5	1515	8.74	87.0	1830	8.44	83.0	2300	8.28	80.0

From: Falter, C.M. and Jack Skille. 1975. University of Idaho, Contract DACW-68-76-M-3433, U.S. Army Corps of Engineers, Walla Walla District, Washington.

Table 3. **Diurnal oxygen data (mg/l) collected by the Bureau of Reclamation on drains in the Boise Valley (September 29-October 3, 1975).**

Time	Ten Mile Creek (B.O.R. No. 007)	Dixie Drain (B.O.R. No. 120)	Indian Creek (B.O.R. No. 018	Indian Creek (B.O.R. No. 014)
0900	—	—	8.2	—
1000	—	9.4	8.6	8.6
1100	9.4	9.5	9.0	8.7
1200	9.8	10.1	9.2	9.0
1300	10.1	10.6	9.2	9.2
1400	10.2	11.0	9.1	9.3
1500	10.1	11.1	8.7	9.4
1600	9.8	10.9	8.1	9.3
1700	9.4	10.6	7.0	9.1
1800	8.8	10.0	5.8	9.0
1900	8.2	9.4	5.2	8.6
2000	7.7	8.6	4.8	8.4
2100	7.5	8.0	4.8	8.2
2200	7.2	7.7	4.8	8.0
2300	7.2	7.4	4.9	7.8
2400	7.2	7.3	5.1	7.6
0100	7.2	7.3	5.2	7.7
0200	7.2	7.2	5.2	7.7
0300	7.3	7.2	5.2	7.7
0400	7.3	7.3	5.3	7.6
0500	7.3	7.3	—	7.7
0600	7.4	7.4	—	7.7
0700	7.5	7.4	—	7.7
0800	7.5	7.8	—	7.8
0900	7.6	8.2	—	7.9
1000	7.7	—	—	8.0

From: Falter, C.M. and Jack Skille. 1975. University of Idaho, Contract DACW-68-76-M-3433, U.S. Army Corps of Engineers, Walla Walla District, Washington.

Table 4. Estimated August daily ranges of dissolved oxygen (% saturation)

Drain	Time of Day of August Sampling	Percent Oxygen Saturation at August Sampling (Corps Data)	Percent Oxygen Saturation at September Sampling (from O_2 Diurnal Curves	September Daily Peak (from O_2 Diurnal Curves	September Daily Peak O_2 as % of O_2 at the Stated Time (Col. 4 Col. 3)
Hartley Drain	1145 hrs	91.3% O_2	82% O_2	83.2% O_2	101%
Mason Drain	1025	90.1	85%	94.0	111%
Middleton North	1005	88.5	82%	94.3	115%
Middleton South	0950	88.8	83%	95.3	115%
Ten Mile Creek	0940	88.3	81%	96.2	119%
Upper Indian Creek (018)	1330	100.8	72%	82.3	114%
Dixie Slough	1130	85.5	90%	105.8	118%
Conway Gulch	1100	90.3	86%	86.5	101%

From: Falter, C.M. and Jack Skille. 1975. University of Idaho, Contract DACW-68-76-M-3433, U.S. Army Corps of Engineers, Walla Walla District, Washington.

Table 5. **Periphyton and submerged vascular plant standing crop estimates (g/m² oven-dry weight) in drains of the Boise Valley, September 24-27, 1975.**

Drain	Average Periphyton Standing Crop	Average Submerged Vascular Standing Crop	Average Total Standing Crop
East Hartley Drain (#114)	26.3 g/m₂	130.0 g/m₂	156.3 g/m₂
Mason Creek (#116)	7.0	97.5	104.5
Middleton North Drain (#111)	8.8	105.0	113.8
Middleton South Drain (#112	15.8	112.5	128.3
Ten Mile Creek (#007)	24.9	156.0	180.9
Field Tributary of Ten Mile Creek	14.0	606.7	620.7
Upper Indian Creek (#018)	7.0	520.0	527.0
Dixie Drain (#120)	22.4	71.5	93.9
Conway Gulch (#121)	22.8	32.5	55.3

NOTE: Ash-free weight of most macrophytes approximates 80% of oven dry weight. Organic carbon approximates 35-40% of oven-dry weight for most species of submergents.

From: Falter, C.M. and Jack Skille. 1975. University of Idaho, Contract DACW-68-76-M-3433, U.S. Army Corps of Engineers, Walla Walla District, Washington.

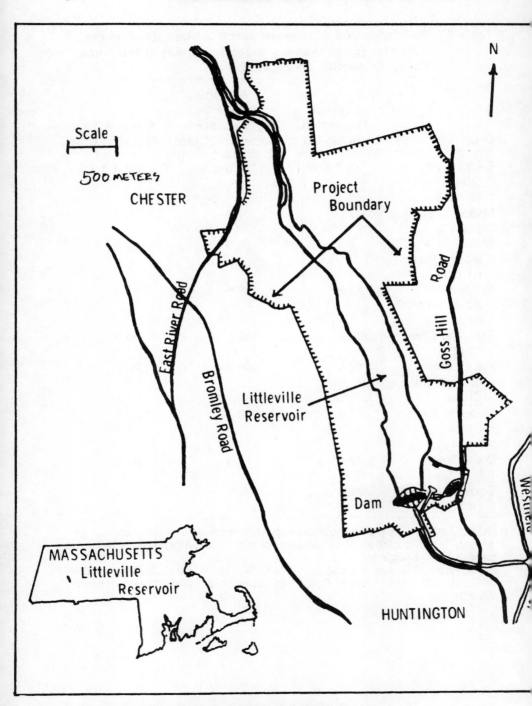

re 15.1 Littleville Reservoir and associated project features.

Figure 15.2 Stocking largemouth bass in the downstream area. (Courtesy of the US. Army Corps of Engineers, New England, July 1978).

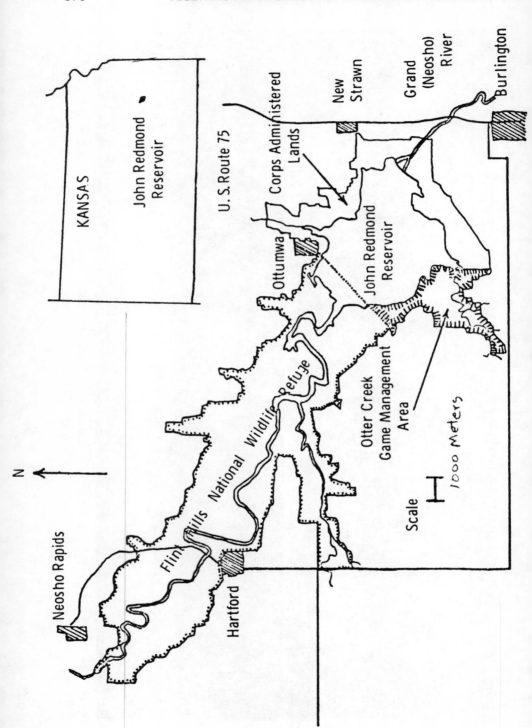

Figure 15.4 Nice catch of largemouth bass from the John Redmond Reservoir. (Courtesy of the U.S. Army Corps of Engineers, Tulsa District, July, 1978).

SELECTED TOPICS IN FRESHWATER VEGETATION

MANAGEMENT

Subject Index